WO

WITHOUT

AIDS

STEVEN RANSOM
& PHILLIP DAY

 Credence Publications

WORLD WITHOUT AIDS

TABLE OF CONTENTS

"Buried deep within the secretive and well-guarded dogma that AIDS is a plague caused by the lethal virus known as HIV, there is a time-bomb of potentially explosive contrary information."

Gordon Stewart MD, Emeritus Professor of Public Health, Glasgow University

World Without AIDS brings you this
contrary information. Be warned however.
The information is indeed explosive. You will be
accessing some 'highly restricted areas'.
You will also be accessing information that
certain authorities do not want you to see.
This book will change you.
We believe it will change everything…
for the good.

Credence Publications

"Ransom and Day are the Woodward and Bernstein of AIDSgate, exposing the corruption, fraud and lies on which the multi-billion dollar HIV industry is based."

Alex Russell, Associate Editor, Continuum Magazine.

"'WORLD WITHOUT AIDS' is the perfect read for everybody to understand what is really going on behind the scenes in the field of AIDS. Both from a scientific and political point of view, nowhere is AIDS better and more simply explained. A masterpiece."

Dr Stefan Lanka, virologist, Vice President of the humanitarian organisation "Science, Medicine and Human Rights"

" 'WORLD WITHOUT AIDS' is a magnificent book. As a Ugandan woman who has worked with many AIDS-related organisations and individuals, I have found out that most people are put off books on AIDS because of the confusing scientific language. This book is very easy to read and understand, and a real eye-opener for us all. For our own education, it is my wish that everybody reads this book. I highly recommend 'WORLD WITHOUT AIDS' as a wake up call to Africa, to save our continent before it is too late. For with the knowledge contained in these pages comes power. God bless the authors and all those who have contributed to this fantastic book."

Winfred Mwebe, Ugandan health advisor.

ALL TOOLED UP FOR CUTTING THROUGH

Hello. We are Phillip Day and Steven Ransom. Thank you for choosing to read *World Without AIDS*. You are reading this book either because you're curious, or maybe you have been diagnosed 'HIV positive' or told you are 'suffering from AIDS' and have received a copy from a well-intentioned friend or relative. Some people buy copies and pass them out to their families because they feel the information contained within these pages can quite literally save a loved one's life. Actually, it doesn't really matter how you ended up with this book in your hand, only that you have.

Phillip Day

This book will accomplish five goals:

- **EXPOSING THE POLITICS OF AIDS** - You will discover that AIDS is primarily not a medical problem at all. It is a series of scientific and political lies, masquerading as medical science, which has come about through man's rapacious appetite for money, power and control. Most directly at fault are those in key positions within certain sections of the medical, **Steven Ransom** chemical, pharmaceutical and AIDS-related fund-raising ('charitable') industries. Their aim is to ensure the lucrative cash-flow from the AIDS 'epidemic' remains uninterrupted by continuing to propagate the myths and lies surrounding AIDS.

- **EXPOSING HIV** - You will learn that almost everything you have been told about AIDS and HIV is either a series of half-truths or complete nonsense. Discovering this to be the case will serve as a valuable reminder not to take accepted truths at face value but always to exercise critical discernment before falling into line with any 'perceived' wisdom.

9

- **EXPOSING THE REAL CAUSE OF AIDS -** You will find out what has really been killing those who have been pronounced 'dead from AIDS' - a death toll that includes some of the world's most renowned performers and public figures; a death toll that is now apparently sounding its knell across the vast expanses of the sub-Sahara and Third World; and just as tragically, a death toll that perhaps includes the lives of some of your own loved ones in its statistics.

- **REPORTING THE MANY CASE HISTORIES OF AIDS 'SUFFERERS' - NOW COMPLETELY FREE OF AIDS AND HEALTHY -** If you have been diagnosed 'HIV positive', or 'suffering from AIDS', you will learn the simple information you need to know in order to make an informed decision on how to start getting better - IMMEDIATELY. The condition known as AIDS need NOT be terminal, despite the overwhelming public message to the contrary.

- **ENDING THE FEAR THAT CLOUDS MANY LIVES –** The information contained in the ensuing pages will help bring an end to the longstanding fears surrounding AIDS and HIV. Those fears have hung over everyone for the last twenty years and are still with many of us today, clouding relationships and causing immeasurable heartache and emotional pain. *World Without AIDS* brings liberating truth to all those whose lives, in one way or another, have been touched by the concepts of AIDS and HIV.

The information you are about to read has been compiled from the desks of some of the world's most renowned medical personnel, biochemists, and researchers - those who have been intimately connected with the research on AIDS. Some of these professional men and women realised, from the very beginning of the AIDS story, that something was gravely amiss and, in spite of threats and intimidation, began to speak out.

What follows is the exposure of greed, pseudo-science, lies, moral bankruptcy and a plague of negligent homicide on a scale so breathtaking, it defies belief. It may interest you also to know that AIDS is by no means the only global disease where this has happened,[1] but AIDS is the focus of our study here today.

We are not doctors, medical practitioners or healthcare specialists and we do not offer medical advice. The facts presented in this book are intended for information and educational purposes only. This book does not instruct the reader to buy products or take any particular course of treatment, nor does it seek wilfully to undermine the advice and recommendations of qualified medical personnel or their institutions. The immuno-deficient condition known as 'AIDS' is of course a serious health concern and consultation with professionally qualified healthcare specialists is always advised. However, in the light of the information we will reveal in the ensuing chapters, the patient should exercise a special discernment when considering the treatments offered to them.

Who are we? Credence Publications is an independent research organisation whose personnel have been reporting on contentious medical issues for over ten years. Whilst we are not medical practitioners, we are certainly qualified to collate and pass on information already in the public domain and report the statements put out by medical and other professional researchers at the forefront of their particular field. Our statement of purpose can be described as follows:

> **Credence Publications** brings to light certain truths which are being distorted and/or deliberately withheld by influential institutions to suit their own specific agendas. Where the withholding of these truths is detrimental to public health, Credence Publications believes that these institutions by their actions are worthy of exposure.

The purpose of this book is to allow the reader to exercise a valuable right – the right to informed choice; in other words, the right to make a decision on choosing treatment or preventative methods based

---

[1] See section entitled *Entrenched Scientific Error.*

on as much evidence as is currently available. In the realm of AIDS and HIV at the present time, this right is being deliberately denied you.

The facts you will learn are presented in a simple, easy-to-understand format. Understanding AIDS and the science behind it isn't complicated. In fact, as you will discover, it was the medical industry's assumed and unquestioned superiority, coupled with their impressive-sounding scientific terminology, that brought the notion of a 20th century plague into our lives in the first place.

The information contained in this book will surprise and may well anger those who have lost loved ones to AIDS as well as those who are working with all good intention in the AIDS environment. Whilst we regret this possibility, our position remains to draw attention to the fact that the current state of affairs concerning AIDS is simply unacceptable. If there is a sadder truth than the thousands who have needlessly perished through lack of knowledge about Acquired Immune Deficiency Syndrome, it is the conniving and the duplicitous nature which lies at the heart of some sections of the highly profitable medical and pharmaceutical industries. Regrettably the attitudes and agendas of these institutions and the agencies supporting them are proving to be a lot more destructive than AIDS itself.

While there are many aspects to the AIDS story which make for sobering reading, *World Without AIDS* brings an end to the fear of this enigmatic syndrome. **And the best news of all!** Every day, people are recovering - healing themselves of AIDS! And no, we are not just talking about a few isolated cases. You will read inspiring accounts of how ordinary men and women, 'positively imprisoned' and sent home to die by the specialists they trusted, resolved to survive against the odds, simply by asking pertinent questions, studying the facts on AIDS and HIV for themselves and daring to tread the unconventional path.

This book is dedicated to the following: To all who have helped in whatever way in the preparation of this book. To the men and women, the whistle blowers, who defied their peers in bringing to light the truth about AIDS and HIV. To anyone who ever smelt a corporate rat but didn't spring the trap. May this book inspire you to immediate action. And finally, to the 'positively imprisoned' men and women everywhere, and to the voiceless ones especially - the children. May this book cut through the ties that bind, and set the captives free.

Part 1

'WESTERN' AIDS

A STRETCHING EXERCISE

the dawn of AIDS

William was down to 98 pounds and he was a mess. His face was haunted and sunken, the look that all had come to expect from AIDS. His skin had taken on an unhealthy, ghostly patina. His surroundings mirrored the same sense of neglect and despair – clothes strewn haphazardly about the place, uneaten fly-infested food and dirty plates piled in the sink.

"OK," said William. "I've read what you sent me. I've decided to do it."

I was overcome by an unexpected relief. I don't know what it was about William that made him choose to fight. Perhaps it was the dawning realisation that if he didn't take responsibility for his own health and life - and rapidly - no one was going to do it for him. This would have become increasingly apparent to William as his condition deteriorated in spite of the efforts of the world's most advanced medicines to reverse it.

"How do you feel about what you have decided to do?"

"I'm gonna die, aren't I...?" he mumbled, suddenly shivering and wrapping his arms around himself. My heart went out to him.

"Come on, let's do it. Then I'll treat you to some lunch down at the Moustache Café."

William gave a small smile. The café on Melrose in West Hollywood was his favourite place. He got up and made his way over to the kitchen cupboard. As he opened the door, some of the contents fell out, so crammed full was the cupboard with what had been put into it.

What William did during the next two minutes was to cure him completely of AIDS. Admittedly it would take some months for the body fully to recover. But the direct consequence of

William's 'senseless act' (as it was later termed by his doctor) would be that in the space of a single day, in body, in mind and in spirit, William would realise he was being dragged away from death and back towards the light of health, vigour and sanity.

Today, eight years after that day, William is an irrefutable example of health and vitality and has been free of AIDS for seven and a half years. Running his own actors' management agency in Los Angeles with the support of his loving parents, William demonstrates no trace of his former condition. To those who know only the outline of William's story, it seems that a miracle has occurred. After all, William once had full-blown AIDS... and today he is completely healthy. [2]

* * * *

In late 1980, a young researcher in immunology named Michael Gottlieb, working at the medical center of University of California Los Angeles (UCLA), embarked upon a study to examine the immune system. *"I assigned a student to track down for me any unusual cases of immuno-suppression."* [3] With the help of his student, Gottlieb began scouring hospitals and clinics to find evidence of patients demonstrating immune deficiency diseases. By November of that year, Gottlieb had found one such case suffering from a yeast infection in his throat as well as a rare pneumonia that refused to disappear. Gottlieb knew that the *pneumocystis carinii* microbe causing the pneumonia was extremely common across the world. In fact, in a dormant state it is thought to inhabit the lungs of nearly every human on the planet. [4] This pneumonia very rarely strikes anyone other than cancer patients, and then, only those whose immune systems have been severely damaged by the application of chemotherapy or radiotherapy treatments. [5] What attracted Gottlieb's particular interest was that, in this particular case, the young man in question had undergone no such chemotherapy treatment and should by rights have been in the peak of health.

---

[2] Day, Phillip, from personal notes.
[3] **Ransom, Steven**, from a telephone interview with Dr M Gottlieb, 13th December 1999
[4] **Duesberg, Peter H** *Inventing the AIDS Virus*, Regnery Publishing, Inc. Washington DC, 1996 p.147
[5] Duesberg, Peter H, *Inventing...* ibid.

Over the following weeks, Gottlieb's search yielded three more cases of immune deficiencies. All displayed the same candidiasis (yeast infection) and pneumocystis carinii pneumonia (PCP) Gottlieb had found in his first subject. Also, according to Gottlieb's new testing protocol, each case had 'low' T-cell immune lymphocyte counts. By April 1981, Gottlieb was convinced he was on to something. He contacted Wayne Shandera, a local public health official who had been trained by the Epidemic Intelligence Service or EIS.

Gottlieb asked Shandera whether his local health department had any reported immune deficiency cases. Shandera said that he had, and was able to add another patient to Gottlieb's list. Recalls Gottlieb: *"We didn't know what this illness was at the time, but I remember being able to tell the CDC: 'I think we have a new disease.'"*[6]

Gottlieb was by now noticing another intriguing factor. All five patients were male and active homosexuals. Gottlieb was convinced he had unearthed something unique. He telephoned the *New England Journal of Medicine*: *"I've got something here that's bigger than Legionnaires'!"* he remarked with excitement.[7] Shandera meanwhile, intrigued too by the homosexual connection, contacted James Curran at the Venereal Disease Division of the Centers for Disease Control (CDC). Curran, in turn, wrote *"Hot Stuff! Hot Stuff!"* on his announcement and had an article on the syndrome hastily published in his agency's *Morbidity and Mortality Weekly Report*. The report came out on 5th June 1981 and implied that the syndrome suffered by the five subjects could represent a major new and hitherto unknown sexually transmitted disease - this despite the fact that the five subjects had experienced no sexual contacts with each other.[8]

Once published, the article attracted other, similar cases which were being reported to the CDC. At this time, the report writers recognised that some of the patients they were studying were suffering from rare blood-vessel tumours and skin disfiguring lesions known as Karposi's Sarcoma (KS). Gottlieb's early patients had another striking

---

[6] Ransom, Steven, telephone interview with Dr M Gottlieb... ibid.
[7] **Shilts, Randy** *And the Band Played On*, St Martin's Press, New York: 1987 p.63
[8] **Gottlieb, M S, H M Schanker, & A Fan** "Pneumocystis Pneumonia - Los Angeles" *Morbidity and Mortality Weekly Report* 30 (5th June 1981): 250-252

similarity in common: they were all heavy users of recreational drugs, including nitrite inhalants such as 'poppers', the volatile liquid used by homosexuals to facilitate anal intercourse and heighten orgasm. The CDC did at one point entertain the notion that part of the problem could be a bad batch of 'poppers', but subsequent investigations failed to turn up a 'bad lot', and so the theory was discounted. [9]

Further studies by the CDC confirmed that the men demonstrating such rare and fatal diseases had all been part of the promiscuous homosexual scene for many years, generating many hundreds of sexual contacts. When the CDC began tracing the contacts of those exhibiting Gottlieb's syndrome, more and more immune deficiency patients appeared. Such 'infection clusters' were producing impressive circumstantial evidence that the syndrome was spread sexually by homosexuals.

Meanwhile in New York, a Dr Friedman-Kein, independent of Gottlieb's research, had also been tracking the same curious phenomenon. Up to this point, the information gathered on this syndrome had largely remained within the confines of the investigative medical authorities. But now its existence was set to reach a far wider audience. Reporting on the work of Dr Friedman-Kein, a *New York Times* article of 3rd July 1981 began:

> *"Doctors in New York and California have diagnosed among homosexual men, 41 cases of an often rapidly fatal form of cancer, with Karposi's Sarcoma appearing in one or more violet spots anywhere on the body. The cause of the outbreak is unknown. Doctors who have made the diagnoses are mostly in the New York City and San Francisco Bay area, and are alerting other physicians in an effort to identify more cases. Dr Friedman-Kein described the appearance of the outbreak as rather devastating."*

While the CDC investigators concentrated their efforts on tracing the sexual contacts provoked by each newly discovered patient, Karposi's Sarcoma and Opportunistic Infections task force members[10]

---

[9] **Etheridge, E W** *Sentinel for Health: A History of the Centers for Disease Control*, University of California Press, Berkeley, CA 1992 p.326
[10] KSOI - another division of the CDC

were examining the plausibility of a new apocalyptic fear. Building on the circumstantial premise that Gottlieb's new syndrome was sexually transmitted, the CDC were now speculating: Was this syndrome, to date found only in homosexual drug-users, now spreading into the heterosexual population? Using the infection pattern of hepatitis B as their model, investigators began their search.

Quite calculatedly however, the CDC did not conduct their search across the usual cross section of the populace. To determine the spread of Gottlieb's syndrome into the heterosexual population, they began by examining non-homosexual heroin addicts and haemophiliacs. [11] Before too long, they were able to confirm the same worrying statistic: that the group they were examining had a low T-cell (immune lymphocyte) count. And sure enough, they also shared a number of immuno-deficient health disorders.

But even though the illnesses they recorded in this new group were, in some cases, not even similar to the diseases suffered by Gottlieb's homosexuals, the CDC once again classified these two groups as falling into this 'new emerging immune deficiency epidemic'. Homosexuals, haemophiliacs and now heroin addicts. Rationally or otherwise, it appeared the new epidemic was spreading.

But from the sidelines, a number of independent researchers were far from happy with the manner in which the CDC had been amassing their data. As we will find out later, one or two even went so far as to accuse the CDC of fabricating a new epidemic just to keep appropriate sections of their work force in well-paid employment. Such accusations are not as far-fetched as they first appear. A brief examination of what became known as 'the swine flu outbreak' brings to light the actions of one particularly powerful, yet little known section of the US medical research community - the Epidemic Intelligence Service (EIS), a department within the Centers for Disease Control.

In January 1976, five soldiers succumbed to a particular strain of flu. The EIS was the first to sound the alarm. The interestingly named Epidemic Intelligence Service was formed in July 1951 by Alexander Langmuir, an associate professor at Johns Hopkins University School

---

[11] Duesberg, Peter H, *Inventing...* ibid. p.135

of Hygiene and Public Health. Langmuir had persuaded US health officials and Congress to grant the CDC special contingency powers to deal with future potential public health emergencies. The Epidemic Intelligence Service came into being and was granted significant spending powers and unlimited access across the medical institutions to give advanced warning of any perceived health threat, however remote. Such was the autonomy enjoyed by the EIS that one of Britain's senior epidemiologists, Dr Gordon Stewart, described them as *"the medical CIA."* [12]

The considerable budget allocated to the EIS helped fund the positioning of agents into local health departments and corporations throughout the United States and even abroad. Acting as the eyes and ears of the CDC, the mission of these agents was primarily to act as guardians of America's health and report on even the most insignificant outbreaks of illness. Such was the mandate of the EIS that, from the outset, finding new diseases and tracking existing viruses and bacteria became fundamental to its worth and purpose.

The disease emerging that January was nicknamed 'swine flu' by the EIS, based on the prevailing speculation that pigs had served as the reservoir for the supposed virus. Such were the frightening predictions put out by the EIS concerning the destructive potential of the 'new' disease that President Ford and Congress panicked, allocating large funds for another flu vaccine – a sum of money which would spread itself liberally down through the epidemic research chain. The program stalled however when insurers discovered that the vaccine itself could produce extraordinary side effects, ranging from severe fevers and malaise to paralysis and death.[13]

To the intense chagrin of the White House, except for the five soldiers, no flu epidemic ever materialised, and nothing remotely akin to an epidemic ever ventured onto the horizon. Unless Congress could be convinced the danger was real, the lucrative vaccine program would be terminated, severely depleting the coffers of the CDC. A battle plan was needed and fast. In their book, *Anatomy of an*

---

[12] Duesberg, Peter H, *Inventing…* ibid. p.135

[13] **Ellison, Bryan** *Rethinking AIDS* Homepage: www.rethinkingaids.com, December 1999

Epidemic, Gordon Thomas and Max Morgan-Witts describe the CDC's preparations:

> *"The large Auditorium A, located in CDC headquarters in Atlanta, became the command centre - called the 'war room.' Set up especially for this occasion, it contained banks of telephones, teleprinters, and computers, the hardware for an unprecedented monitoring system which, to work, also required a typing pool, photocopy machines, and doctors sitting at rows of desks in the center of the room."* [14]

The CDC and the EIS worked around the clock, week after week, following up every rumour of flu outbreaks. And then, on the horizon – a sighting. A cluster of pneumonia cases suddenly appeared in Philadelphia. This pneumonia had manifested itself in a group of elderly American Legion members several days after returning home from their July convention. The EIS sprang into action. On Monday 2nd August, within three hours of receiving word of this outbreak, its officers flew up to Philadelphia. They were joined by dozens of experts from the CDC.

On arrival, the CDC then began wilfully to feed rumours that this was the start of the swine flu epidemic they had predicted. To cover the rampaging 'swine flu' story, the CDC assigned none other than EIS-trained Lawrence Altman, now chief medical correspondent to the *New York Times*. Altman rose to the challenge magnificently.

And so, following the *New York Times'* run on the swine flu epidemic, Congress suddenly changed its mind and approved the CDC's request for a mass swine flu vaccine program. What followed was nothing short of a catastrophe. Over 50 million Americans were inoculated during the following months, ultimately producing at least 1,000 cases of severe nerve damage and paralysis, dozens of deaths, and nearly $100 million in liability claims. As if that were not enough, within days of the legislative approval for the vaccine program, the EIS was compelled to acknowledge that the minor pneumonia outbreak was not actually related to swine flu at all.

---

[14] Ellison, Bryan, *Rethinking AIDS*, ibid.

The EIS rode out the whole sorry affair by blaming the outbreak on some newly isolated bacterium. In reality, those stricken ex-servicemen were later found to be a group of elderly men, several with kidney transplants, who had all become extraordinarily drunk at their convention – combined risk factors well known for inviting the onset of pneumonia. Such minor outbreaks are relatively common, though rarely fall into the public spotlight. What made this situation disturbingly different was that, in their pursuit of a disease and a dollar or two, the CDC's only success had been in bringing virtual panic and not a little death to a nation of 250 million and compelling many millions of people to accept an untested and unsafe vaccine treatment they otherwise would not have taken – all over a harmless bacterium found in the plumbing systems of almost any building.[15]

With little outward sympathy for either the CDC or the EIS, Congress was considering a drastic reduction in their budget. It was now 1981, and the CDC were in dire need of some national threat to health to revive their tarnished image and avert an imminent cash crisis. In that same year, AIDS appeared. And as Bryan Ellison, co-author of *Inventing the AIDS Virus*, wryly comments, *"not a moment too soon."*[16]

The CDC were now contacting hospitals across the US in an effort to trace patients with unusually low immune system T-cell counts. Jackson Memorial Hospital in Miami reported that, whilst they had no cases exactly fitting the CDC requirements, they had recently taken in a number of undernourished Haitian boat people. The close confinement of their extremely arduous sea journey had left all passengers sharing a virulent form of tuberculosis, salmonellosis, and a variety of gut parasites, leading to diarrhoea and malnutrition.[17] On the strength of that description alone, the CDC were satisfied the Haitians were suffering from Gottlieb's syndrome. The epidemic was spreading! In fact, could the outbreak have originated in Haiti itself? Harry Haverkos from the EIS was sent to Haiti to study that possibility first-hand.

---

[15] Duesberg, Peter H, *Inventing...* ibid. pp.56, 144

[16] Ellison, Bryan, *Rethinking AIDS*, ibid.

[17] **Shenton, Joan** *Positively False*, Tauris Publishers, 1998

Joan Shenton, author of *Positively False,* has also studied the Haitian problem, but from a very different perspective. Her chapter entitled "Whatever Happened to AIDS in Haiti?" gives a penetrating insight into the havoc wreaked so indiscriminately by the 'big boys' from across the water:

> *"The effect of all of this on Haiti was dramatic. The tourist industry collapsed and with it the economy. In the US, Haitians all over the country lost their jobs. Incensed by this, Haiti's Minister for Health, Ari Bordes, demanded the CDC strike Haiti off their list of risk categories. The CDC reluctantly agreed, and with a little juggling of statistics, they reallocated the Haitians to different specific disease groups."* [18]

But the damage had already been done. Once again, even though the range of diseases found in the largely undernourished Haitian population were different to those being reported on mainland America, the definitions for the syndrome were simply expanded further to include the Haitian diseases. In what amounted to no more than a cynically contrived data-stretching exercise, the little island of Haiti was ruined almost overnight, was then exited just as quickly and left to pick up the pieces of its shattered economy. It has taken many years for Haiti to recover from its visit from the CDC. Unfortunately, it seems that history is about to repeat itself again for Haiti, albeit from a different angle of attack this time, as this release from The United States Department of Agriculture reveals:

> ***GLICKMAN MAKES $5.3 MILLION AVAILABLE TO KEEP CLASSICAL SWINE FEVER AT BAY. WASHINGTON, March 19, 1999*** *- Agriculture Secretary Dan Glickman has authorised an emergency transfer of $5.3 million to guard America from classical swine fever, currently in Haiti and the Dominican Republic. It was eradicated from the United States in 1978 after a 16-year effort by federal and state governments. If a similar eradication effort were attempted today, the estimated cost would exceed $500 million. "We are taking this action to protect our nation's hog farmers," Glickman said. "By helping our neighbors understand this disease and teaching them to guard against it, we can prevent classical swine fever*

---

[18] Shenton, Joan, ibid.

from entering the United States and infecting our hogs. "

The US enforcement agencies had stepped in to 'help their neighbours' in Haiti once before in 1983, over the pig issue. A pig 're-population' program was ordered after US agricultural officials announced another sighting on the horizon, this time of 'African swine fever', which, unless expeditiously acted upon, was feared might migrate from Haiti to mainland US. The United States Government offered local farmers three US 'whites' in exchange for one Haitian 'rustic', the local pig and well adapted to its environment. US enforcement officers were despatched to the island and the Haitian pigs were slaughtered by the thousand. With Haitian agronomists arguing against the severity of the so-called epidemic, the US pigs began arriving at Port-au-Prince, but in far less numbers than originally agreed, many of the arrivals soon dying from the heat. Those that did survive suffered severe sunstroke, required constant expensive US medicines and could digest only US imported feed. In Haiti, a pig is a person's livelihood. Once again, the unnecessary actions of Haiti's meddlesome neighbours would serve only to set back the Haitian economy for a number of years to come.[19] And now, as Glickman hands over $5.3M to the Investigative Enforcement Services team of APHIS (Animal, Plant Health Inspection Services) to protect US hog farmers, Haiti will no doubt find itself once again having to contest these generally destabilising claims. [20]

But to return to mainland America and the crisis at hand. The CDC were now taking known and classified conditions such as TB, malnutrition and salmonellosis and reclassifying them as 'strange unknowns' under the umbrella of Gottlieb's new syndrome. As a result of adding more diseases to the syndrome profile, it appeared to the public that the epidemic was growing steadily. The CDC then embarked on a program to publicise the new syndrome, and in July 1982 named it the Acquired Immune Deficiency Syndrome or AIDS. Announcing it as 'BIG' they then solicited the help of powerful

---

[19] *Albany Business Journal*, 8th March 1999

[20] **Franklin, Jane** *Cuba and the United States*, Ocean Press, August 1997. Among other things, a revealing account of US government involvement in the deliberate infection of Caribbean livestock. See also **de Wind, John** "Aiding Migration - The Impact of International Development Assistance on Haiti," Columbia University Research Program 1987 – a study of the ultimately self-serving intentions of the corporate lending agencies purportedly giving financial aid to Haiti.

politicians Henry Waxman (Los Angeles) and Philip Burton (San Francisco).[21] As AIDS was apparently decimating their constituents, both men wasted little time in raising a furore and compelling Congress to consider crash spending programs to combat the new AIDS threat. The first in a series of emotionally charged media articles began to appear as a result of the political lobbying of these men, whose efforts later succeeded in diverting millions of additional dollars into the coffers of the Centers for Disease Control.

Waxman and Burton's high profile orchestrations were difficult to ignore. Soon every major newspaper, news agency and talk-show was getting in on the act. By late 1982, hundreds of articles were appearing in the news media about the new syndrome known as AIDS. *Time* and *Newsweek* ran front-page stories of the mystery killer syndrome and hypothesised about its danger to world populations. Gruesome 'before and after' pictures appeared. On 12th April 1983, *Newsweek* ran its cover on the subject and labelled AIDS "The Public Health Threat of the Century". Every article began by asking the same central questions: What was causing it? Who was most at risk? What was being done by government to combat this new apocalyptic threat to public health?

Bizarre and fanciful predictions of entire populations being wiped out appeared in the less responsible tabloids across the globe. The question hotly debated in medical circles became: Was AIDS being caused by a virus or bacteria? And just as the bounty on Jaws led to shark hunters of all shapes and sizes putting frenziedly out to sea in the search for that dreaded great white, so too did AIDS attract the immediate attention of the virus hunters. And then, one press conference in April 1984 instantly changed the whole future of AIDS and AIDS research. A hunter had apparently speared a new virus – the virus identified as Human Immunodeficiency Virus, or HIV.

But not all were convinced by the party line that had rapidly taken shape concerning AIDS.

Very soon after the announcement that HIV was the cause of AIDS came news of a new 'virus identification' procedure, now commonly

---

[21] Duesberg, Peter H, *Inventing…* ibid. p.151

known as 'the AIDS test'. The test was marketed to a fearful public as highly specific and accurate. A suspected carrier could now be tested. The social penalty the test exacted on the 'positive ones' would very quickly become known.

By now the media machine was unstoppable. HIV could live on toilet seats for up to three weeks. It lurked on the doorknobs of homosexual bedrooms. By late 1986, the world was awash with documentaries featuring tales of HIV-infected, killer prostitutes with grudges against males, or sex-crazed rape villains blackmailing defenceless housewives with HIV infection. Firemen became fearful of giving car-crash or drowning victims the kiss of life. Dentists squirmed for the first time when they looked into an open mouth. Says one 'positive' individual who remembers all too well:

"I was treated like a leper and a fiend. My family abandoned me. They refused to eat with me until checking it was safe with the doctor. When I had dental treatment, the dentist wore a helmet and a visor. I became so afraid I might infect others, I would wash my hands over and over again with bleach until they were raw."[22]

The declared pathological make-up of AIDS was also a horror. Here was a virus (HIV) which could creep into your system and remain dormant for up to 10 years before striking. All over the world, doctors began announcing a new and shocking diagnosis: *"You have HIV, the virus that causes AIDS. There is no cure."* One day - nothing. The next, lesions all over the body, barrier nurses face-masking around you, friends and relatives making excuses and disappearing. And then the spasms, the haemorrhaging and the croaking of your last breath before becoming another one of the horrifying and mounting AIDS statistics.

The press scare stories became so virulent that virtual panic broke out in the gay communities of the Castro, San Francisco and West Hollywood, Los Angeles. Rallies of the fearful hit the streets of major cities throughout the world. As AIDS appeared to spread into middle-class heterosexuality, fear began to play on those deemed outside the declared high-risk groups. Newspapers fed the public bewildering

---

[22] Shenton, Joan, ibid.

stories of poor souls who, upon receiving the dreaded HIV positive result, had climbed the stairs to the hospital roof and launched themselves into oblivion.[23] Husbands, wives and lovers began to whisper, *"Not tonight, Joseph/Josephine,"* looking at each other, wondering if perhaps their previous history had now somehow rendered them irreversibly 'armed and biologically dangerous'. Everyone was a target. Everyone was at risk.[24]

Through the power of the media, the AIDS monster was loosed upon a dazed and tremulous world.[25] AIDS was uniting the public with princesses, politicians and the paparazzi at the bedsides of Rock Hudson, Liberace, Freddie Mercury, Arthur Ashe – their gaunt faces and final harrowing days broadcast around the world. From Philadelphia (Tom Hanks) to Britain's most popular soap, East Enders (Todd Carty), 'facts' about AIDS were dramatised and driven home into an unquestioning collective psyche. Something grotesque was stalking our planet and the future looked bleak.

Today, in our battle against AIDS, the international medical community and the major pharmaceutical companies appear to be pulling out all the stops in an effort to combat this dreadful disease. AIDS, we are told, is only just being contained in the West, thanks largely to the new drugs being developed which have the potential to retard the spread of HIV infection. But the research is very costly and success has been limited to date. Key global health agencies such as The World Health Organization tell us that with no money to buy the

---

[23] *"I'd Shoot My Son if He Had AIDS."* So ran the *Sun* newspaper headline on 14th December 1985. The headline was accompanied by a photograph of Dad holding a shotgun to his son's head. Commenting on this, Kenneth Thompson, author of *Moral Panics*, stated *"The coverage managed to combine some of the most potent images of threats to normal life, family breakdown, infanticide, teenage sexuality, homosexuality and contagious disease."* (**Thompson, Kenneth** *Moral Panics*, Routledge Press, 1997. An analysis of how perceptions are shaped and reflected through the media over time).

[24] *"Why Must The Innocent Suffer?"* *Daily Express* 25th September 1985. *"AIDS: The NEW Holocaust."* *Sunday Telegraph*, November 1985. *"All Are Potential Victims."* *Sunday Times*, November 1985. See also *Guardian Newspapers*, 14th September 1995: *"Angel of Death"* - the story of a mysterious young woman who had apparently infected nine men within a six-month period. Despite the £10,000 offered by various newspapers for her name and whereabouts, no 'angel' was ever traced. The hundreds of UK and overseas journalists who had converged on the tiny Irish town of Dungavon all left within a few days.

[25] In November 1986, the UK government announced a £20 million ($32 million) advertising campaign, which included leaflets delivered to every door, nation-wide posters, radio, TV and cinema coverage of the horrors of AIDS.

necessary drugs, AIDS is now devastating the continents of Africa, South East Asia and India. There seems to be no let up in the gloomy forecasts. Associated Press, broadcasting on WorldNetDaily on 23rd November 1999, reports:

"Despite powerful new drugs and massive information programs, the AIDS virus is spreading at a growing rate with an estimated 33.4 million people said to be carrying HIV, according to a report released today. The UN program on HIV/AIDS and the World Health Organization said it expected the number of infections world-wide to continue to grow, fuelled by an increase in the use of injected drugs.

According to the report, 33.6 million people, including 1.2 million children, are carrying HIV, the virus that causes AIDS. It said sub-Saharan Africa continues to be the worst hit, with close to 70 percent of the global total of those with HIV. Most will die in the next 10 years, joining the 13.7 million Africans who have already died of AIDS, increasing healthcare costs and cutting productivity, the report said."

And so there appears to be little hope of relief in sight. Nothing about AIDS which was incurable in 1985 is curable today, in spite of the billions we have spent. The condoms, the safe/safer sex education programs and plethora of drug treatments seem to be having little impact. Almost twenty years into the history of AIDS, it appears that all the money, the red ribbons, the super-technology, the strident politicians and AIDS rallies in the world are useless in the face of the implacable and unrelenting new HIV micro-enemy. AIDS is still the merciless ravager of our planet, and for the last 20 years the world has been shivering involuntarily with the titillation and the terror of it all.

This is the story the world has been given.

And the world has bought it all.

* * * * *

30

The following is a summary of what the public understands about AIDS today:

- AIDS is a range of diseases arising from infection as a result of the virus known as HIV.
- The AIDS test is a simple and accurate method of detecting HIV.
- The virus is contracted and spread in humans through 'one-off' and/or promiscuous unprotected homo/heterosexual activity, through the sharing of intravenous drug users' contaminated needles or through contaminated blood supplies.
- Pregnant women who test positive can pass the virus on to their unborn child. HIV can also be transmitted to the baby outside of the womb through breast-feeding.
- In the West, HIV infection is spreading among women and heterosexual men and is increasing exponentially every year.
- Drugs are available to treat AIDS patients but they are very expensive. A new range of anti-HIV drugs, the 'protease inhibitors', are now believed to be more effective.
- AIDS is devastating the Third World.
- There is currently no cure for AIDS.

With the exception of AIDS drugs being expensive, _everything you have just read in the above summary is entirely false and has no scientific validity whatsoever_. In beginning to unravel the incredible deception that has been woven around the whole myth of AIDS, it has firstly been necessary to examine the vital role played by the CDC and EIS in helping to establish the AIDS crisis.[26] There were however a number of other key players fulfilling critical roles in the formative years of this 'crisis'. Our attention will now focus on one individual in particular, that most celebrated of virus hunters - the spearer of the infamous HIV, Dr Robert Gallo.

---

[26] _Plain Dealer Online_, 8th November 1998. **"CDC Flouts its Own Human Rights Rules"**
"...fashioning scientific partnerships on nearly every inhabited continent, and undertaking medical research without obtaining basic agreements to avoid abuses. Medication was dispensed without assurance that patients be fully informed, monitored for safety or free to refuse experimental drugs in all 96 research projects conducted by the CDC in the last 10 years," say investigators Epstein and Sloat.

It is George Orwell's apocalyptic 1984, and America is in the grip of a new and terrifying enemy that is predicted to wipe out entire nations in the next few decades....

FAKE DIAMONDS
AND UNATTENDED IGNITION KEYS

Gallo's early years

23rd April 1984 and The National Academy of Sciences auditorium in Washington DC was packed with journalists and television crews abuzz with anticipation. US Health Secretary Margaret Heckler emerged and greeted the assembled throng, declaring: *"Today we add another miracle to the long honour roll of American medicine and science. Today's discovery represents the triumph of science over a dreaded disease."*

The miracle Heckler announced was that a team of virologists led by Dr Robert Gallo had isolated a virus that was apparently causing AIDS. This was a tremendous announcement and the enormity of Heckler's words, coming at a time when the climate of AIDS-induced fear was at its height, could not be under-estimated. Speaking of Gallo's work as an all-American miracle discovery, Heckler reminded the public of the gratitude it owed to medicine for triumphing over this dreaded disease.

And then it was the turn of Dr Gallo: *"Dr Gallo, Sir! Dr Gallo, this way! Sir, this way!"* chorused the hordes, the whirring and flashing bank of cameras more befitting a royal arrival. The jostling photographers vied for that special Gallo victory pose to accompany next day's world editorials which would triumphantly announce: *"The beginning of the end of the scourge of AIDS!"* With no demanding questions being asked of Dr Gallo, the likeable, but rather nervous-looking doctor produced what he described as photographic evidence of the cornered virus and briefly outlined the supporting science behind the discovery. And all the time, the flashing and the whirring. This was big, big news, and Gallo was quite literally being fêted as the saviour of the human race.

But how very different the future of AIDS and HIV might have been, had Margaret Heckler opened the press conference thus:

"Science and research must be studied in the context of all the interested parties involved. The questions centre on

determining the relative weight of the various allies in the 'fact-creating' process - e.g. funding bodies, businesses, departments of state, professions and other scientists. In analysing scientific debates, <u>one should always ask what social, institutional, political and philosophical interests lie behind often apparently 'neutral' and 'technical' knowledge claims.</u>"[27]

An important piece of advice, ten years too late and in any case forgotten in the razzmatazz of the public canonisation of Dr Gallo. After all, for the good of mankind, science and scientists had been pulling out all the stops to bag possibly the biggest killer this planet had experienced since the plagues of the 15th century. And of course, in this all-out mercy mission to save so many human lives, it goes without saying that nothing improper would have been taking place... doesn't it?

To our very great cost, and hence the reason for this book, we shall see that such trust and benevolence extended towards the science supporting AIDS and HIV is misplaced and naïve in the extreme. A special panel of the National Academy of Sciences would, a few years after the Gallo announcement, be meeting to discuss:

"...a persistent pattern of behaviour on Dr Gallo's part of repeated misrepresentation, suppression and distortion of data, and the misrepresentation of findings in such a manner that would enhance Dr Gallo's claim to priority."[28]

As we shall see, the above panel was by no means the only one that would be urgently convened over the years following the 1984 press conference to discuss the methodology of Dr Gallo. What exactly was this man getting up to in the enclosed and almost impenetrable world of beakers, bunsen burners and centrifugal separation? Before we visit the Gallo laboratories in Bethesda, Maryland, it is important to examine the scientific and medical culture into which the AIDS crisis reared its head in the first place. Establishing what attitudes prevailed towards the causes of illness and disease at that time will highlight why

---

[27] University of Manchester Institute of Science & Technology (UMIST) research methodology course handout, 1994

[28] *Chicago Tribune*, "Scientific Panel Accuses Gallo of Recklessness," 27th March 1992

the search for the cause of AIDS was so dominated by the virus hunters.

The National Institutes of Health (NIH) in America began in 1887 as the Hygienic Laboratory. An insignificant organisation at the time, it was actually affiliated to the Public Health Service, which itself was affiliated to the US Navy. The NIH has retained its military connections, the Surgeon General to this day wearing a white uniform. In the 1930s Congress created the National Cancer Institute (NCI), which became the first subdivision of the NIH to focus on any particular illness, and the organisation became known as the National Institutes of Health. James Shannon became the director of the NIH in 1955, taking up his position at a time when the US was being ravaged by a polio epidemic. Shannon persuaded Congress to release considerable amounts of money to fund an all-out medical war against polio. With the natural waning of the polio epidemic in the early 1960s, the many students who had been trained to battle against this disease were trained exclusively in virology, and they were now specialists in their field.

After polio, these same specialists began casting around for further employment and began concentrating their efforts on the search for the cure for cancer. And being virologists, they were all hunting for the virus that must surely lurk behind one of mankind's biggest killers. Any ideas that cancer might be a toxic, metabolic, environmental or radiation-based disease were given little credence.[29] It was a virus and a virus only they hunted - nothing else was considered. Gallo himself would later remark: *"Sometimes we virologists have a virus in search of a disease."*[30]

As we shall discover, the narrow ambitions of the virus-hunting establishment have produced some highly embarrassing and extremely costly medical research failures. This is particularly true of the research commissioned by Congress for Richard Nixon's 1971 War on Cancer, the NCI announcing in that same year that a vaccine

---

[29] **Day, Phillip** *Cancer: Why We're Still Dying to Know the Truth*, Credence Publications, 1999. ISBN: 0953501248

[30] Maggiore, Christine *What If Everything You Thought You Knew About AIDS Was Wrong?* AFFA Publications, 1999

against cancer would be available by 1976.[31] The dominant power the virus establishment wielded and its disconcerting ability to get things badly wrong on occasions is highlighted most succinctly by South African barrister and AZT critic Anthony Brink:

"As we've all seen, when these oracles mumble and the press trumpets blare, the entire world eagerly gobbles up every word without demur. How many fake health crises have they delivered still-born into the popular consciousness? Take the idle herpes scare in the 70s, the phantom syphilis epidemic of the 30s and 40s, the great swine flu fiasco and that shining emblem of medical idiocy, the pellagra plague in the first four decades of this century, treating the people with arsenic and ruthless quarantine, which turned out to be plain malnutrition among the politically awkward droves of poor whites in [America's] deep south industrial towns.

We need contagious epidemics to fight. Even imagined ones. They're tremendously psychologically useful. Germ theory so dominates contemporary medicine that it seeks germs everywhere, the more virulent the better, and especially if they can be linked to our culture's great taboos - sex and death. Anything to avoid facing up to unappealing political realities like widespread chronic under-nourishment among a shameful number of our countrymen as the time-honoured and common-sense cause of broken health."[32]

Regular intakes of nutritious food - an excellent remedy for the maintaining of health it seems, but a sensible prescription often lost in our overall reverence for the pharmaceutically driven medical model.[33]

When a disease fails to perform to a given pattern, it is vital to the medical establishment that they are seen by the general populace to be in control of the situation and understanding of all its complexities. It was virologist Carlton Guidachek who first put forward the notion of the slow virus – that an invader could gain entrance to the body, hide up and strike, perhaps years later. Although sounding quite plausible to

---

[31] *In These Times*, 8-15th August 1992

[32] **Brink, Anthony,** *The Pope of AIDS,* http://www.virusmyth.com/aids/data/abpope.htm

[33] See section entitled *Entrenched Scientific Error*

the laity and even to some medical experts, the idea of the slow virus would eventually be consigned to the scrap-heap once the true research data became available. In reality, actual causes of disease are not dominated by the virus. Bryan Ellison comments:

> It was a few virologists in the early sixties who simply invented the notion of the slow virus, [a concept] which was actually awarded the Nobel Prize in 1976. Of course, once the concept of slow viruses had come to be accepted, it was possible to blame conceivably any disease on a virus, no matter how uninfectious the disease was....."[34]

We also had the combined influence of the CDC and the EIS shaping our understanding of health and disease. In a discussion on 'shaped' understandings and preconceived ideas, Noam Chomsky, Professor of Linguistics and Philosophy at Massachusetts Institute of Technology, stated that:

> "Hundreds of billions of dollars are spent every year to control the public mind."[35]

Subliminally or otherwise, is it that inconceivable that such vast sums of money might be influencing attitudes towards illness today? Bryan Ellison thinks not:

> "By the time AIDS came along, the virus hunters controlled all the reins of power in the biomedical research establishments, and so naturally they dominated the research on AIDS. The very first person to describe AIDS cases - Michael Gottlieb in Los Angeles describing five homosexual men with pneumocystis carinii pneumonia - himself was already suggesting that it was caused by the herpes-type virus, cytomegalovirus. That was the result of the virus hunters being in a dominant position in the establishment."[36]

There was no choice in the matter. Until proven otherwise, any new and emerging disease from the early sixties onwards was first and foremost going to be viral. And that was also true for some of the well established diseases, especially cancer.

---

[34] **Ellison, Bryan,** "Rethinking AIDS" interview, March 1994, www.rethinkingaids.com
[35] *Continuum Magazine*, October 1996. Today the NIH annual expenditure is in excess of $10 billion (*Rethinking AIDS* interview).
[36] Ellison, Brian, ibid.

It was now the early 1970s and Robert Gallo was working out of laboratories in Bethesda, Maryland, under the wing of the National Cancer Institute, and reporting to the immensely powerful Litton Bionetics. Gallo, a fully trained virologist, had been set a specific brief. Steven S Hall, author of *Commotion in the Blood*, says this of Gallo's early calling:

> *"Gallo set the research agenda, did the hiring and ran the lab meetings. Every lab has an overriding mission and Gallo's was no exception. Like many virologists, Gallo had been looking for a human virus believed to cause several forms of human cancer..."* [37]

Gallo was hunting a particularly nasty virus, a virus hidden deep perhaps, but a virus he believed existed and could be detected - the virus most likely responsible for the dreaded leukaemia.

Leukaemia is the umbrella term to denote the unrestricted growth of under-developed 'rogue' blood cells. In failing to mature properly, they create greater and greater numbers of themselves until they crowd out the healthy blood cells, bringing the immune system to a kind of leukaemic gridlock. In their attempt to validate the 'leukaemia as virus' hypothesis, Gallo's lab technicians would obtain the cancerous leukaemia cells and concentrate primarily on trying to manufacture a 'culture' in which the cancerous cells might live. This would then allow the researchers time to study the cells, in order to try and identify any attacking virus.

As a point of interest, more prized than isolating any virus, the virologists' Holy Grail was independently to create in these cultures the infamous killer T-cells. Just as the alchemist pursues the life force, the fifth essence (quintessence), and the astrophysicist the single-line equation explaining the universe, so the virologist dreams of creating T-cells – those unique and incredibly complex fighters in our immune system...(*"Having such killers at our beck and call would surely then make it possible for us to manipulate them, train them even and then direct them to destroy any invading cancerous cells."*) Discovering the recipe for promoting the growth of the T-cell was an ongoing pursuit.

---

[37] **Hall, Stephen S** *A Commotion In The Blood*, Little, Brown and Co. 1997

And creating the 'culture' in which the cells might grow was, and still is time-consuming and expensive. The laboratory beakers containing Gallo's precious and painstakingly prepared cultures were all meticulously labelled and kept refrigerated at the necessary low temperature.

And then, in late 1974, after almost three years of experimentation, a leukaemic virus was apparently isolated, which Gallo named Human Leukaemia 23 (HL23V). Gallo immediately reported the discovery to the local scientific community, and submitted a paper on the isolated virus to *Science* which was published in January 1975. Newspapers were quick to report on Gallo's remarkable achievement, but his peers were even quicker to question his claims, asking what culture he used, how he had prepared it and how he had gone about his experiments. Gallo hedged and would not reveal the chemistry of his culture, nor would he share the exact manner in which his virus had been isolated - only that it had. Concerning the validation of scientific claims, Geoff Watts, author of *Pleasing the Patient*, reminds us of traditional scientific methodology:

> *"Researchers are required not only to publish their findings, but also to describe their method in sufficient detail to allow others to repeat the work. Indeed the repeatability of an experiment is one of the criteria by which scientists judge the claims of their peers."*[38]

Gallo's reluctance to conform to this sensible scientific methodology served only to anger his peers. Their questions became more forcefully posed: *"Where's the virus, Dr Gallo? And how do you preserve the cells?"*

With pressure mounting on Gallo to produce the necessary evidence to support his 'discovery', suddenly... a calamity! One morning lab workers arrived to find that the refrigerator containing the supposed leukaemia virus and the precious 'cultures' had been mysteriously unplugged. Any evidence of the HL23V, supposedly preserved in the secret 'culture', known only as WHE, had now been ruined. Says Gallo of this unfortunate but quite timely disaster:

---

[38] **Watts, Geoff** *Pleasing the Patient*, Faber and Faber, 1992

"We were screwed. We were only able to say, 'Honest, we had it!' and prove it to nobody." [39]

Popular medical literature of the day however makes no mention of these 'minor' irregularities along the way, and credits Gallo with all the 'leukaemia breakthrough' headlines. It was Robert Gallagher, a technician at Gallo's lab during this period, who later stated that they hadn't *actually* wrapped their hands around an *actual* virus; rather they had inferred its presence based on a number of intricate virological predictions. [40] Exactly the same species of 'virtual truth' can be found propping up much of what we know as quantum physics. Anyone wishing for direct evidence that various exotically named particles such as quarks, nuons and gluons, actually exist are quite breezily quoted Heisenberg's Uncertainty Principle. *"One can estimate where the particle might be going and where it might have been, but not actually where it is."* That in laymen's terms is the central tenet of particle physics. The virtual existence of the quark and the massive funding to track it down bears uncanny resemblance to the chemokines and cytokines rearing their virtual heads in the blood sciences of today - equally exotic and authoritative in name as the quark family, but equally elusive to the rational, enquiring mind. Similarly, in the case of Gallo's HL23V, the overriding question is this: *"Was there ever really a virus in the first place?"*

And what about that secret 'culture' known only as WHE? It was perhaps prudent of Gallo that he did not expand on its exact make-up. The initials WHE stand for 'whole human embryo'. Aborted whole foetuses, developed no further than the first trimester, had various cell extractions performed upon them, the extracted cells forming the base composite for the melted HL23V. Readers comforting themselves that foetuses not exceeding the first three months are probably just underdeveloped cell matter may be shocked to discover otherwise, as the following extract from "Love Your Unborn Neighbour" reveals:

"By the sixth week from fertilisation, tiny fingers appear, followed within days by toes. At the same time the eyes develop the lens and retina and the eyelids begin to appear. Brainwaves can also be detected. At seven weeks the child has

[39] Hall, Stephen S, ibid.
[40] Hall, Stephen S, ibid.

its own fingerprints, the outer ear is present and the inner ear, with its hearing and balancing mechanisms, is well established. At twelve weeks the child's features become more defined. The unborn baby can open or close the lips, wrinkle the forehead, raise the eyebrows and turn the head. The baby's sex is easy to determine, the baby measures about 90mm and weighs 45 grammes and she is also sensitive to touch."[41]

Three years' lucrative funding and thousands of man-hours later and finally… a virus that existed only by the word of Dr Gallo. And now it had melted! With his reputation severely dented, and Gallo still insistent that he had isolated the leukaemia virus, he immediately began scouring the labs for a cell specialist, someone with the necessary qualifications to resurrect his battered HL23V program. Steve Hall recounts:

"It would not be exaggerating to characterize the mood in the lab as scientifically based hysteria. And into this dark environment of desperation, suspicion and frantic scientific scrambling arrived Doris Ann Morgan…" [42]

With a Phd in Biochemical Genetics, Doris Morgan joined Gallo from Litton Bionetics where she had held the post of senior scientist in cell biology. Working alongside Frank Ruscetti, her brief from Gallo was *"Get me that HL23!"* Steven Hall again:

"Ruscetti's tack was to test every known bone marrow cell line and as many embryos as possible to see if he could scare up the same factor that had disappeared in the great refrigerator meltdown, and he did a prodigious amount of work. Before he finally stopped looking he had tested close to 250 cell types, all failures.

Morgan took a different tack. She decided to stick with the existing system of growing leukaemic cells and see if she couldn't tinker with the conditions enough to nudge the cells into expanded growth. While working in Houston she had managed to keep a number of white blood cells taken from

---

[41] *New Scientist*, "Earliest Feelings Help to Develop the Senses," 7th May 1987. Quoted in *Love Your Unborn Neighbour,* SPUC Publications, London, 1994
[42] Hall, Stephen S, ibid.

mice, known as granulocytes, in test tubes for up to 3 weeks, which at the time, was considered a phenomenally long out-of-body experience for a blood cell. The leukaemic cells Gallo studied were also granulocytic, also of myeloid (bone marrow) origin. Perhaps Morgan could tweak the system a bit."[43]

And in March 1975, after much tinkering, Morgan noticed the appearance of cells apparently not seen before. Could they be the hallowed T-cells, the Holy Grail of immuno-biology? Said Gallo at the time: *"My God, this is important! But we've gotta be sure we're right."*[44]

Gallo soon began informing his peers that his lab had discovered the recipe for T-cell growth culture. His peers abruptly sat up. This was a massive step towards the elusive cure for leukaemia, and for the war against cancer in general. The administration of a strain of this factor in the patient could promote an absolute proliferation of killer T-cells, that would in turn make short shrift of any cancerous cells.

This time Gallo did share his recipe for human T-cell growth factor with the scientific community, submitting his research for full publication in *Science*, March 1976. Gallo subsequently received hundreds of calls from immunologists, complaining that they couldn't get the growth factor to work. Says Ruscetti, *"They were saying we were crazy, but it was only because they didn't really want to accept it."*[45]

Another dead end. But Gallo, impervious to the scepticism of his peers, sensed that Morgan's discovery was going to be big, and he calculatedly made a phone call upstairs. Stephen Hall again:

"Given the personalities of Gallo and Ruscetti, it's just one of those things in human dynamics. They saw the significance of it; this was Nobel Prize stuff. Those personalities never concerned themselves with personal aspects, just with the scientific problem, and Doris got left in the dust. Finally around 23rd January 1978, Phillip Markham from Litton Bionetics

---

[43] Hall, Stephen S, ibid.

[44] Hall, Stephen S, ibid.

[45] Hall, Stephen S, ibid.

informed Morgan in a letter that her job would be terminated."[46]

Morgan was being moved on. Asked if Gallo ever treated her badly, Morgan's only regret was that Gallo had taken all the credit for the discovery of the special factor, which, perhaps for Morgan was a blessing in disguise. Gallo's growth factor, instead of being rightfully discarded, was adopted by Steve Rosenberg, and its name changed in 1979 to Interleukin 2, IL2 for short. Rosenberg, who would later become Ronald Reagan's cancer surgeon, took IL2 to new and dizzy heights. IL2 was fêted as a 'cancer breakthrough' on the front cover of *Fortune* magazine on 25th November 1985 and Rosenberg was awarded the $100,000 Armand Hammer cancer prize the same year for his work.

Anyone wishing to embark on a study of the long history of 'cancer breakthroughs' will find the exercise a very sobering one. The NCI cancer vaccine, promised for 1976, has of course failed to materialise. And when traced with any objectivity, the history of IL2's 'effectiveness' in treating cancer is a horrendous litany of medical disaster. Almost every patient treated with IL2 suffered fever, malaise, nausea or vomiting, diarrhoea, sharp drops in blood pressure, skin rashes, breathing difficulties, liver abnormalities and irregularities in blood chemistry. Rosenberg himself details a number of horrifying case histories, and one in particular where the administration of IL2 had precipitated amongst other things, vomiting, swollen joints, lung fluid and 'vascular leak syndrome' where blood would ooze through the vessel walls and collect under the skin. [47] Reading between the lines, it is evident that many a hapless patient died of his oncologist. Charles G Moertel, a renowned and respected physician at that time, delivered the following opinion on the benefits of Interleukin 2 in the *Journal of the American Medical Association (JAMA)*, 12th December 1986.

> *"The treatment itself is an awesome experience, usually requiring weeks of hospitalisation, much of which must be spent in intensive care if the patient is to survive the devastating toxic reactions. In short, IL2 is associated with unacceptably severe toxicity and astronomical cost. This is not balanced by any persuasive evidence of true net therapeutic*

---

[46] Hall, Stephen S, ibid.

[47] **Rosenberg, Steven** *The Transformed Cell,* Putnam, New York: 1992

gain. IL2 would not seem to merit further application in the compassionate management of patients with cancer."

And today, thirteen years later, the Chiron Corporation, pharmaceutical manufacturers and suppliers of Interleukin 2, state on their web page that *"...many people are leading normal lives because of IL2."* Credence has requested details from Chiron Corporation on the specific manner in which people have been helped by IL2. To date there has been no reply.

In reality, Doris Morgan's much vaunted IL2, remembered only as Gallo's discovery, has proven to be yet another dead end in a history of dead ends for our senior virologist. And he never won the Nobel Prize either.

What then of Gallo's credentials to date? Anthony Brink is brief and dismissive about the early days of 'the Pope of AIDS':

> *"Gallo's disgraceful behaviour in relation to his AIDS research was no first. Had he not ascended to such power and influence within the federal health bureaucracy, it is likely his claims to have found a single infectious cause for the disparate diseases grouped together as AIDS in the early 1980s would have been laughed out of court.*
>
> *After all, this was the bright spark who, with almost as much fanfare as that at his flash-bulb popping HIV press announcement, had loudly touted his discovery of what he claimed to be the first identified human retrovirus, HL23V, in the mid 1970s. After another look, this exciting find turned out to be nothing of the kind, just another accidental laboratory artefact. His laboratory hadn't done the most basic controls. To his great embarrassment, Gallo had to retract his claims, and HL23V then modestly retired as a virus from the scientific lexicon."[48]*

And what of Gallo's team? What of their credentials? A brief trawl through the records reveals that Syed Zaki Salahuddin, one of Gallo's closest lab associates, was convicted of using Gallo's laboratory credit card to purchase supplies from the NIH central stores; supplies which he then spirited out in order to set up his own research laboratory.

---

[48] Brink, Anthony, ibid.

Having established his own lab, Salahuddin then installed his wife as director. Running alongside this venture, Salahuddin also arranged for various 'private interest' items to be manufactured, all within Gallo's own laboratory, which were then sold to outside competitors.[49] Dr Dharam Ablashi, a fellow worker at Gallo's laboratory, was recruited as a sales rep for this clandestine outfit. Salahuddin was ordered to repay $12,000 and complete 1,750 hours community service. Salahuddin was also one of the principal authors of the early papers announcing the discovery of an HIV. Gallo's second-in-command at the lab, Prem Sarin, would later find himself on trial for directing $25,000 into his own account which should have been spent hiring a lab technician. Sarin was equally involved in the early papers on the 'discovery' of HIV.[50] In his "Lab Rat" article, Seth Roberts summarises the early years thus:

> *"Gallo's lab has been described by past and present employees as a 'den of thieves' and as being 'full of mediocrities'. In its quantity of intrigue and capricious purges, it resembles a 'medieval Italian town', says one former employee. He adds, 'I'm surprised somebody hasn't killed someone there.'*
>
> *Without AIDS, Gallo would have been simply another grasping, over-productive, underscrupulous scientist. Dozens of awards, hundreds of papers, thousands of tantrums, a vast phone bill, a ringside seat at the discovery of IL2 and HTLV1, and a handful of derailed careers - that would have been the Gallo legacy. AIDS, however, gave him the chance to really make a difference."[51]*

And 'make a difference' he did. IL2 was becoming a fading memory for Gallo. It was now the early 1980s, and Gallo's attention was becoming increasingly diverted towards Gottlieb's up-and-coming, but as yet unnamed AIDS syndrome. But just prior to Gallo's full pursuit of the virus that *'must surely lie at the heart of AIDS'*, another startling claim was made by some members of his team. In 1980, Frank Ruscetti and fellow biologist Bernard Poiesz apparently isolated the very first human cancer retrovirus, naming it Human T-cell Leukaemia Virus or HTLV1 for short. The 'discovery' of the cancer

---

[49] **Oostram, Neenyah** *New York Native,* 14th August 1989, issue #330

[50] Shenton, Joan, ibid.

[51] *Rethinking AIDS* Homepage, December 1999

retrovirus (a generalised description of this interesting little molecule being *"I can't see it under the microscope, and you can't see it either. But if Gallo's lab tells us there's one there, then what reason do we have to disbelieve them?"*) has subsequently precipitated massive injections of cash into virus labs the world over. It will come as no surprise to the reader that yet again, HTLV1 has proven to be just another of those 'Gallo lab discoveries' that no-one has yet been able independently to verify. This fact does not stop Robin McKie, science editor for the *Observer* newspaper from writing:

> *"Once a contender for the Nobel prize, for discovering the first human cancer-causing virus, Gallo...."* etc, etc. [52]

But it was to be one artefact in particular, the elusive HIV, which would prove to be the most destructive 'quark' in the history of immunology.

1983 was the beginning of Robert Gallo's public ascendancy into the AIDS debate. The following chronology traces the key events leading up to Gallo's world-wide announcement of his 'discovery' of HIV and that 'HIV was probably the sole cause of AIDS'.

In May 1983, fellow virus hunter Luc Montagnier from the Pasteur Institute trustingly submits a paper to Robert Gallo, outlining what Montagnier believes is a new type of virus. Gallo senses that Montagnier may be on to something and edits the paper in such a manner that the reader would concur that the Montagnier virus is a member of the same family as Gallo's HTLV1 virus, regardless of the fact that HTLV1 had been completely discredited.

In July 1983, Gallo receives a shipment of factor for his inspection, which Montagnier states contains his virus, named Lymphadenopathy-associated Virus or LAV. Montagnier believes that this is the virus which may lie at the heart of AIDS.

On 14th September 1983, unaware of the growing US interest in his findings, Montagnier lectures on the blood test he has developed, which can apparently detect certain antibodies in the blood - antibodies

---

[52] **McKie, Robin** *Observer Newspapers*, "Resurrection of the AIDS Pioneer," 22th December 1996

that might indicate the presence of his virus, and hence, the onset of AIDS.

On 15th September 1983, Montagnier files for a UK patent on his potentially lucrative AIDS blood test. Throughout all of these proceedings, Gallo has been in attendance at a number of meetings where the technicalities of Montagnier's virus and its supporting science are intimately discussed. These and other factors would later add weight to accusations that Gallo was attempting to plagiarise and then 'cash in' on Montagnier's work.

On 22nd November 1983, after close observation of Montagnier's potentially momentous discovery, Gallo announces that his lab too has isolated certain particles, which might also be the AIDS virus. Not unsurprisingly though, an independent analysis of the samples submitted by Gallo for verification produced no trace of a virus. To counter these embarrassing findings, Gallo's lab almost immediately announces the discovery of yet another virus, which is named HTLVIII. Gallo states that this is most definitely the much sought-after AIDS virus. A subsequent enquiry to establish the actual existence of Gallo's HTLVIII (later renamed HIV) determines that yet again, Gallo had failed to isolate any virus. Roche Laboratories found no trace of HTLVIII in the ten samples submitted to them.

On 12th March 1984, despite the fact that HTLVIII does not exist, James Curran from the CDC meets with Gallo, and tells him that the blood test procedure that Gallo has been working on confirms the presence of Gallo's HTLVIII virus in blood samples of suspected AIDS patients. In other words, Gallo claims discovery of a virus, and then claims a method to detect said virus. This 'full-circle' scenario is then scientifically validated by a close colleague in an influential position. More respectably translated, the CDC has just informed the NIH and the NCI that everything is satisfactory. Gallo's two inventions will go on to 'confirm' to the waiting world that the epidemic known as AIDS is viral. Says Gallo later: *"In Curran's view, we had determined the cause of AIDS."*[53]

---

[53] History of key events, 11th August 1986. Robert Gallo's sworn declaration.

In the same month, Gallo's well-timed letter to the *Lancet* is published, telling of his 'struggle' to isolate Montagnier's LAV, the virus that Montagnier believed was responsible for AIDS.[54] And indeed, several years later, Montagnier would confess that his own lab had never actually isolated the virus known as LAV, according to the standard rules for isolation.[55]

On 23rd April 1984 Heckler introduces Gallo to the world. That same day, Gallo submits his blood test kit for a US patent. Anthony Brink drily comments:

> *"In cravenly seeking the endorsement of Big American Science, Montagnier naively left his keys in the ignition, and the next thing it was gone. Gallo resprayed Montagnier's LAV as HTLVIII. It was later renamed HIV on the basis of Gallo's claims, without proof to warrant its fearsome title."*[56]

In short, at that Washington press conference which proclaimed the discovery of the vicious virus causing AIDS, there was no virus.

May 29th 1985 Gallo's patent on his own blood test is granted. Montagnier's patent is still pending at this time. (The patent was never granted.)

December 1992 Robert Gallo is convicted of science fraud by the Office of Research Integrity, an oversight department of the National Institutes of Health (NIH), based on his declaration that he had discovered HIV.

* * * * *

Anthony Brink comments:

> *"Having sneaked through a patent application on the blood test, thus guaranteeing him a fortune in royalties, Gallo went on to publish four papers in the prestigious if dowdy journal*

---

[54] *Lancet*, 5th March 1984

[55] Q. *"Could it be anything else than a retrovirus?"* A: *"No, well... after all, yes. We did not purify."* Extract from an interview between Luc Montagnier and Djamel Tahi. **'Did Montagnier Discover HIV?'** Continuum Vol 5, No 2, January 1998

[56] Brink, Anthony, ibid.

Science *two weeks later. Then the trouble started: an exuberant international dispute over who stole the fake diamonds. For Gallo, this was the Paula trouble that led to Monica.*"[57]

And fake diamonds they were too. For the habit of *inferring* the presence of a virus without actually being able to lay hands on one is a habit not solely confined to the Gallo labs. To loyal readers of *The National Enquirer*, Montagnier's money-spinning LAV may well be alive and well (along with the obligatory photographs of Elvis). To the rational enquirer however, Montagnier's LAV remains elusive to this day. The scandalous use of 'inferred' photography in modern-day science and its accompanying pitfalls is discussed in more detail later.

Montagnier was incensed when he learned of Gallo's televised announcement. He believed that Gallo had quite simply stolen his virus and was now going to reap the rewards. Montagnier was not going to forego his cut. Branching away from the usual loose laboratory rules for virus verification, Montagnier pressed for definite proof that his share of the expected proceeds would be 'isolated', verified and then visibly transferred into his own bank account. He wasn't going to rely on Gallo only inferring that this would soon take place. Virtual funds would not suffice in this instance.

The subsequent wranglings between Gallo's laboratory and the Pasteur Institute and between the French and US governments became increasingly acrimonious, with accusations of scientific plagiarism and 'inexplicable' cross-contamination of evidence. Presidents Reagan and Chirac persuaded Montagnier and Gallo to meet up to sort out their differences. They emerged from their meeting in a Frankfurt hotel, agreeing to share the royalties on the blood testing kits, which, by 1994, would amount to $35,000,000.[58] Whether or not Montagnier has ever forgiven Robert Gallo for exhibiting a photograph of Montagnier's unsubstantiated 'virus' at that Washington press conference, claiming it as his own, will probably never be known.

---

[57] Brink, Anthony, ibid.
[58] Shenton, Joan, Ibid.

So where was Montagnier's virus? Where was Gallo's virus? In truth, on that spring day in April 1984, reinforced with the full backing of the American medical, political and scientific establishment, a photograph of someone else's *virtual* virus, no virus of his own, and a lucrative patent application at the back of his mind, Dr Robert Gallo braced himself to enter the world's stage. Brushing down his suit, he entered the whirring, flashing arena of the National Academy of Sciences auditorium, announced a major breakthrough in the battle against AIDS, and quite unabashedly soaked up every last little bit of the worship bestowed upon him.

COOKING UP HIV

What an ugly stew...

The Emperor's New Clothes: *Many years ago lived an emperor, who thought so much of new clothes that he spent all his money in order to obtain them. One day two swindlers came to his city and declared they could manufacture the finest cloth to be imagined. Their colours and patterns, they said, were not only exceptionally beautiful, but the clothes made of their material possessed the wonderful quality of being invisible to any man who was unfit for his office or unpardonably stupid.*

"That must be wonderful cloth," thought the emperor. "I must have this cloth woven for me without delay." Advancing a large sum of money to the swindlers, he requested they set to work immediately. The swindlers set up two looms, and pretended to be very hard at work. They asked for the finest silk and the most precious gold-cloth; all they were given, they secreted away, working at the empty looms till late at night.

"I should very much like to know how they are getting on with the cloth," thought the emperor. But he felt rather uneasy when he remembered that he who was not fit for his office or unpardonably stupid could not see it. Personally, he was of the opinion that he had little to fear, yet he thought it advisable to send somebody else first to see how matters stood.

So he sent one of his ministers. The good old minister went into the room where the swindlers sat before the empty looms. "Heaven preserve us!" he thought, and opened his eyes wide, "I cannot see anything at all." But he did not say so. Pointing to the empty looms, both swindlers requested the minister to come near, asking him to admire the exquisite pattern and the beautiful colours. "Oh dear," he thought, "can I be so stupid? I cannot say that I am unable to see the cloth." The minister praised the weavers and exclaimed, "What a beautiful pattern, what brilliant colours! I shall tell the emperor that I like the cloth very much!"

The swindlers worked about in the air with big scissors, and sewed with needles without thread. "The emperor's new suit is ready now," they said at last. The emperor and all his ministers came into the hall. The swindlers raised their arms as if they held something in their hands and said: "These are the trousers! This is the coat! And here is the cloak! They are all as light as a cobweb, and feel as if one has nothing at all upon the body; but that is just the beauty of them."

"Indeed!" said all the courtiers. But they could not see anything, for there was nothing to be seen. The emperor undressed, and the swindlers pretended to put the new suit upon him. "I am ready," said the emperor. "Does not my suit fit me marvellously?" The emperor marched in the procession and all who saw him exclaimed: "Indeed, the emperor's new suit is incomparable! What a long train he has! How well it fits him!" Nobody wished to let others know that he could see nothing, for then he would have been unfit for his office or unpardonably stupid. Never were the emperor's clothes more admired.

Suddenly, amongst the gathered onlookers, a lone voice was heard. "But father, the emperor is naked. He has nothing on at all," said a little child. "Good heavens! Listen to the voice of the innocent child," said the father, one whispering to the other what the child had said. And very soon did the whole people cry, "He is naked. The emperor is naked. He has nothing on at all!" This made a deep impression upon the emperor, for it seemed to him that they were right; but he thought to himself, "Now I must bear up to the end." And so it was that the king walked with still greater dignity before the crowd. And with full ceremony did his courtiers carry the train of his garments, the garments that did not exist.

* * * * *

After Gallo's 1984 press conference, the world witnessed the AIDS establishment commencing its pursuit of HIV with a single-mindedness that bordered on religious obsession. HIV became THE world threat - no longer a shadowy, ephemeral enemy. According to the Gallo camp, HIV was now a proven virus with its own pathology, biochemistry, and one heck of an impressive name. Human Immunodeficiency Virus was now officially Public Enemy No1.

After the historic announcement, the amount of artillery the CDC and other health organisations wheeled up to the battlefront to face HIV was awesome. The public was certainly impressed with the apparent high level of science being brought to bear on AIDS. After all, if two presidents had to meet just to adjudicate the row over who discovered HIV, this whole thing had to be for real.[59] The problem was, dissident researchers also visited the front-line to peer curiously at mankind's new virus enemy for the first time. They were at first surprised and then unnerved to find a naked emperor facing them. While there were vague photographs of something referred to as HIV, no one could produce any scientific, definitive proof that the virus had been successfully isolated and catalogued in the usual scientific manner. The subsequent dispute going on that spring over who had first claim to the supposed discovery of HIV (Gallo or Montagnier?) completely masked the more unsettling question of whether the virus existed at all.

Nobel Laureate Dr Kary Mullis, the well-known AIDS dissident and author of numerous works denouncing the 'AIDS as virus' hypothesis, writes as follows:

"In 1988 I found myself writing a report on our progress for an HIV project, sponsored by the National Institutes of Health, when I found that I did not have the scientific reference for a statement I had just written: "HIV is the probable cause of AIDS". I turned to the virologist at the next desk, a reliable and competent fellow, and asked him for the reference. He said I didn't need one. I disagreed. While it's true that certain scientific discoveries are so well established that their sources are no longer referenced in the contemporary literature, that didn't seem to be the case with the HIV/AIDS connection.

Of course, this simple reference had to be out there somewhere. There had to be a published paper, or perhaps several of them, which taken together indicated that HIV was the probable cause of AIDS. There just had to be. I was going to a lot of meetings as part of my job. I got in the habit of approaching anyone who gave a talk about AIDS and asking

---

[59] *Newsweek*, "The End of a Scientific Feud", 25th July 1994

him or her what reference I should quote for that increasingly problematic statement, "HIV is the probable cause of AIDS".

After ten or fifteen meetings over a couple of years, I was getting pretty upset when no one could cite the reference. I didn't like the ugly conclusion that was forming in my mind: The entire campaign against a disease increasingly regarded as a 20th century Black Plague was based on a hypothesis whose origins no one could recall. That defied both scientific and common sense. Later I discovered why I was having so much trouble finding the references that linked HIV to AIDS. There weren't any."[60]

And later...

"10,000 people in the world now specialize in HIV. None has any interest in the possibility that HIV doesn't cause AIDS, because if it doesn't, their expertise is useless."[61]

Dr Stefan Lanka has studied the nature of virus behaviour at the University of Konstanz in Germany and has a wide-ranging scientific background in researching the HIV/AIDS dispute in all its forms. He is part of a growing medical consensus that believes that 'HIV' is nothing but a complete myth. Lanka explains his position:

"Viruses can reproduce themselves only by infecting a suitable host cell and appropriating the chemical machinery they find there. The proteins making up the viruses are characteristic for each species of virus, the composition of proteins for a given virus results in a specific shape for the virus particle. This much is known.

Less well known is the existence of other particles, which look like viruses but aren't, and are nonchalantly referred to as 'virus-like' particles. Such particles are far from rare - they are found, for example, always in placentas, and very frequently in the artificial environment of laboratory cell cultures. They have served to muddy the waters considerably as far as AIDS

[60] **Mullis, Kary** Foreword to *Inventing the AIDS Virus,* Duesberg, Peter H, Regnery Publishing, 1997
[61] **Hodgkinson, Neville** *Sunday Times of London*, "Experts Mount Startling Challenge to AIDS Orthodoxy," 26th April 1992

research is concerned, because particles just like these have been called HIV. To date, none of these has been characterised and shown to exist as an entity which one may justifiably call a virus." [62]

What disturbs scientists such as Lanka is that all known and accepted scientific investigative techniques have so far failed to prove one single aspect of the existence of HIV. Why should this be, argues Lanka, if HIV is an actual virus, as is being claimed the world over? Professor Beverly E Griffin is Director and Professor of Virology at the Royal Postgraduate Medical School in London. In May 1990, she stated in *Nature*:

"It would be irresponsible to produce guidelines on AIDS until an infectious micro-organism is identified and the means by which it causes disease are understood."

What Professor Griffin was diplomatically highlighting was that six years after Gallo made his HIV=AIDS announcement on prime-time television, a single infectious micro-organism that causes all AIDS-defining diseases had still to be identified. *Continuum*, a quarterly magazine campaigning against the fraudulent HIV=AIDS hypothesis, offers a cash reward for any proper, no-nonsense evidence for the existence of HIV. To date, this reward remains uncollected.

Neville Hodgkinson, a former science and medical correspondent for the *London Times*, was at the forefront of breaking the AIDS story as it unfolded in the mid-1980s. He remembers:

"There was never really to my mind, and I have looked at this very closely now, evidence of a new virus actually being isolated…. I think, in that second half of the 1980s, it was a great story and we took it on board as a kind of public health emergency too. And that's a danger with any group of professionals, whether they are media workers or scientists, to get too close to the sort of propagandising that happened with AIDS. We lost our sense of judgement, I'm afraid, on this issue, because we felt that sense of fear and urgency. It was like a war and in those circumstances, critical judgement went out of

---

[62] **Lanka, Stefan,** *Zenger*, December 1998

the window, I'm afraid, for too many of us." [63]

Aside from the complete lack of evidence for the existence of an HIV, the whole manner in which documented viral illness behaves is in complete contrast to the pattern of pathological behaviour manifesting itself in AIDS. Health researcher Christine Johnson lists out the common characteristics of infectious diseases:

- ***They spread equally among the sexes and across the age range.*** In its early years, AIDS cases were being reported almost exclusively in younger males.
- ***They cause primary illness in the diseased person soon after infection.*** AIDS supposedly takes from months to years to develop in an HIV positive person. In some cases it never appears at all.
- ***In ALL cases, infectious diseases correspond with a common, active, abundant and detectable infectious microbe.*** [64] HIV was and still is *not detectable* as a microbe.
- ***The disease kills more cells than the host can spare or regenerate.*** HIV cannot be seen to be killing any cells it is supposedly infecting. Cell depletion witnessed in AIDS patients is more often than not directly attributable to AIDS medication. This is discussed in more detail in a later chapter.
- ***The disease generates a predictable pattern of symptoms.*** There was, and still is no predictable pattern of which symptoms an AIDS patient will manifest. An AIDS patient with *Karposi's Sarcoma* is said to infect another person who could then go on to develop, not *Karposi's Sarcoma*, but *pneumocystis pneumonia* (PCP) or diarrhoea or candidiasis, etc.

Johnson's reasoning is an accumulation of observations based on proven medical science. Another well documented way in which new diseases may be identified is by employing Koch's Postulates. In use for over a century, Koch's Postulates are the most widely accepted scientific criteria for identifying the guilty pathogen for a disease. Koch stated that three main factors must exist in a diseased person in order

---

[63] *AIDS: A Second Opinion*, a video documentary, Gary Null & Associates, PO Box 918, Planetarium Station, New York, NY 10024 USA Tel: (212) 799-1246 Fax: (212) 769-3566

[64] **Johnson, Christine** *Perceptions*, "No Proof that HIV = AIDS", Summer 1994

to prove that the micro-organism under scrutiny is the primary cause of the disease being observed:

1) *"...it must be present in all cases of a specific disease..."* As we will learn, there are many patients diagnosed with AIDS who do not test positive for 'HIV'.[65]
2) *"...inoculations of its pure culture must produce the same disease in animals..."* All efforts to produce AIDS by inoculation of an 'HIV culture' have failed. No pure HIV culture has ever been produced.
3) *"...and from these it must be obtained in pure cultures and propagated."* i.e. the virus must be isolated and observed. To date, this has never been accomplished.

When pressed on these matters, Harold Jaffe, the senior AIDS and HIV investigator at the CDC, and Professor Robin Weiss, a British AIDS researcher, both argued:

> *"It seems bizarre that anyone should demand strict adherence to these unreconstructed postulates 100 years after their proposition."*[66]

Gallo too saw no problem dismissing one of science's time-tested, primary check and balance systems:

> *"Rules were needed then, and can be helpful now, but not if they are too blindly followed. Robert Koch, a great microbiologist, has suffered from a malady that affects many other great men: he has been taken too literally and too seriously for too long."*[67]

Journalist John Lauritsen became intrigued with the arguments put forward by those opposed to the HIV theory of AIDS. In preparing for an interview with AIDS dissenter Professor Peter Duesberg, a retrovirologist renowned for asserting that HIV does not cause AIDS, Lauritsen decided to do some groundwork. He telephoned the CDC and NIH to interview officials concerning HIV. Finally getting in touch

---

[65] US CDC report of AIDS cases without the presence of HIV - December 1992

[66] *In These Times*, 5th August 1992

[67] **Gallo, Robert C** *Virus Hunting - AIDS, Cancer, and the Human Retrovirus: A Story of Scientific Discovery*, Basic Books, New York, 1991

with the National Cancer Institute's press officer, Lauritsen demanded definitive proof that HIV caused AIDS. She could not give an answer and postponed the call until the following day when the persistent Lauritsen confronted her again. He was read a hastily prepared response. When this failed to address his arguments, Lauritsen quizzed her about HIV not meeting the criteria for infectious disease as laid out in Koch's postulates. Not having heard of Koch's Postulates, the press officer asked when they were formulated. On being told they had been in existence for about 100 years, she replied: *"Oh, well then, would you say that those apply now?"* [68]

Koch's Postulates have remained one of medicine's primary benchmarks for over a century. Now, because they do not fit the HIV profile but rather expose it, they are apparently not to be *"...taken too literally and too seriously..."*

AIDS also fails the test of another proven medical maxim, known as Farr's Law. Farr, a 19th century British epidemiologist, traced the trends of seasonal microbial epidemics occurring at his time and noticed several solid rules that governed their rise and fall.

- Epidemics spread exponentially into any given population.
- They do not discriminate between the sexes.
- They decline within months due either to the deaths of their victims or most often by natural immunity being acquired by the survivors.

Since Farr formulated his law, all epidemics have followed his rules by the letter. And then along comes AIDS and Farr's Law, along with other well established medical codes, is immediately thrown out of the window. Professor Duesberg is concerned at the low level of science surrounding Gallo's investigations into HIV. His concerns prompted him to state:

> *"If you think a virus is the cause of AIDS, do a control without it. To do a control is the first thing you teach undergraduates. But it hasn't been done. The epidemiology of AIDS is a pile of anecdotal stories selected to fit the virus-AIDS hypothesis. People don't bother to check the details of popular*

[68] **Lauritsen, John** Notes on conversations with CDC/NCI personnel, 11th-12th June 1987.

dogma or consensus views."[69]

With HIV undetectable and AIDS not conforming to infectious disease patterns, could this illness be in any more disarray? Unfortunately, yes. Another anomaly in the AIDS equation was that a number of people who had been diagnosed as HIV negative were being documented as suffering from symptoms identical to those who were deemed HIV positive.

Upon discovery that AIDS was being diagnosed in patients who were HIV negative, Project AIDS International (PAI), a Los Angeles-based AIDS research organisation, attempted several times to clarify this seeming incongruity with the Centers for Diseases Control. CDC at first explained that these cases had different viral causes, but later, after being quizzed repeatedly by PAI chairman Jeremy Selvey, the government agency then tried to deny any knowledge of such cases.[70] Even though this issue was clearly of major importance to public health, PAI was cautioned by CDC that these findings were not for general broadcast. [71]

After continued pressure from Project AIDS International, CDC finally submitted documentation of at least 30 cases of HIV-free AIDS. By 31st December 1992, the CDC had reported 97 such cases. These were to be the tip of the iceberg. Later in *Science*, Peter Duesberg would report over 2,000 cases of HIV-free AIDS in existence.[72] Since 1985, many other cases of HIV-free AIDS have been reported.

Reflecting also on the absurdity of HIV=AIDS when there are so many HIV-free AIDS patients in evidence, Robert Root-Bernstein, Associate Professor of Physiology at Michigan State University, declared:

"On the existence of HIV-free AIDS, it's time to re-evaluate the HIV/AIDS hypothesis."[73]

---

[69] Maggiore, Christine, ibid.

[70] **Selvey, Jeremy** *Public Information Dossier and Report to the United Nations*, 15th March 1993. PAI, 8033 Sunset Blvd #2640, Los Angeles CA 90046 USA

[71] Selvey, Jeremy, ibid.

[72] **Duesberg, Peter H** *Science*, September 1992

[73] Selvey, Jeremy, ibid.

As mentioned, Robert Gallo was convicted of science fraud in December 1992 by the Office of Research Integrity, a department of the National Institutes of Health. His conviction was based on his declaration that he had discovered HIV. Up until 1994, Robert Gallo remained under investigation by the United States Congress on various other charges of scientific fraud. Today he is back in the fold, reinstated at the forefront of AIDS research in the United States.

By the end of the 1980s, Gallo's well-reported lack of laboratory ethics was beginning to concern other scientists around the world. As the depth of Gallo's scientific fraud unfolded, it became evident that neither Gallo nor Montagnier had actually used accepted scientific methods to report the virus they had allegedly found. Upon publicly questioning his old friend Gallo's HIV hypothesis in a paper published in *Cancer Research*, Duesberg's laboratory at Berkeley had its funding suspended.[74] Journalist Frank Prescott notes that during this period, Duesberg remained unruffled and stuck to his guns:

> *"HIV does not cause AIDS,"* the scientist would tirelessly repeat. *"The point that everyone is missing is that all those original papers have been found fraudulent... The HIV hypothesis was based on those papers."*[75]

Despite his long-standing reputation as an outspoken critic of AIDS being caused by an infectious virus, Duesberg the retrovirologist is nevertheless still mounting arguments for the existence of HIV, but attributing to it only harmless, retrovirus-like qualities.[76]

A more prosaic description of HIV retrovirology could be *'convincing terminology supporting the search for a biological entity supposedly lurking inside yet another biological entity, neither of those entities yet proven to exist'*. Hardly the most exacting of sciences. We must remember that it was Robert Gallo who laid claim to the first human retrovirus 'discovery'. Both Gallo and Duesberg were 'retro-colleagues' in the early 1970s, and for Duesberg, the retrovirus remains a reality. However, for all the years Duesberg has spent

---

[74] *Cancer Research*, Vol 47, 1199-1220, 1st March 1987

[75] **Prescott, Frank** *"At Last. The Proof Sex and HIV Are Not the Real Causes of AIDS" Perceptions*, Summer 1994

[76] Duesberg, Peter H, *Inventing....* ibid. pp.175-178, 335, 338

relentlessly pursuing and 'inferring' the presence of the HI retrovirus, so far he has not persuaded this enigmatic little snipe to put in even the briefest appearance. What then is one to make of the 'inferred' science of retrovirology?

In his commentary on the ease with which fundamental error can become established 'scientific truth', W Deutscher's succinct statement more than adequately applies to Peter Duesberg's chosen profession:

"We concentrate on consistency without much concern of what it is we are being consistent about, or whether we are consistently right or wrong. As a consequence, we have been learning a great deal about how to follow an incorrect course with the maximum of precision."[77]

Duesberg and other retrovirologists continue to validate their calling and justify pursuit of a missing retrovirus, telling us that the necessary proof is just around the next lucratively funded corner. This is simply not acceptable, says Dr Stefan Lanka:

"Why do 'HIV'-virologists never subject their viruses to the same generally accepted standard techniques of molecular biology as all other virologists and biologists do?"[78]

And further -

"Such evidence up till now has never been produced for HIV. No photograph of an isolated HIV particle has ever been published. No control experiments as mentioned have been published to date. What has been shown are photographs of virus-like particles in cell cultures, but none of isolated viruses, let alone a structure within the human body having the shape ascribed to HIV. What the whole world has seen are models representing HIV with dish aerials, said to be receptors with which the virus attaches itself to cells."[79]

Thus we find ourselves in an ever-expanding No-Man's Land; that gulf separating 'virtual truth' from sensible science. And at this point, it

---

[77] **Deutscher, W** University of Manchester Institute of Science and Technology course handout, 1994

[78] **Lanka, Stefan** *HIV: Reality or Artefact?* http://www.virusmyth.com/aids/index/slanka.htm

[79] Lanka, Stefan, ibid.

is surely not unreasonable to equate HIV and other such 'retroviruses' with those finely woven garments spun from a deceptively empty loom. Donald Gould, the former editor of *New Scientist*, warns of the dangers we invite by going that one step further and admiring the cut of the emperor's cloth:

> *"Why not make the most of what the non-conformists have to offer and to hell with uncharitable logic? There is, I suggest, a powerful reason for rejecting this superficially attractive option. Truth is a fundamental value. If we accept uncritical thinking in one area of our lives for the sake of convenience or because of the popular appeal of a seductive myth and the short-term comfort to be gained by believing in the unbelievable, or because a false answer lets us pretend we are completely coping with a painful problem we haven't truly tackled, then we are all the more likely to adopt the same strategy in other situations; from dealing with the family, to managing the national economy, and from chairing the parish council to handling arsenals of nuclear weapons. The result is likely to be unhappy and stands a decent chance of proving a disaster. Irrational beliefs are always dangerously corrupting, even when they only relate to the cause and cure of piles."*[80]

Karl Krafeld is not a popular man in some circles. In 1989 he received two prison warrants for disclosure of corruption in financial services, and for revealing that the German government was concealing information pertinent to human rights. Krafeld argues that preventing certain actions from becoming known puts them outside of the realm of the thinkable. *"When it is not allowed that reality can become thinkable, then it is not possible to find the right ways and means to solve problems."* [81] Krafeld introduces us to the idea of HIV being a 'psycho-product'. In commenting on Duesberg's role in perpetuating the mindset of HIV, Krafeld makes the following observations:

> *"In their fight over who discovered HIV, Montagnier and Gallo promoted the retrovirus construct in a roundabout way. Duesberg publicly claimed the 'Missing Virus' award even after several scientists, including Dr Lanka, had published beyond*

---

[80] **Gould, Donald** *The Black and White Medicine Show*, Hamilton 1985
[81] **Krafeld, Karl** *Inventing the AIDS Virus?* Continuum. Vol 5. No 1, 1997

reasonable doubt that there was never any such discovery. Acting thus, was Duesberg mindless of the fact that with his collaboration, millions of people would remain scared to death and continue dying? ...If in future Duesberg does not want to be named in the same breath as Gallo and Montagnier, he has to present biological proofs, according to the fullest standards of biology, for the existences of retroviruses and HIV before he speaks about them, or claims 'HIV is harmless.' If this is not possible, he must then concur that belief in them is a psycho-product, an idea and biological error. A scientist who wants to be respected must be able and willing to escape the influence of his own psycho-mechanisms. With AIDS and HIV, lives are at risk. Lies and scientific slop work are unacceptable."[82]

It must be noted that, while Professor Duesberg appears to demonstrate intellectual inconsistency in his continued belief in the elusive HIV, he has nevertheless made many valid contributions to the AIDS debate, which in turn have helped to save many lives.

Dr Robert Willner, author of *Deadly Deception: The Proof that Sex and HIV Absolutely Do Not Cause AIDS*, was another HIV=AIDS dissident up until he was discovered dead in his car. So determined was Dr Willner to prove to the world that AIDS was not spread sexually or through blood contamination, that he stunned the nation of Spain in 1993 by inoculating himself on TV with the blood of Pedro Tocino, a haemophiliac said to be HIV positive. The footage was broadcast throughout Europe. Encouraged by the coverage he was receiving, Willner repeated his performance with different patients in front of the cameras of ABC and NBC. Surprisingly no US network reported this dramatic news on national television.[83] Up until his untimely death, Dr Willner remained HIV negative in spite of constant testing.[84]

Dr Harvey Bialy, editor of *Bio/Technology*, made his views about the HIV hypothesis very frankly known as far back as Spring 1992 in Britain's *Sunday Times*:

---

[82] Krafeld, Karl, ibid.

[83] See Part 2 for an examination into the role of the media in AIDS.

[84] **Willner, Robert** *Deadly Deception*, Peltec Publishing Co., 4400 N Federal Highway, #210, Boca Raton, FL 33431 USA

"The [HIV] hypothesis has become all things to all people. It violates everything we previously knew about virus disease, and allows any kind of therapy, any kind of research, to generate research bucks. What kind of science continues to place all its marbles, all its faith, all its research dollars, in such a theory? The answer I keep coming back to is that it has nothing to do with science; the reasons are all unscientific. We have taken sex and equated it with death, and into that mixture we have thrown money. What an ugly stew." [85]

Nevertheless, despite the overwhelming evidence to the contrary, the orthodox medical establishment is not about to have 'Project HIV' derailed so easily. The ultimate twin heresy of the AIDS orthodoxy remains to this day:

- Questioning the HIV=AIDS hypothesis
- Calling into doubt the infectious nature of AIDS

The reality is that since 1984, over 100,000 papers have been published on HIV. Yet, with all the accepted methods available in biochemistry today, there is still no definitive proof that AIDS is infectious; that HIV causes AIDS; or that HIV even exists to be photographed. As anti-HIV activist Michael Verney-Elliott acidly declared: *"Congratulations. From the people who didn't bring you the virus that causes cancer, it's the virus that doesn't cause AIDS."* [86]

Steve Connor, medical correspondent for the UK's *Independent* newspaper, recently penned an article on the existence of HIV, and supported it with a front-page photograph of something referred to as HIV, where the 'virus particles' had been highlighted in luminous green for his 500,000-plus readership. Connor was contacted by Credence researchers on this matter. He was reminded that this colouring-in technique was actually standard *'inferred presence only'* practice in HIV virology. Since HIV had never been isolated, and was therefore invisible, it naturally followed that a luminous green overcoat was vital in order to help make its 'presence' known. Credence asked Connor why he had not mentioned or explained the colouring-in technique in

[85] Hodgkinson, Neville, *Sunday Times of London*, ibid. pp.12-13
[86] Maggiore, Christine, ibid.

his article. Connor replied that our line of argument was unconventional and most offensive to the many, many thousands who had so far died of AIDS.

Connor, himself an author of a book on HIV=AIDS, stated further that our questioning him on this matter also flew in the face of the overwhelming evidence that HIV had been isolated. *"Those who question the HIV hypothesis,"* Mr Connor told us, *"also argue that the earth is flat."*[87]

Alex Russell is assistant editor at *Continuum* magazine. On a number of occasions Russell has had reason to write to the Press Complaints Commission concerning HIV journalism, and particularly Steven Connor. This letter includes the following observation:

Alex Russell

> *"I would like to warn The Press Complaints Commission that Steve Connor is a well-known 'HIV' propagandist and will use highly emotive rhetoric to defend his 'HIV' credo. When it comes to reporting on 'HIV', he is not a critical, disinterested, or objective journalist but a fundamentalist defending his fanatical 'HIV' faith. Yet in a court of law, Steve Connor could not prove that 'HIV' exists.*

> *I ask the Commission to take up my complaint against the editor of The Independent and Steve Connor for misleading their readership with this fraudulent [coloured-in] image. I have written three letters to the editor of The Independent, a) asking him to reconsider publishing my original letter, which was not published, b) to publish the letter in the correspondence pages,*

[87] **Ransom, Steven** Personal telephone conversation with Steven Connor on 21st December 1999 in regard to Mr Connor's article dated 16th December 1999

which was not done, and c) to ask the editor why he has not responded to my complaint. I look forward to hearing from the PCC in due course. Alex Russell, Assistant Editor, Continuum magazine."

Steve Connor is one of hundreds of journalists responsible for perpetrating the unproven HIV hypothesis. Does it concern Mr Connor that there has been not one iota of evidence for the existence of HIV published, photographed or proven with the precise methods available in biochemistry today?

In an interview for *Zenger* magazine, Dr Lanka recounts his course of action when he discovered that there was actually no evidence for the existence of HIV:

"I was afraid of speaking about this with my friends and family. They would think I was absolutely crazy. So for a long time, I studied virology, from the end to the beginning, from the beginning to the end to be absolutely sure that there was no such thing as HIV.... I realised that the whole group of viruses to which HIV is said to belong, the retroviruses – as well as other viruses which are claimed to be very dangerous – in fact do not exist at all." [88]

Lanka's personal quest to get to the heart of a matter, in this case HIV, serves as a reminder to us all that truth is not always presented on a plate. There are times when we must accept the responsibility to make that truth-seeking journey for ourselves.

On the science supporting HIV, Martin Walker, author of *Dirty Medicine* stated:

"Had Gallo presented his theory in a reputable scientific journal, rather than the Washington Press conference, his proposal would have been tested by his peers. A focused, centralised authority which had responsibility for evaluating scientific knowledge would have made a judgement, its clinical basis would have been replicated and a dialectic process would have hopefully forged the truth. As it was, there was no proving, no dialectic process, no clinical proof, no biological proof, no

---

[88] *Zenger*, December 1998. p.7

peer review, no open public critique. Gallo's idea was passed down in tablets of stone. HIV was found the guilty party without any kind of trial or search for the truth…. The idea that HIV is the cause of AIDS-associated illnesses is just that – an idea. There is even now no evidence, but only supposition to support it." [89]

Dr Valendar F Turner, a Fellow of the Royal Australasian College of Surgeons, has long been arguing against the HIV=AIDS hypothesis. On being asked in an interview to expand on his statement that not one antibody-positive person in the world is infected with HIV, he replied:

"No one has yet proved the existence of HIV using the proper method, based on the definition of a virus, as discussed at length at the 1973 Pasteur Institute meeting [90] …No research group has ever presented evidence for the existence of HIV according to the proper rules." [91]

Fellow colleague of Turner, Eleni Papadopulos-Eleopulos is a bio-physicist at the Royal Perth Hospital in Australia. She has long been proclaiming the falsity of HIV=AIDS.

"What nobody can deny is that HIV has never been accorded reality according to the correct definition [of a virus]…. Instead everybody's opted for a set of non-specific criteria and appear to imagine that if you put all these together, they must somehow metamorphose into the right answer…. In our view the greatest single obstacle to understanding and solving AIDS is HIV." [92]

Here, Eleopulos and her colleagues are arguing that it is the use of the 'HIV' term itself that is the obstacle. Alex Russell adds body to this argument by stating:

---

[89] **Walker, Martin** *Continuum* "A Seller's Market," Vol 5, No 1, October 1997

[90] **Sinoussi F, Mendiola L, Chermann, J C** "Purification and partial differentiation of the particles of murine sarcoma virus (MSV) according to their sedimentation rates in sucrose density gradients." *Spectra*, 1973; 225-235.

[91] **Turner, Valendar** "Do Antibody Tests Prove HIV Infection?" *Continuum* Magazine, Vol 5, No 2, December 1997

[92] Eleopulos and Johnson Interview, "Is HIV the cause of AIDS?" *Continuum*, Vol 5, No 1, October 1997

"HIV imprinting has become subconsciously internalised on such a global scale that people will not be able to accept the brute reality that HIV does not exist." [93]

It was physicist Carl Popper who, in his defence of guarding the rules for logical argument, stated that no one can ever say there is no such thing as a white crow. One can only state that *"to date, and according to my experience, I have not yet seen a white crow."* Whilst there is certain merit in this line of cautious argument, this approach has wreaked considerable damage to the valuable role played by absolutism. At what point does the crowd finally admit that the emperor is actually naked? Eleopulos, Lanka, Turner, Krafeld and Russell are to be congratulated for taking an absolute position in the HIV debate.

HIV does not exist. There. The silence has been broken. Those taking a sharp intake of breath at this point are invited actively to pursue the path taken by the above truth-seekers. Now, if the virus *does* exist, let's gather all the dissident dignitaries around the table and take a good look at the little critter. For the HIV-propagandists, surely now is the time for them to "Put up or Shut up".

It is at this point in the AIDS story that we must now unavoidably head towards much bleaker terrain. What has perhaps been a gradual and somewhat uncomfortable downward slope for the reader who is new to the world of AIDS, now precipitates into a steep and horrifying descent, as the full implications of an HIV positive diagnosis are examined. One day, an everyday, healthy individual; the next, an abrupt HIV positive diagnosis and the death sentence is passed. And all it takes to know for sure is Robert Gallo's patented 'AIDS test'.

---

[93] *Positive Nation*, January 1998. "HIV Does Not Exist."

POSITIVELY NEGATIVE

Examining the 'AIDS test'

"Have you considered an 'AIDS test'...?" Those two words instil only fear. Who isn't aware that an HIV positive diagnosis is synonymous with a suspended death sentence? In reality, the term 'AIDS test' is fraudulently misleading. There is not, nor ever has been, a 'test for AIDS'. Neither of course has there ever been a successful 'test for HIV' - the virus that not only does not cause AIDS, but also has never even put in an appearance. About the best job the ELISA and Western Blot tests are doing today is generating enormous incomes around the world for their respective manufacturers.

These two tests, we are told, identify HIV antibodies that have been created by a person's immune system in response to 'HIV invasion'. This statement is nonsense, and dangerous nonsense, as we will soon discover. So what are these tests – the ELISA and the Western Blot - and how are they supposed to work?

The ELISA (Enzyme-Linked Immuno-Absorbent Assay) and Western Blot tests are designed to highlight the presence of the supposed HIV, not by identifying the virus itself, but by identifying the presence of antibodies in the blood, allegedly unique to, and stimulated by the virus. The only real difference between the two tests is that the ELISA is supposed to measure reaction to HIV as a whole, whereas the Western Blot measures reactions to separate proteins supposedly making up the virus. As a result of this claim, the Western Blot method is deemed by most in the AIDS industry to be more specific than the ELISA test, and will often be used to confirm a positive ELISA test. [94]

To carry out the test, the clinician introduces a foreign protein (antigen) into the blood sample and then monitors the blood for any signs of unique activity as the invader meets up with the immune system's antibodies. And it is here that we immediately encounter the

---

[94] **Lake, Douglas** *The Biology Project* University of Arizona School of Medicine.

first hurdle. Introducing a foreign body into the bloodstream will always provoke a response from the immune system, the foreign presence releasing killer blood cells to combat the invading germ. This is what our immune system has been designed to do. The problem is that no antibody is ever specific to any one disease - a fact that has been widely known in science for a number of years. The ELISA and Western Blot tests are both marketed as being highly specific and accurate in identifying the presence of HIV antibodies in a person's body. But, as Christine Maggiore explains:

> *"Both tests are non-specific to HIV antibodies and are highly inaccurate. Non-specific means that these tests respond to a great number of non-HIV antibodies, microbes, bacteria and other conditions that are often found in the blood of normal, healthy people. A reaction to any one of these other antibodies and conditions will result in an HIV positive diagnosis. A simple illness like a cold or the flu can cause a positive reading on an HIV test. A flu shot or other vaccine can also create positive results. Having or having had herpes or hepatitis may produce a positive test, as can a vaccination for hepatitis B. Exposure to diseases such as tuberculosis and malaria commonly cause false positive results, as do the presence of tape worms and other parasites. Conditions such as alcoholism, liver disease and blood that is highly oxidated through drug use may be interpreted as the presence of HIV antibodies. Pregnancy and prior pregnancy can also cause a positive result."* [95]

Yes, you read correctly. **A simple illness like a cold or flu can cause an HIV positive reading.** You could be suffering from a relatively innocuous viral infection, and your immune system, functioning quite normally, has detected the presence of an invader and ordered the defender blood cells into action. The activity of those perfectly healthy killers working away in the blood can be interpreted by the 'AIDS test' and the experts administering it as indicative of the presence of HIV. **Did you know that?**

Christine Johnson of Project HEAL in Los Angeles, a voluntary organisation dedicated to exposing the myth of viral AIDS, has compiled and referenced some sixty different conditions that can

---

[95] Maggiore, Christine, ibid.

cause a false HIV positive reading. Some of these conditions have been included below for sober consideration.

"Naturally occurring antibodies, recent viral infection or exposure to viral vaccine, flu, flu vaccination, tuberculosis, renal failure, hepatitis, organ transplant, haemophilia, tetanus vaccination, leprosy, alcoholic liver disease, blood transfusions, malignant cancers, proteins on the test filter papers, rheumatoid arthritis, herpes, Hepatitis B vaccination, healthy individuals as a result of poorly understood cross reactions…. [plus forty-six others]." [96]

In the case of haemophilia and AIDS, it is Factor VIII, the man-made compound used to help in the coagulation process, that in the main has been responsible for false HIV readings.[97] Introducing this agent into the bloodstream to help stem blood flow will naturally provoke an antibody response, the immune system demonstrating it is functioning properly. This activity is mistakenly read by scientists as indicative of the presence of HIV. Haemophiliacs, by the very nature of their condition, are prone to a number of life-threatening illnesses, and many do indeed die – but not from HIV.[98] The popular tabloids of course prefer to blare out *'HIV INFECTED BLOOD FOUND IN BLOOD BANKS MAY INFECT THOUSANDS'* rather than report the prosaic truth. Explaining the subtleties of opportunistic infection and blood-test cross-reaction does not sell newspapers.

Prior to AIDS, **the presence of antibodies had *never* been used as an indicator of any illness.** Yet since Gallo's HIV hypothesis was popularised, antibody testing has become *de rigeur* in the AIDS establishment as the indicator of infection, when the presence of

---

[96] Johnson, Christine *Continuum*, September/October 1996

[97] Haemophiliacs lack key components that allow their blood to clot. In the 1970s-80s however, scientists developed Factor VIII, a product that contains the protein composites haemophiliacs need to restore the clotting ability they lack. Haemophiliacs are now living longer, but another problem has been widely recognised, as recorded by Professor Peter Duesberg: *"Hemophiliacs lose immune competence according to the cumulative amount of Factor VIII consumed: However, when the clotting factor is highly purified, the immune system remains healthy. Cost unfortunately bars many hemophiliacs from using purified Factor VIII. [Those] treated with commercial Factor VIII consequently develop some opportunistic infectious diseases in the long run, particularly pneumonia and yeast infections."* (Duesberg, Peter H, *Inventing… p.287*)

[98] **Duesberg, Peter H** "Is HIV the Cause of AIDS?" *Lancet,* 346 (1995): pp.1371-1372

71

antibodies actually denotes a normal healthy response! The following extract from *Foundation News* is a glaring example:

> *"Professor Andrew McMichael in Oxford announced that 50 Nairobi prostitutes had high levels of killer T-cells in their bodies, which suggested they had been exposed to HIV. The Nairobi research was complemented by Oxford studies in Gambia which yielded similar results. Said Dr Omu Anzala: 'This was further evidence that it was the presence of T-cells which was holding the virus at bay'."*[99]

The possibility that the test kits could merely be reacting with parasites, TB bacilli and other medical conditions common to Africans is rarely considered by these doctors, even though the problem of inadvertent cross-reaction is common knowledge. In reality, a 'positive' reading is actually a 'false positive', the tests confirming only that the immune system is functioning satisfactorily.[100]

The potential for false diagnosis with HIV tests has been noted in mainstream publications such as *The London Times, USA Today, The Telegraph* and *The Wall Street Journal*, which on 11th January 1995 reported that the FDA were recalling HIV testing kits due to problems with high rates of 'false positives'.[101]

Frank Prescott, writing on behalf of Peltec Publishing in *Perceptions Magazine* in 1993, tells us:

> *"The London Times reports a major research group has recently proven the test for HIV to be completely invalid and 'riddled with false positives'. Malnutrition, multiple infections, having once had the flu, measles or a simple flu shot can all result in positive HIV diagnosis."*[102]

This one fact alone destroys any validity of an 'AIDS test'. But there are more....

---

[99] *Foundation News,* Issue #34, September 1999

[100] *Bio/Technology Journal,* 11:696-707, June 1993

[101] *Wall Street Journal,* 11th January 1995, Health, page B-8

[102] *Perceptions,* ibid.

The US Food and Drug Administration also admits that the 'highly specific' AIDS test has some worrying glitches, as the following *USA Today* bulletin tells us:

"People who receive gamma globulin shots for chicken pox, measles and hepatitis could test positive for HIV even if they have never been infected. The Food and Drug Administration says that a positive test could be caused by antibodies found in most of America's supply of gamma globulin. Gamma globulin is made from blood collected from thousands of donors and is routinely given to millions of people each year as temporary protection against many infectious diseases. Dr Thomas Zuck of the FDA's Blood and Blood Products Division says the government didn't release the information because 'we thought it would do more harm than good.'"[103]

US News & World Report had this to say on the subject on 23rd November 1987:

"With public health officials and politicians thrashing out who should be tested for HIV, the accuracy of the test itself has been nearly ignored. A study last month by Congress's Office of Technology Assessment found that HIV tests can be very inaccurate indeed. For groups at very low risk - people who don't use IV drugs or have sex with gay or bisexual men - 9 in 10 positive findings are called false positives, indicating infection where none exists."

The New England Journal of Medicine recorded the following:

"The techniques of the HIV test have not been standardized, and the magnitude and consequences of inter-laboratory variations have not been measured. Its results require interpretation, and the criteria for this interpretation vary not only from lab to lab, but also from month to month."[104]

What one of the most respected medical journals in the world is trying to tell the reader here is that the HIV test is about as useless as it gets. A tacit endorsement of these sentiments comes from a

---

[103] *USA Today*, 2nd October 1987
[104] *New England Journal of Medicine*, 317:238-241

surprising and unexpected source - the manufacturer's leaflet which accompanies the Western Blot (HIV) test kit itself!

"The test for the existence of antibodies against AIDS-associated virus is not diagnostic of AIDS and AIDS-like diseases. Negative tests do not exclude the possibility of contact or infection with the AIDS-associated virus. Positive tests do not prove AIDS or pre-AIDS disease status nor that these diseases will be acquired."

This from the test which is supposed to confirm the ELISA test! In other words the test kit is saying: *"Thank you for spending your money on me. In return for your considerable investment, I can predict <u>absolutely nothing except that your blood sample contains antibodies.</u>"*

Medical researcher Dr Roberto A Giraldo is very familiar with the ELISA, Western Blot and Viral Load tests. He works at a laboratory for clinical immunology in one of the most prestigious university hospitals in New York City. When Dr Giraldo first came across the ELISA, he was surprised to learn that, to run the test, a patient's serum required diluting 400 times with a special specimen diluent. Most serological tests that search for the presence of antibodies against germs, such as those for syphilis, hepatitis A and B and the rubella virus, use neat or undiluted serum. The obvious questions facing Dr Giraldo were: What made HIV so unique that the test serum needed to be diluted 400 times? And what would happen if the patient's serum were not diluted?

Dr Giraldo ran extensive tests on blood samples that tested negative at 1:400 dilution. The same samples conducted with neat serum ALL showed positive. Dr Giraldo further found that if any person's blood, including his own, was tested with neat serum using the ELISA, the test came out positive! Dr Giraldo concludes that the tests are worthless, once again merely highlighting the presence of non-specific antibodies in the patient's blood serum.[105]

It is standard practice in most UK haematology and/or other blood testing laboratories to conduct at least two tests if the first test reads 'positive'. Confirmatory testing is usually carried out at any one of a

---

[105] **Giraldo, Roberto** "Everybody Reacts Positive on the ELISA Test For HIV," *Continuum*, Vol 5, No 5, pp.8-10

number of Public Health Laboratory Service centres across the UK. Credence Publications contacted the virus reference library at the UK's leading PHLS in Colindale, north London, in order to determine if they had ever been able directly to identify the presence of HIV in any of the blood samples sent to them. Was it rather the case that their blood test was designed to measure the presence of antibodies only? The representative from the lab informed us that he was not permitted to answer any of our questions, referring us instead to their press office. On asking the press office for the references that would point to HIV having been independently isolated, we were informed that of course HIV had been identified. *"The virus was isolated as far back as 1983 by Drs Gallo and Montagnier."*

Concerned at the high level of ignorance demonstrated in this reply from a leading virus laboratory, an attempt was made to speak to someone at management level at Colindale. A Mr John Parry, deputy head at the virus library, could make only vague references to papers he believed proved the existence of HIV, and he admitted that the testing procedures employed at the laboratories were not precise, particularly the Polymerase Chain Reaction Test or PCR.[106] This highly complex technique is supposed to be able to detect fragments of genetic material in the blood that allegedly indicate the presence of HIV. The Roche PCR testing kit actually contains a warning against using PCR as a test for the presence of HIV. *"The test is not to be used as a screening test for HIV or as a diagnostic test to confirm the presence of HIV."* [107]

This significant fact was pointed out to Mr Parry. During the course of the conversation Mr Parry was also reminded of the fact that Kary Mullis, the Nobel laureate inventor of PCR, referred to his own diagnostic invention as *"inappropriate for use in AIDS medicine."*[108] Startled perhaps that an ordinary member of the public actually knew what PCR stood for, knew its history of unreliability, and then had the

---

[106] Polymerase Chain Reaction or PCR is another 'method' of HIV detection. PCR is invariably quoted as highly specific by those unacquainted with its true history. Neither approved nor recommended by either the FDA or the CDC, the application of this equipment in AIDS research has been described as *"...far more misleading then useful."* Maggiore, Christine, ibid.

[107] Roche Amplicor PCR Diagnostics HIV-1 Monitor test kit pamphlet.

[108] Index for Free Expression. *Big Science and Little White Lies.* March 1999

audacity to question what went on within Colindale Laboratories, Mr Parry chose to offer no further reply.[109]

And the simple question which remains for the reader? Would you trust your blood sample to this methodology? The stark truth here is that a blood sample, quite falsely deemed HIV positive by the highly inaccurate ELISA test, is then sent on to Colindale and other 'specialist' laboratories to be *'confirmed as positive or otherwise'* again by ELISA and then secondarily tested in the same establishment by the equally inaccurate PCR. Another glaring example of following an incorrect course with the maximum of precision.

And in the case of the Western Blot test, the positive criteria differ from continent to continent! (see photo section) You can be tested positive in one country, and negative in another.

Yet another hurdle the 'AIDS test' has quite disastrously failed to clear is what is known as 'The Gold Standard Test'. Christine Maggiore explains:

> *"HIV tests have been developed without verification by an independent 'gold standard'. In medical science, a gold standard means that viral isolation has been used as an independent means of establishing the presence or absence of a virus. This process is essential for the authentication of any diagnostic test. Without a gold standard, it is impossible for a doctor or scientists to know if a positive antibody test indicates infection or what it may indicate."[110]*

Gary Null is an independent AIDS researcher whose work has taken him around the world, resulting in film documentaries, countless interviews with medical personnel and media articles presenting his findings. Null runs his own nutrition clinic and hosts *Natural Living* on New York City's WBAI Radio. An excerpt from his program, broadcast on 21st March 1996, had him addressing the 'gold standard' issue:

> *"No one, I repeat, no one under ANY circumstances should have an HIV test. It is a fraud. A complete and total fraud. Why is it a fraud? Because there is no 'gold standard'. I have just*

---

[109] Credence telephone conversation with Colindale staff on 14th March 2000
[110] Maggiore, Christine, ibid. p.42

gone all over the world trying to find the independent verification of this test. I have not found it."[111]

Of course none of the above information is shared with the patient at the point of testing. As if all this wasn't bad enough, a new form of diagnosis came into being in late 1987. The *Los Angeles Weekly* explains:

"In the 4th September issue of the Journal of the American Medical Association [JAMA], *the CDC announced that a diagnosis of AIDS no longer requires an AIDS test. The government now considers you are an AIDS carrier if you suffer from any of the maladies on its new list of diseases indicative of AIDS, including such relatively common infections as herpes simplex, tuberculosis, salmonellosis and a shockingly broad 'other bacterial infections'. This broad definition will lead to countless new AIDS diagnoses - whether or not the person actually has AIDS. A major problem with the new AIDS definition is that it ignores the many environmental causes of immune suppression. Exposure to toxins, alcoholism, heavy drug use or heavy antibiotic use all can cause onset of the list of 'diseases' indicative of AIDS."*[112]

And the CDC itself, in a stunning remark, conceded:

"The diagnostic criteria accepted by the AIDS surveillance case definition should not be interpreted as the standard of good medical practice."[113]

Presumptive diagnosis was born. Now the orthodoxy was able to diagnose any patient as an 'AIDS carrier' simply by looking at their lifestyle and asking whether they had any one of a handful of common symptoms that people have been suffering from for centuries. On the basis of this unscientific determination alone, tens of thousands of Americans have been given the fateful diagnosis. Seldom considered are the appalling consequences and the private grief for the individual once a positive result is announced. Iola Martin was one such person given a positive diagnosis. Here she recounts her own particularly traumatic experience at the hands of the AIDS establishment.

---

[111] see also Maggiore, Christine, ibid. p.5
[112] *Los Angeles Weekly*, 18th December 1987
[113] *Los Angeles Weekly*, ibid.

"In 1990, it was recommended that I took an HIV test because I was pregnant. The first test came back inconclusive, the second was positive. The positive result left me in total shock. I was told that I would have to decide what to do about my baby. The information I was given left me without much choice. They said there were two scenarios. I could live long enough to watch my baby die of AIDS, or I could leave my baby without a mother, when I died of AIDS, knowing that my baby would die soon after me. Believing in the death sentence I had been given, I agreed to a second trimester abortion. It was a terrible, terrible experience, and the decision haunts me to this day."

Today, ten years later, Iola is still with us. She is alive and physically well. But her experience has taken its emotional toll. Iola's long-term relationship has ended: *"I was so bitter, sad and angry and caught up in the idea that I was going to die."* [114] Discovering the truth about AIDS in 1996 came too late for Iola, and far too late for her unborn child.

Relationships severed - marriages called off - innocent lives inadvertently ended - social ostracism - mental torture – suicides - negligent homicide? All this even before the supposed HIV has begun its deadly work. The physician then warns us that as the disease progresses, its victims will die a slow and agonising death. And as we witness the onset of AIDS in the individual, the unsuspecting among us believe we are witnessing a death that can only be the result of the deadly virus. But this is not the case at all. Death will be exacted by a method we least suspected….

AIDS by prescription.

---

[114] Maggiore, Christine, ibid.

THE AIDS PHARMACY

"We are apt to shut our eyes against a painful truth, and listen to the song of the siren till she transforms us into beasts. For my part, whatever anguish of spirit it may cost, I am willing to know the whole truth, to know the worst, and provide for it."
Patrick Henry on the brink of The American Revolution

A healthy individual given an HIV positive diagnosis following an 'AIDS test' is generally recommended 'early intervention' treatment with the drug Azidothymidine (AZT) and/or its derivatives. An AIDS physician suggests this course of action because this is what he has been taught to do through the medical briefs sent regularly to him. It is generally believed that early intervention treatment reduces the rate at which HIV spreads, thus raising the levels of immune function T-cells, which then do battle with the virus, and thus delay the onset of AIDS-related diseases in the patient.

Let us now trace what happens to that individual, who maybe feels a little run down, and who has decided to go to the doctor. We'll call him Chris. Perhaps Chris belongs to one of the AIDS risk groups popularised by an emotionally charged media (active multi-partner, fast-track hetero/homosexual and/or drug user). Perhaps his tiredness and flu-like symptoms coincide with his having recently returned from a trip abroad. Perhaps his tiredness and flu-like symptoms are just that - flu. In any case, Chris's doctor is aware of the AIDS risk categories and advises Chris to get tested for HIV.

Chris is not aware of the truth concerning AIDS, he has only been told that HIV is an incredibly volatile viral agent capable of spreading easily through bodily fluids and through the transfer of blood products. So Chris takes the extremely unspecific 'AIDS test', and after two weeks of inner turmoil waiting for the result, he is told he has 'the AIDS virus.' As Joan Shenton says:

"The inexorable death sentence – 'you have ten years at most' pronounced by doctors on young men and women, has led to some of the most intense human suffering imaginable. It

has broken up families, alienated individuals from their communities and led to psychological death and suicide."[115]

Looking quite unwell through the stress of it all, Chris is now recommended one of two courses of action:

- Early intervention treatment with anti-viral therapy (AZT, ddl, ddC, d4T, etc.)... *or*
- Go home untreated and come back when AIDS symptoms start to manifest.

Chris decides on early intervention with AZT - after all, his doctor knows best and this is modern medicine. Had Chris elected not to have AZT to begin with, but to go home and wait for the AIDS symptoms to manifest, he would not have long to wait before starting to notice a number of physical symptoms. That is because Chris is already showing signs of illness through stress alone. He has been persuaded by his doctor and a relentless media into watching for the common symptoms of AIDS. These indicators are 'something like flu', diarrhoea and pronounced fatigue. Notice that these are also psychosomatic symptoms, each of which can be brought on by simply the worry of being HIV positive and thus 'prone to AIDS'. [116]

Gary Null has studied in detail the correlation between receiving bad news (a 'positive' result) and the onset of ill health. Says Null:

"I've looked at all the literature on psychoneuroimmunology and I have seen an abundant series of articles that show that if you give a person some bad news, all the quantitative measurements of immune function - natural killer cells, T-cells, phagocytes etc - go down. In a matter of hours, the entire immune system can become depressed. Now give them bad news that is only going to get worse and you're putting that person's psychoneurological immune system into a tailspin." [117]

---

[115] Shenton, Joan, ibid.

[116] **Brown, George** *Life Events and Illness*, Guildford Press, 1999. Assembles examples of findings where the LEDS (Life Events and Difficulties Schedule) is used to examine the onset of a range of disorders. In consultation with psychiatrists, GPs and related healthcare professionals, Steven Ransom has compiled a list of over 70 physical and mental conditions that can manifest as a direct result of life stresses. Details available from Credence Publications.

[117] **Null, Gary**, *Zenger*, August 1997

Chris has not opted to go home and wait. Having been passed the equivalent of a verbal death sentence and now not feeling well at all, Chris has decided on the doctor's suggestion of early intervention treatment with AZT.

So what is AZT? Researcher Christine Maggiore introduces us to this widely prescribed AIDS drug.

"AZT is not a new drug. It was not created for the treatment of AIDS and is not an anti-viral. AZT is a chemical compound that was developed - and abandoned - over 30 years ago as a chemotherapy treatment for cancer. Many cancer patients do not survive chemotherapy due to its destructive effects on the immune system. Because of the damage it causes, chemotherapy is never used as a prevention and is only administered for very limited amounts of time.

Since cancer is made of persistently growing cells, AZT was designed to prevent formation of new cells.... In 1964, experiments with AZT on mice with cancer showed that AZT was so effective in destroying healthy growing cells that the mice died of extreme toxicity. As a result, AZT was shelved and no patent was ever filed."[118]

It has been reported by Project AIDS International that Richard Beltz, the creator of AZT, called for the abandonment of this drug because 1) its extreme toxicity made it unsuitable for any chemotherapy - even short term, and 2) it was carcinogenic (cancer causing) at any dose. [119] [120]

Barrister Anthony Brink remarks:

"In truth, AZT makes you feel like you're dying. That's because on AZT you are. How can a deadly cell toxin conceivably make you feel better as it finishes you, by stopping your cells from dividing, by ending this vital process that distinguishes living things from dead things? Not for nothing does AZT come with a skull and cross-bones label when

---

[118] Maggiore, Christine, ibid.

[119] Selvey, Jeremy, ibid. p.7

[120] **Cohen, S S** *New England Journal of Medicine*, 317 (1987): 629

81

packaged for laboratory use."[121]

And indeed that is the case. With a skull and cross-bones on the outer label (see photo section) and a reminder to wear *suitable protective clothing when handling,* the inner contents of the AZT packaging include the following side-effects advisory notice:

WHOLE BODY: abdominal pain, back pain, body odour, chest pain, chills, edema of the lip, fever, flu symptoms, hyperalgesia.

CARDIOVASCULAR: syncope, vasodilation.

GASTROINTESTINAL: bleeding gums, constipation, diarrhoea, dysphagia, edema of the tongue, eructation, flatulence, mouth ulcer, rectal haemorrhage.

HAEMIC AND LYMPHATIC: lymphadenopathy.

MUSCULOSKELETAL: arthralgia, muscle spasm, tremor, twitch.

NERVOUS: anxiety, confusion, depression, dizziness, emotional lability, loss of mental acuity, nervousness, paresthesia, somnolence, vertigo.

RESPIRATORY: cough, dyspnea, epistaxis, hoarseness, pharyngitis, rhinitis, sinusitis.

SKIN: rash, sweat, urticaria.

SPECIAL SENSES: amblyopia, hearing loss, phxotophobia, taste perversion.

UROGENITAL: dysuria, polyuria, urinary frequency, urinary hesitancy.

Dr Stefan Lanka has this to say:

"...The use of AZT and other 'anti-retrovirals', which are supposed to target HIV replication, but actually kill cells indiscriminately (and ultimately the whole body), must be stopped immediately. It is especially distressing to note that AZT and its analogues preferentially attack those cells which divide most rapidly, namely cells in the intestines causing diarrhoea and malabsorption of food, and in bone marrow, ironically, the primary production site for cells of the immune system." [122]

---

[121] **Brink, Anthony,** *AZT and Heavenly Remedies,* Rethinking AIDS Homepage: www.rethinkingaids.com

[122] Lanka, Stefan, ibid. Also **Lauritsen, John** *Poison by Prescription: The AZT Story,* Asklepios, New York, 1990. Also **Lauritsen, John** *The AIDS War. Propaganda,*

The horrific toxicity of AZT brings on the symptoms of AIDS: diarrhoea, malabsorption of food leading to rapid weight loss and immune deficiency disorders. This of course has led some doctors to maintain the dosage of AZT or even increase it in the patient, as they perceive that the medication 'isn't working' and more is required. This in turn accelerates the degradation of the patient. More AZT is given. The patient relapses further... and so on, down the slippery slope to death. More disturbingly, while most chemotherapy agents are only administered to the patient for a strictly limited period of time in view of their toxicity, AZT is prescribed until the very end.

Chris is now quite literally dying. In being prescribed AZT, Chris is receiving white capsules with a blue band. Chris doesn't know about the protective clothing worn in the labs. He's read the side-effects insert, but he's resolved to fight his dreadful 'illness'.

Chris will not live much longer. His doctor has advised that his dosage be increased in order to try and combat the ravaging effects of the 'AIDS virus'. Chris agrees to the increased dose. And when Chris eventually dies of liver and heart damage, malnutrition and dramatic weight loss through internal haemorrhaging and other complications, his family will mourn the passing of a dearly loved husband, father or son who was brave to the very end, but who finally succumbed to the dreadful AIDS.

But Chris did not die of HIV/AIDS. Chris's death was by prescription.

In exactly this manner, thousands upon thousands of men and women have been persuaded to take AZT, a drug believed by the more discerning in the scientific community to be the leading cause of AIDS in the western world. Researcher Newly Abbott remonstrates:

"AIDS is truly an iatrogenic disaster of the primary magnitude. By 'iatrogenic', we mean that clinical AIDS is a syndrome that is primarily being caused in the western world now by doctors and their medicine. I'm not sure what's more terrifying: that this state of affairs continues to exist at all in spite of all the obvious

---

Profiteering and Genocide from the Medical-Industrial Complex, Asklepios, New York, 1993

evidence, or that the English language actually has a word for it. "[123]

Despite this catastrophic history, Glaxo-Wellcome rises defiantly in defence of the positive benefits of its most infamous product. In fact, its information leaflet, incongruously titled *Positive Benefits*, states *"... there are no life-threatening side-effects associated with zidovudine [AZT]."* Wellcome further cites numerous studies to substantiate its claims that AZT both *"prolongs life"* and *"enhances its quality".* The problem is, the only studies that appear to demonstrate these *"positive benefits"* are the studies that have been funded, either directly or indirectly, by the Wellcome Foundation.[124] As we shall see, independent studies conducted on AZT paint an entirely different picture.[125]

So how is it that such a drug can ever be prescribed today? Twenty years after AZT was shelved as an unusable poison, HIV was the talk of the medical establishment after Gallo's press conference. The emergence of the phenomenon of immune suppression known as AIDS presented an incredibly lucrative new opportunity for someone to come up with a drug to combat the supposed causative virus. David Barry, UK drug company Wellcome's head researcher in the United States, was a man who knew a golden opportunity when he saw one. Barry had a number of advantages working for him. He knew US FDA drug approval procedures after having worked at the federal agency during the 1970s as a virologist. But Barry's main advantage was that he worked for Wellcome, whose unusual non-profit charity status enabled the corporation to donate large sums of tax-free grant money to strategic institutions throughout government, universities and the corporate world.[126] Wellcome thus had many grateful and influential friends.

David Barry turned his attention to the company archives in search of previously rejected compounds. The race was on for an AIDS drug. There was no time to research a new substance from scratch, go

[123] **Abbott, N** "AIDS - Examining the Politics of Medical Genocide," a special report. Sydney, Australia 1994
[124] Project AIDS International, Public Information Dossier, 15th March 1993. p.9
[125] **Hamilton et al**. VA Study 1990. Also CDC unreleased study 1990
[126] Duesberg, Peter H, *Inventing...* ibid. p.310

through the interminable FDA approval procedures and expect to be first into the new and wide-open AIDS market. Barry knew that if he could find a suitable existing substance, Wellcome would save millions in research and development money in addition to being perfectly positioned to corner sales. Barry selected a group of drugs and forwarded them to his friend Dani Bolognesi, a professor at North Carolina's Duke University and a former colleague. Bolognesi tested the substances in his lab to see if any proved to demonstrate an ability to halt viral cell multiplication. One drug, code-named Compound S, was wildly successful. Bolognesi wasted no time in sending his approval back to Barry for Compound S, or, as the archive tag in Barry's office would later identify it, AZT.[127]

Bolognesi subsequently referred David Barry to Sam Broder, the man in charge of Robert Gallo's laboratory at the National Cancer Institute. Barry and Wellcome needed the clout the new Pope of AIDS, Robert Gallo, was able to bring to bear to get AZT through the FDA approval procedure.[128] Barry duly sent Sam Broder a sample of Compound S in late 1984. The drug's ability to interrupt cell multiplication impressed Broder right away. Broder was later to become known in research circles as 'Mr AZT', such was his new-found religious enthusiasm for the drug.

Barry and Broder were the right men at the right time for AZT, Bruce Nussbaum recalls:

"David Barry was the puppet master, and his favorite marionette was Sam Broder. While Broder was charging around promoting AZT at the National Institutes of Health, Barry was working quietly behind the scenes, orchestrating a whole panoply of actors who would ensure the drug's ultimate commercial success." [129]

Broder hurried AZT through its Phase 1 trials. Unprecedented FDA co-operation was extended because of the extreme pressure being

---

[127] Duesberg, Peter H, *Inventing...* ibid. p.311

[128] **Nussbaum, Bruce** *Good Intentions: How Big Business, Politics, and Medicine are Corrupting the Fight Against AIDS*, Atlantic Monthly Press, 1990

[129] Nussbaum, Bruce, ibid. Also **Wyatt, E A** "Rushing to Judgment," *Barron's,* 15th August 1994, p. 23-27

brought to bear on the US government by pro-medication AIDS activist groups determined to see a drug onto the market as quickly as possible. Duesberg records what was happening in these hurriedly approved AZT trials:

"Sixty-six AZT recipients suffered 'severe' nausea... as compared to twenty-five in the placebo group. All AZT users saw their muscles waste away, while only three placebo recipients suffered this symptom. And a full thirty in the AZT group survived only with multiple blood transfusions to replace their poisoned blood cells, compared to five similar cases among the placebo users."[130]

A follow-up study shattered anyone's illusions that AZT was in any way beneficial when all the patients were put on the drug. An unacceptable rate of fatalities prompted urgent calls for the trials to be stopped. Bruce Nussbaum:

"A move to stop the trial began immediately. The toxicity of AZT was proving to be extremely high, much higher than indicated by Sam Broder's safety trials. PIs [Principal Investigators] began to worry that AZT was killing bone marrow cells so fast that patients would quickly come down with aplastic anemia, a murderous disease. This was terrifying to many PIs. "There was enormous pressure to stop," recalls Broder. "People said, 'My God, what's going on? We're getting these anemias. What's going on?' We never saw this level of anemia before."[131]

Unknown to Broder however, another disastrously unscientific situation was developing. Some of the patients, completely sold on media rumours of AZT's miracle healing powers with AIDS, were determined to get their hands on the drug and forget the placebo. Discussions among the patients began, with some tasting another's medication. Some of the placebo group, unknown to the investigators, began taking AZT, further corrupting any blinding value the trials may have had in determining the effectiveness of the drug. Also, some of the AZT recipients simply weren't able to complete their courses of

[130] Duesberg, Peter H, *Inventing...* ibid. p.317
[131] Nussbaum, Bruce, ibid.

AZT, due to the drug's extreme side-effects. Margaret Fischl, who headed up the study, admitted:

> *"Drug therapy was temporarily discontinued or the frequency of doses decreased... if severe adverse reactions were noted. The study medication was withdrawn if unacceptable toxic effects or a [cancer] requiring therapy developed."*[132]

Here Fischl blatantly admits that doctors knew all along who was using AZT. So much for the double-blind, placebo-controlled trial. Christine Maggiore records other trials, not funded by Wellcome, which were producing a similar worrying picture:

> *"A multitude of independent studies including the Concorde study - the largest (1,749 subjects) and longest (three years in duration) - concluded that AZT increases T-cell counts only moderately and briefly without improving health (clinical status), and that it does not delay the onset of AIDS indicator diseases.*[133] *Following recommendations for 'early intervention', one third to one half of those who take AZT begin treatment before manifesting any symptoms of AIDS,*[134] *although independent studies have shown that AZT actually accelerates clinical decline and decreases quality of life, at times even causing death before any AIDS defining illnesses appear - an occurrence officially described as 'death without any preceding AIDS-defining event.'"*[135] [136]

British and French scientists organised what became known as the Concorde study in 1991. The purpose of the three-year study was to test whether AZT prevented the onset of AIDS indicator diseases in HIV positive but otherwise symptomless individuals, as compared with those who were already demonstrating the onset of AIDS. Evidently as the study progressed, arguments between the scientists erupted over whether to continue the trials in view of the appalling toxic attrition they were witnessing. They nervously agreed to continue.

---

[132] **Fischl et al** The AZT Collaborative Working Group, "Efficacy of Azidothymidine", 185-191
[133] *Lancet* 343:871, Concorde Coordinating Committee
[134] *British Medical Journal*, 15th July 1995, p.156-158 (49%); *Science Magazine*, 24th February 1995, p.1080 (34%)
[135] *JAMA* 260:3009, 1998; *New England Journal of Medicine* 326:437, 1992
[136] Maggiore, Christine, ibid.

After three years, the researchers published their results. Their indictment of AZT was total. The death rate in the AZT group who were taking the drug to avoid developing AIDS was 25% higher than the control group.[137] Some of those who survived could no longer stand the nausea, vomiting and anemia, so they flushed their AZT capsules down the toilet.[138] The day before this news was reported in England, Professor Tony Pinching, director of immunology at St Bartholomew's Hospital, London, went on record in the *Daily Telegraph*, warning HIV positive, symptomless individuals that they would be better off without drug therapy. Not surprisingly, the *Concorde* report also clearly showed that AZT did not halt the development of AIDS.[139]

Even Jerome Groopman, one of the participating scientists, had serious doubts about the humanitarian nature and efficacy of AZT. He gave it to 14 patients in his Boston hospital on a compassionate basis. Three months later, only three were still able to take AZT. *"We found it nearly impossible to keep patients on the drug,"* Groopman admitted.[140]

Gay historian and AIDS dissident John Lauritsen was incensed:

"The multi-center clinical trials of AZT are perhaps the sloppiest and most poorly controlled trials ever to serve as the basis for an FDA licensing approval... Because mortality was not an intended endpoint, causes of death were never verified. Despite this, and a frightening record of toxicity, the FDA approved AZT in record time, granting a treatment IND [investigational new drug] in less than five days and full pharmaceutical licensing in less than six months."[141]

Dr Joseph Sonnabend, an American AIDS researcher, had this to say about AZT:

[137] **Seligman, et al.** "Concorde: MRC/ANRS Randomized Double-Blind Control Trial."

[138] **Hodgkinson, Neville** "The Cure that Failed." *London Sunday Times*, 4th April 1993

[139] *Daily Telegraph*, "HIV Carriers Advised to Stop Their Treatment," Peter Pallot. 3rd April 1993

[140] **Kolata, G** "Imminent Marketing of AZT Raises Problems," *Science*, 235 (1987): 1462-1463

[141] Lauritsen, John, ibid.

"It is beyond belief. I don't know what to do. I'm ashamed of my colleagues. I'm embarrassed. This is such shoddy science. It's hard to believe nobody's protesting. Damned cowards! The name of the game is to protect your grants. Don't open your mouth. It's all about money. It's grounds for just following the party line and not being critical when there are obvious financial and political forces that are driving this."[142]

And Dr Harvey Bialy, molecular biologist and science editor of *Bio/Technology,* states:

"I'm stunned by the low quality of science surrounding AIDS research. I'm horrified by the widespread use of AZT. Not just because it is toxic, but because the claims of efficacy are false. I can't see how this drug can be doing anything other than making people extremely sick."[143]

Another alarming trend noticed was that longer term treatment with AZT brought on lymphoma (a type of cancer) in around half of the patients.[144] Incredibly, even then, the virus hunting lobby rushed to defend the drug, declaring that patients were living longer on AZT and therefore merely stood a higher statistical risk of developing cancer![145] Dr Sonnabend filed a report with the Food & Drug Administration questioning the criteria and basis for the licensing of AZT. He never received a reply either from the FDA or from Burroughs-Wellcome. [146]

In spite of these and other drug trial fiascos, the Food & Drug Administration approved AZT as an anti-retroviral treatment for AIDS. Once approval was granted, AZT became THE AIDS drug. Almost overnight the demand for the expensive and exclusive AZT became so fierce that Wellcome was hard pressed to supply the quota.

Despite the widely reported failures, Wellcome's income from AZT very quickly became the envy of its counterparts. Soon other

---

[142] Quote recorded by **Jeremy Selvey**, PAI Archives.

[143] Project AIDS International, Public Information Dossier, ibid.

[144] **Pluda et al.** "Development of Non-Hodgkin Lymphoma in a Cohort of Patients with Severe Immunodeficiency Virus (HIV) Infection on Long-Term Anti-Viral Therapy." *Ann. Intern. Med.,* 113 (1990): 276-282

[145] Pluda et al. ibid.

[146] **Sonnabend, J A** Report on MultiCenter Study of AZT to FDA, 1987

pharmaceutical giants began vying for a piece of Wellcome's AIDS pie. Hoffman La-Roche produced dideoxycytidine (ddC) and Bristol-Myers Squibb marketed its version, known as ddI. During testing, ddI was found capable of destroying nerves throughout the body and causing fatal damage to the pancreas,[147] something not even AZT was reported to do. Doctors began experimenting with ddI, giving it to patients who were unable to tolerate AZT.[148] Many patients inexplicably died during these unofficial trials, but once again, the FDA were able to staunch the inevitable flood of complaints.

AZT and its derivatives are still prescribed with reckless abandon. But, just as the turbulent history surrounding the radioactive Windscale nuclear power plant necessitated a politically expedient name-change to Sellafield, Wellcome and other manufacturers are now giving their window display a fresh new look. At the 1996 Conference on Retroviruses and Opportunistic Infections, a new generation of AIDS drugs known as 'protease inhibitors' was launched. Protease inhibitors, or 'combo cocktails', are said to enhance dramatically the effects of AZT and ddI. Drug companies are pushing the latest 'great news' on AIDS, stridently insisting that their cocktails be taken, like margaritas, in large doses for life, but in the small print stating *"...the long-term effects of protease inhibitors are unknown."*[149] Christine Maggiore explains the drug companies' continued psychological conditioning of their vulnerable patients:

> *"The absolute compliance required for protease treatment is a popular subject of news reports and AIDS organization seminars. Patients are required to pop 30 to 50 pills a day on a 24-hour-a day schedule - some taken with food, some on an empty stomach. Patients are warned that if they do not rigorously adhere to the strict protocol schedule, their virus will mutate into new, drug resistant strains."*[150]

Drug company Merck muscled to the front in getting FDA approval for its protease inhibitor cocktail drug, Crixivan. Such was the hype

---

[147] Merck Index

[148] Lauritsen, John, *AIDS War*, ibid.

[149] Wording which appears on the Merck protease inhibitor product Crixivan.

[150] Maggiore, Christine, ibid. p.17

surrounding the new scare that the drug received FDA approval in just 42 days. Christine Maggiore again:

"Crixivan's FDA approval broke a 72-day record for the fastest approval in FDA history, previously set by the protease inhibitor Ritonavir. Newsday articles noting the toxic effects of these drugs - diarrhea, nausea, fungal infections, bloody urine, kidney stones, weakness, headaches and liver inflammation requiring "doctor visits and additional medicines" - were ignored by AIDS organizations who pressured the FDA for fast track approval.[151] Recently reported side-effects include CMV retinitis, diabetes, liver failure, 'buffalo humps' (large fat deposits at the base of the neck), acute kidney failure, acute pancreatitis, grade four diarrhea and sudden death."[152]

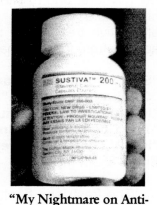

"My Nightmare on Anti-HIV Therapy" - On the second day of treatment, one young man became confused and scared. He began to hear strange, non-existent sounds which were the start of a series of hallucinations. *"I couldn't find my way home. I couldn't remember how to put a record on or how to use a computer."* He was taking Efavirenz, Abacavir and d4T. Within 48 hours of stopping the drugs, everything returned to normal.
(*Positive Nation Magazine.* "The Crazy Beat of Those Combo's", January 2000)

Protease inhibitors have been wildly successful in one area however - breathing new life into the AIDS industry and increasing the cash-flow ever further. In 1997, sales of anti-retrovirals amounted to $2.3 billion, and are estimated to double by 2002.[153] Drug companies are promoting their protease inhibitors in an orgy of marketing excess. Billboards and magazines advise 'AIDS-infected positives' to *"be smart about HIV"* by *"hitting early and hard"* with the new generation of AIDS wonder cocktails.

Straight Up is a glossy African AIDS community magazine promoting the latest

---

[151] *Newsday Magazine*, 30th January 1996

[152] *Lancet*, 1st June 1997. Vol.349, p.1745; *Philadelphia Inquirer*, Associated Press Report, 13th June 1997; *Rolling Stone Magazine*, "Special Report: Dr David Ho and the Lazarus Equation", 6th March 1997; *The Valley Advocate*, "The Big 'Tease", 20th February 1997

[153] Reuters Health, January 1999. www.reutershealth.com

'breakthroughs' in the war against AIDS. Included is a section on various alternative treatments for HIV positive sufferers, including the highly favoured homoeopathy. The basis of homoeopathy's alleged curative powers is to administer to the patient minute doses of the main aggravating agent, thus conforming to the principle of 'like cures like'. Where, one might legitimately ask, does the homoeopath obtain his minute quantities of HIV?[154] Alongside other highly dubious alternative treatments, the magazine also includes several full-page adverts from the pharmaceutical industries:

"Stay Strong... HIV Care" - Glaxo Wellcome
"Celebration of Life..."
"Investing in Your Future" - Pharmacia & Upjohn
"The Tide is Turning in HIV Therapy" - Boehringer Ingelheim
"In HIV Therapy, There is Hope... We're Working on It"...Merck, Sharp & Dohme[155]

The fresh and healthy promises, a central feature of these multi-million-pound PR campaigns, mask the ugly clinical reality concerning these drugs. And what is the ugly clinical reality? It is that protease inhibitors have been a dismal failure from the very start. Merck actually delayed marketing their own protease inhibitors for four years because the drugs were killing their laboratory animals.[156] This ethically controversial data was not made known to those people taking part in the protease inhibitor trials. Little wonder the *New York Times* reported that *"...unexpected deaths amongst human protease inhibitor consumers are rising."*[157]

Even Dr Michael Saag, a paid consultant for AZT's manufacturer Glaxo-Wellcome and other pharmaceutical corporations, confesses

---

[154] **Ransom, Steven** *Homoeopathy, What Are We Swallowing?* Credence Publications, 1999. An examination into the fraud and charlatanism predominant in alternative medicine.

[155] All advertisements from *Straight Up*, Axiom Publishers, London: December 1999

[156] *Dayton Daily News, New York Times*, August 1997. Quoted in *Continuum* Magazine, Vol 5, No 1, October 1997. The National AIDS Manual reports that Efavirenz causes abnormalities in animal offspring and therefore should not be taken during pregnancy. Psychological changes in the first four weeks with Efavirenz can include euphoria, vivid dreams, psychotic episodes and suicidal thoughts. *Anti-HIV Drugs*, NAM Publications, First Edition, 1999.

[157] *Dayton Daily News*, August 1997, ibid.

that the cocktail dam holding back AIDS is already springing serious leaks:

> *"Failures* [with Highly Active Anti-Retroviral Therapy (HAART)] *are occurring right and left,"* Saag confides. *"[Doctors] should expect failure with whatever* [HAART cocktail they] *first use. We should plan on it. We should prepare for it. Clinicians should expect failure."* [158]

Fellow protease expert Dr Rasnik is equally dismissive. For Rasnick, the press ecstasy and back-slapping over the release of protease inhibitors recalled the previous euphoria over AZT.

> *"Once again, all we have are researchers talking to reporters about incomplete studies that haven't been scrutinized by the scientific review process. And the researchers involved are funded by the companies that make the drugs in question. There is no justification for the claims coming from these sources, particularly when we have seen it all before* [with AZT]." [159]

Gallo too, in a break from his usual upbeat tradition, stated that *"... these drugs are toxic... The longer you take the drugs, the greater the toxicity."* [160]

One would imagine that an organisation such as The AIDS Treatment Project would take the comments of Saag, Rasnick and Gallo into consideration when dispensing their advice to the HIV positive community. Sadly, this is not the case. In their leaflets entitled *An Introduction to Combination Therapy* and *Changing Treatment*, there are numerous warnings to adhere strictly to the regime and not miss medication times:

> *"Use a pill beeper or alarm watch to set dose times.... If you are going away for a few days, take extra drugs.... If you have been taking all your drugs at the right time, but you have not had a very good response, you may need a drug concentration test. The £25.00 test will check to see if you are absorbing enough of the drugs.... The chance to return to the*

---

[158] *Esquire Magazine,* April 1999
[159] Maggiore, Christine, ibid. p.20
[160] Maggiore, Christine, ibid. p.18

luxury of a drug-free period can help improve adherence to the regimen.... It is always safer to use a stronger combination than a weak one...." [161] (emphasis ours)

Stephen Rogers recounts his nightmare encounter with protease inhibitors. Heralded as the Wonder Drug and possible cure for AIDS, Stephen was recommended to take part in a clinical trial for one of the new protease inhibitor products, Saquinavir. [162] Stephen's account has necessarily been condensed, but the thrust of his story is self-evident:

"These new protease inhibitors are marvellous." said my consultant. "Pretty soon everyone will be on them." My trial consisted of AZT, ddl, and Saquinavir. During the first year, I needed a blood transfusion. During the second year I developed a mild attack of shingles and I became affected by the condition Lypodistrophy, with changes in my body shape and veins of the lower limb beginning to protrude and the skin on my thighs becoming more transluscent. [163] *My medication was changed to Ritonavir.* [164] *My doctor brushed aside my concerns that some people had died of liver failure through this drug.*

The first two weeks brought no side-effects and then... the onslaught. Numbing and tingling in the lips, lethargy, insomnia, crippling stomach cramps and chronic diarrhoea. My doctor then reintroduced Saquinavir, alongside the Ritonavir. I developed a skin abscess, which swelled to the size of a golf ball. My doctor tried to blame it on my sexual pursuits.... My clinic appointments were now a torture, occurring every two to four weeks. I began to feel more like a lab rat than a person. The mountain of pills

---

[161] ATP Guides to 'Combination Therapy', August 1999, and 'Changing Treatment', July 1999

[162] *New York Times*, 16th May 1999, contains a report on their ten-month investigation into drug companies offering large payments to doctors to recruit patients into testing experimental drugs. Top recruiters can earn $1,000,000 per annum. Says Dr David Shimm of the Ethics Committee at Porter Adventist Hospital, Denver: *"Doctors are enticing and cajoling patients who are in no position to resist, and who do not see a dual agent with divided loyalties."*

[163] *New York Times*, 5th February 1998: *"Paunches, buffalo humps, puffy cheeks and other unusual accumulations of fat are changing the body shape of many numbers of people taking combination therapy."*

[164] Incidence of severe liver damage amongst patients taking Ritonavir were five times higher than among those taking other drugs. *Journal of the American Medical Association*, 5th January 2000

and capsules I had in my hand now filled me with dread. Each time before taking them I would pause and think: 'These drugs are killing me.' I felt confused and frightened. The organisations set up to help people like me had become no more than shadow puppets, projecting the image of living longer and better on combination therapy, but with no actual substance to their claim.

And so, instead of accepting the situation as many do, I began a relentless quest for the truth and began asking lots of questions. When I learned the Viral Load Test is highly inaccurate, my fear turned to anger at being duped. I made a decision to stop taking the drugs".[165]

Amazingly, Saquinavir has been declared a 'Millennium Product' by the Millennium Design Council. Exhibited in the Millennium Dome at Greenwich, London and included in exhibitions in schools and colleges across the UK, a jubilant spokesperson for Roche, the manufacturers of Saquinavir, said, *"We are proud that Saquinavir's contribution to anti-HIV therapy has been recognised and delighted that it has received this award."* [166]

Stephen believes he is alive today largely as a result of ceasing his award-winning medication. The skepticism Stephen showed towards the viral load theory was also not unfounded. Viral load is a recent hypothesis proposing that HIV is replicating in the body at least one billion times a day, thus increasing a patient's 'viral load'. Once again, no evidence has ever been produced to substantiate this claim. Nevertheless, drug researchers and their pharmaceutical companies have used 'viral load' as a fresh new vehicle upon which to launch even stronger cocktails to combat this 'vicious new replicating danger.' The AIDS Treatment Project again:

"Several billion new HIV infected cells are produced in an HIV positive person every day."[167]

Just like a blockbuster Hollywood thriller, it seems that AIDS, the *phantom virus phenomenon* of the 20th and 21st centuries, has a way of

---

[165] **Rogers, Stephen** *Continuum*, Vol 5, No 5, December 1998

[166] UK *Gay Times* magazine, June 1999

[167] ATP Guides to 'Combination Therapy', August 1999, and 'Changing Treatment', July 1999

regularly 'upping the ante'. Following hot-on-the-heels of the public health scare that new antibiotic-resistant superbugs are stalking the planet (inspiring unforgettable tabloid headlines such as "Killer Bug Ate My Face") AIDS researchers are now predicting and promoting a new drug-resistant AIDS epidemic, which is set to engulf us 'very soon'. The following headline is a good example:

> **THE BEST AIDS DRUGS ARE STILL NOT GOOD ENOUGH** - *Scientists at Jefferson Medical College have found evidence for the first time of actively replicating HIV in the bloodstream of patients taking the most powerful anti-AIDS virus drugs available. Scientists knew that the combination of drugs known as HAART, highly active anti-retroviral therapy, did not eradicate the AIDS virus, <u>despite the fact that the virus could not be detected by conventional means in the patient's blood</u> [emphasis ours]. But they thought that the drugs had at least arrested the virus from replicating. No one had been able to find active virus in the blood of patients still on the drugs…. until now. Roger J Pomerantz, MD, professor of medicine, biochemistry and molecular pharmacology, etc. etc….."* [168]

The only measurable contribution this report (and the many similar to it) has made to the debate on AIDS is to increase public fear. As a direct result of this fear-mongering, health officials and legislators in the US have increasing freedom to call for compulsory treatment laws for HIV positive persons, to protect a vulnerable public from a new and potent AZT-resistant AIDS horror. [169] [170]

And in the UK, London's Enfield and Haringey Health Authorities are now committed to screening 80% of their expectant mothers for HIV by 2001. Their *Focus* leaflet says:

> *"In April '98 a working party report called for HIV testing to be made available in all ante-natal clinics in the United Kingdom, and that in areas of high prevalence of HIV such as London,*

---

[168] Jefferson Medical College, 11th November 1999

[169] *Continuum*, Vol 4, No 4, 1996. *"Health officials in San Francisco want to identify everyone who is HIV+ and force them to have drug therapy… City's health director Sandra Hernandez believes this measure 'has potential for curtailing the further spread of the HIV epidemic.'"*

[170] *New York Native Issue*, 15th July 1996. p.691

staff should strongly encourage the women to have the test."[171]

In their misguided attempts to guard the health of all expectant mothers in their area, Enfield and Haringey have absolutely no idea of the horrors they are unwittingly calling down upon the innocents in their care. A healthy, young expectant mother who has just recovered from flu is coincidentally advised to take the ELISA test...? Christine Maggiore again:

> *"The effects of the drugs on the mother include muscle deterioration, severe anemia, nerve damage, liver and kidney damage, diarrhoea, dementia and seizures. The effects of these drugs on the developing fetus include deformities, and other birth defects, spontaneous abortions and the need for therapeutic abortions of severely damaged fetuses. In many states today, children who test HIV positive risk being removed from their homes by the welfare agencies or public health services if the parents do not agree to give them treatment with AZT or other pharmaceuticals."*[172]

It is at this point in the story of AIDS that the enormity of our earlier accusation of negligent homicide is now seen in its proper context. An expectant mother with flu, who tests positive for 'the AIDS virus' through cross-reactions, is then advised to begin 'anti-viral' treatment with AZT or similar drugs as soon as possible *"...For the benefit of your baby, Mrs Smith."* Mother and child then have every likelihood of going on to die a slow and agonising death.

And a recent study in *Lancet* gives tacit admission that as with adults, administering protease inhibitors to children can cause skin and bone abnormalities such as the renowned 'buffalo humps'.[173] Writing in defence of these hump-causing toxic 'medicines', Tim Horn and Linda Grinberg of Act Up Golden Gate Writers Pool scorned the notion that these drugs had bypassed all the normal tried and tested procedures. They went on to state that many people were alive as a result of these drugs. Credence wrote to Horn and Grinberg, asking them to supply further evidence that people's lives had been saved. To

[171] Enfield & Haringey Health Authority, *Sexual Health Promotion*, Winter 1999
[172] Maggiore, Christine, ibid. p.14
[173] **Vigano, Allesandra et al** *Lancet* 352:1905, 12th Decembe 1998

date there has been no reply. Horn and Grinberg's wholly unsubstantiated quote *"Tell that to those whose lives were spared..."* [174] will no doubt be used to support further ill-researched and pharmaceutically funded articles in defence of protease inhibitors.

Those more conversant with the AIDS debate however know very well the dangers of these medications. *People Magazine*, dated 5th October 1998, carries an article about Maine housewife Valerie Emerson whose two children, Tia and Nikolas, were diagnosed as 'carrying HIV'. Her three-year-old daughter Tia was put on AZT and subsequently died in 1997. After ten weeks of AZT treatment, Mrs Emerson saw Nikolas go *"...from being a little boy who was active to being a little boy who lay on the floor and cried."* The article continues:

> *"She took Nikolas off AZT last fall, but by March two doctors advised Emerson, a welfare mother, to begin treating her son with an aggressive new 'cocktail' of drugs that included AZT to combat HIV-related symptoms. She refused. Officials from Maine's Department of Human Services accused her of endangering her child's health and began legal proceedings to take custody of Nikolas.... On 14th September, after a four-month legal struggle, a district judge in Newport, Maine, upheld her right to determine her son's treatment...."*

The August 1999 edition of the widely read *Positive Treatment News*, an ATP publication, contains a variety of information for HIV positive women and pregnancy. Alongside snippets such as *'Sperm washing in the UK – significantly reducing the risk of mother or baby becoming HIV positive...'* and *'...if you're going into hospital, remember to pack your drugs into your hospital bag'*, an interview was included with Dr Karen Beckerman, who manages HIV positive women through their pregnancy at the Bay Area Perinatal AIDS Center in San Francisco. Among the drugs used at the centre are the old favourites Saquinavir, Ritonavir, AZT, ddI and d4T. On being asked what effects anti-retrovirals might have on fertility, Dr Beckerman replied: *"I think they enhance it. Women feel better, they're healthier, they start thinking long-term."* and on her preference for the latest protease inhibitors, Beckerman stated *"I have to be honest with you, I have a*

---

[174] **Horn, Grinberg** *HAART Sick Hoax*, Act Up Golden Gate Writers Pool, 24th February 2000

special fondness for d4T. Many years hence, it may prove to be a better drug than AZT." [175] In what capacity better?

ATP openly declare their publications are copyright free, and that readers may photocopy and distribute material as they wish. In the face of the overwhelming evidence against the efficacy of AZT and its derivatives, disseminating Beckerman's statements would be unbelievably irresponsible. Consider the following report, one of several recent warnings to doctors in the treatment of expectant mothers.

> *"In pregnant women treated with AZT at a hospital in India, Kumar et al. report a shocking number of therapeutic and spontaneous abortions, and of the live births, a number of grotesque birth defects included holes in the chest, abnormal indentations at the base of the spine, misplaced ears, misshapen faces, heart defects, extra digits and albinism."* [176]

And in the UK, a 'Mum on the Run' story was blazoned across the pages of several nationals in late August 1999. The mother had been diagnosed HIV positive nine years ago after submitting to an ELISA test. On discovering her HIV positive status, Camden Council in north London applied to the High Court under the 1989 Children's Act to have the mother's perfectly healthy five-month-old baby girl tested for HIV. The council had taken this unprecedented action because the mother had so far refused their requests, herself knowing full well the true nature of AIDS and AIDS 'medicines'. The case took on added emotional force when, in July 1999, the British government announced plans to include HIV testing in all routine ante-natal examinations *"...in a bid to reduce the UK's exceptionally high transmission rates from mother to child."* [177] In the belief that if the child tested positive she would need the best care and best medical intervention, High Court Justice Wilson declared the baby had 'a right to life' and announced *"I order the test."* Both parents and their baby have subsequently vanished, unwilling to submit to the authorities, to their test or to the horrors of AIDS anti-viral therapy.

---

[175] *Positive Treatment News*, August 1999

[176] **Kumar et al.**, *Journal of Acquired Immune Deficiency Syndromes*, 7:1034-9, 1994

[177] *The Guardian*, 27th August 1999

Project AIDS International's chairman Jeremy Selvey comments on the widely-established practice of prescribing deadly chemicals to babies who inadvertently trigger a positive result on an 'AIDS test':

"The practice of treating HIV positive infants with AZT based on 1) tests with questionable accuracy such as the ELISA and Western Blot, and/or 2) presumptive diagnosis when no clinical illness is present - is <u>*murder*</u>*. Murder as used here means 'the introduction of a known toxic substance that ultimately results in the infant's premature death.'"* [178]

It is for the above reasons that Camden Council are unable to trace the whereabouts of mother, father and precious, healthy child. In keeping with the words of Patrick Henry, no matter the anguish of spirit, Mum and Dad had purposed to discover the truth about AIDS some time ago. They have disappeared because they know the worst. They wish to avoid their infant's premature death at the hands of state legislation. But who will now provide for them?

London's *Evening Standard* recently ran the following headline:

CALL TO TEST ALL MOTHERS AS LONDON HEADS HIV BABY LEAGUE *- All pregnant women should be tested for HIV, particularly in London where more babies are born with the virus than the rest of Britain, experts have warned.... Dr Walters, a senior lecturer in paediatrics and infectious diseases at St Mary's Hospital in Paddington, said "One of the advantages of testing pregnant women is that we are able to offer them healthcare before they become very ill."* [179]

Katrine is another 'mum on the run', determined at all costs to evade conventional 'AIDS healthcare'. Whilst in Africa In 1996, Katrine contracted malaria. On her return home to the US, a doctor took a blood sample, and went on to perform an AIDS test without her permission. As a result of that test, and despite the doctor knowing that she was suffering from malaria (one of the many diseases which can give rise to a false positive), the doctor nevertheless pronounced Katrine an official AIDS case. Katrine has recently had a baby boy. As a result, both Katrine and her husband have vanished with their baby

---

[178] Selvey, Jeremy, ibid. p.8
[179] *Evening Standard*, 24th November 1999

in order to avoid the highly dangerous conventional AIDS healthcare being forced upon them by the authorities, the authorities in this instance being the US Child Protection Services.

> *"Although I planned to deliver at home with a midwife, I asked what would happen if I gave birth at hospital. The answer – 12 hours of intravenously fed AZT, a caesarean and formulae-feeding for the baby with AZT liquid – sealed my decision to stay out of the system.... The CPS questioned my mother and said they would notify the police if she did not reveal my whereabouts.... Ten days after our baby was born at a friend's house, my husband and I packed up our entire lives and fled the state for good. We left behind a home, careers, friends and family. This is what we have to do to keep our son off toxic AIDS drugs, and to ensure that he receives the vital nourishment and immune protection through breast-feeding. As I write this, we have no idea where we are going or what we will do, but at least our son is healthy and in our care.*

> *Katrine. Somewhere in America."* [180]

And what of the effects of AIDS drugs on a mother unaware of the dangers of AZT and its derivatives, trying also to cope with lively school children? The following news item from *Observer Online* is one of many altruistic and well-meaning reports, where neither the reporter nor the sufferer have any idea of the deadly truth that can now be read between the lines. Once again, we are witnessing another needless tragedy unfolding:

> ***MOM WITH AIDS by GIGI ANDERS, Staff Writer –*** *RALEIGH - Matthew and Jonathan, who resemble young McCauley Culkins, must fend for themselves this morning. Their mother's alarm clock went off at 6, as did theirs, but she's too sick to get up with them and make breakfast. More often than not, that's the case. There's a loud crash. Suddenly, their sleepy mother, Nicole, appears in the doorway in a long, white T-shirt and bare feet. The 33-year old has long, blonde hair and an ivory complexion, with reddish spots across her pale arms and strange, pink squiggles on her hands.*

---

[180] Maggiore, Christine, *"What if Everything.."* 4th Edition, 1999

101

"Are you OK, Mama?" Matthew asks, appraising her. "Your eyes are red as rabbits'."

"I'm just real tired, honey. I'll be fine."

From the doorway Nicole watches them run off. She waits to make sure they don't return for something they've forgotten. Now she can begin her ritual, the ultimate secret she keeps from her children. Taking a glass of orange juice into her bedroom, Nicole locks the door. She reaches under a bench and produces a locked metal box. She sits cross-legged on her king-size water-bed and unlocks it. There is a mini-pharmacy inside that box, 25 plastic orange bottles and tiny vials that contain the pills she must take every day to stay alive... When she's too sick to make their meals, Nicole tells her sons she has a bad cold or feels run down. They seem to accept it. Nicole says she doesn't want to burden them with the truth, especially since her time with them may be short: The red spots on her arms are inflammatory lesions, common among people in the last stages of AIDS. Nicole has written her sons a letter that explains the truth. It's kept at a lawyer's office, along with a will." [181]

Credence Publications has contacted the reporter in this instance and supplied some necessary information, which we hope will find its way to Nicole.

Hippocrates stated, *"First, do no harm to the body."* The Hippocratic Oath binds all doctors with this most fundamental axiom. Furthermore, the 18th World Medical Assembly in Helsinki, Finland - convened in June 1964 - binds physicians with the words, *"...the health of my patient shall be my first consideration."* The American Medical Association, the British Medical Association and other medical authorities world-wide are signatories to this declaration. What then is one to make of the murderous quackery practised in AIDS medicine today? What is one to make of the atrocious state of affairs where HIV positive mothers are hunted down by authorities, compelled to submit their child to 'an AIDS test', and then told, upon receiving a positive

---

[181] *Mom with AIDS*, Gigi Anders, 8th January 1999, *News and Observer* online. www.newasandobserver.com

result, *"You are harming your child's right to life by refusing anti-viral treatment for their life-threatening illness"* ?

There is no doubt that extreme drug toxicity brings on the very symptoms of AIDS itself. But this is by no means the whole story. AZT, the first of many AIDS drugs, did not hit the market until 1987. So what was wasting away and killing young homosexual men for at least six years prior to that? To answer this question, it is necessary for us to wind back the clock to the late 1970s, and return to America's beautiful West Coast city of San Francisco. For it is here in northern California that the story of AIDS has its genesis....

ANNIHILATING THE ANNIHILATORS

examining the sexual 'link' to AIDS

*"If I could take any one thing out of my life, it wouldn't be
AIDS. I really didn't have a life before AIDS."*
Former prostitute, drug addict and convicted felon
Cyndi Potete, founder of Positive Voices.

As has already been noted, it was Dr Friedman-Kein who brought
a wider attention to the emergence of *'a rapidly fatal form of cancer'*
being diagnosed in those first 41 men. Dr Friedman-Kein's *New York
Times* article continues as follows:

> *"The reporting doctors said most cases involved
> homosexual men who have had multiple and frequent sexual
> encounters with different partners, as many as ten sexual
> encounters a night up to four times a week. Many of the
> patients had also been treated for viral infections such as
> herpes, Hepatitis B, as well as parasitic infections such as
> amebiasis and giardiasis. Many patients also reported that they
> had used drugs such as amyl nitrites and LSD to heighten
> sexual pleasure."* [182]

A valid question being asked by those opposed to the 'AIDS as
virus' hypothesis was this: How much damage was being wrought on
the human frame by choosing to indulge in such extreme behaviour, let
alone the additional effects a rumoured AIDS virus might be having?

Joan Shenton sheds light on some of the less publicised details of
life in most city/suburban gay communities in the 1980s.

> *"In some New York and San Francisco bathhouses,
> clients were offered a tray as they entered, replete with a range
> of antibiotic cocktails to take as an aperitif, supposedly to help
> protect against the soup of sexually transmissible infections
> waiting inside. Backrooms were to be found in most capital
> cities across America and Europe. These were the special*

---

[182] *New York Times*, 3rd July 1981

areas in popular gay bars where patrons could indulge in wild promiscuous sex involving sado-masochism and all the most excessive forms of gay sex. The sexual activity was of such intensity that drugs were needed to fuel it. At the height of bathhouse and backroom activity, more than seventy different chemical stimulants or depressants were commonly used by the dedicated 'fast-tracker'. Backrooms usually had very low lighting or were pitch black to facilitate anonymity. Before the visit to the backroom or the bathhouse, often came the disco where other dangers lay."[183]

Cathy Kay, RN, Director of National Healthcare Advocates, reveals that, from a hygiene perspective alone, the more extreme homosexual practices can invite all manner of health-related dangers:

"Sodomy... the ingestion of one another's feces; urinating on one another, it's called 'golden showers', and 'rimming' where they lick one another's rectums. These are things that people really don't realise are going on, but it's all part of the behavioural lifestyle that can go along with homosexuality."[184]

Sean and Andrew, both former homosexuals and AIDS patients, had this to say about their former lifestyles:

Sean: *"When I first moved to the city, I was very naïve. But after a couple of years of seeing these things happen in bathhouses, it just gave me the creeps. After a while I knew this was abnormal. 23-year-olds with colostomy bags? Everyone in San Francisco that I knew was getting into this sado-masochism. It was like a spiral funnel. Everyone was gravitating towards this intense sex."*[185]

Andrew: *"I was aware of something deeply disturbing going on [within the gay scene]. I came to realise we were being manipulated in a spiritual fashion by forces beyond our control, which had as their goal our death. Gays know that promiscuous sex in communities such as San Francisco and Los Angeles is a death sentence, but far from responding to our natural instinct*

---

[183] Shenton, Joan, ibid.
[184] *Gay Rights, Special Rights*, a video documentary, Jeremiah Films, PO Box 1710, Hemet, CA 92546 USA, ISBN 1878993445
[185] *Gay Rights, Special Rights,* ibid.

for self-preservation and survival by changing our lifestyles to avoid this miserable death, we are driven by these forces to indulge in it with ever increasing abandon."[186]

And today, Celia Farber writes of barebacking, or 'conscious, unprotected, unsafe sex' - a craze that has apparently been bubbling underground for years.

"The idea is to unapologetically do it raw. In the most hardcore circles, it goes even further. Here HIV-infected semen [if you believe it is infected] is itself eroticised and the ultimate erotic bond is for one man to infect another – consciously. Equated with breeding, some men going as far as to select the man who will father their HIV…. This has less than nothing to do with dangerous dissident movements and everything to do with basic human lust and rage."[187]

The casualness of sex, both homosexual and heterosexual, was adopted without question by many in the 1970s' younger generation - the decade of 'new-found sexual liberation'. Heterosexual promiscuity and its little-mentioned place in AIDS history is explored a little later in this chapter. For the homosexual, abandoned forms of sexual expression were the cornerstones of the 1970s' gay rights movement. Gay Lib epitomised a new lifestyle, which ran counter to one of mankind's most enduring taboos. It offered a daring new sexual freedom to all who would reach out and grasp it. Phillip Gefter's recollections of times spent on New York's notorious Fire Island at the height of the gay liberation movement of the 1970s succinctly capture the mood of the period:

"The Ice Palace was the most fabulous disco I'd ever been to - two thousand writhing, drugged, beautiful bodies on the dance floor. By 6am we were outside across the pool dancing under the stars as the sun was coming up. And I believed at this moment in time that we were having more fun than anybody in the history of civilisation had ever had. The sexual tension, the drugs, the music and the sun coming up created a special kind of thrill and excitement. I can remember the sexual

---

[186] Day, Phillip, personal notes.

[187] **Farber, Celia** *Continuum*, Vol 5, No 5, December 1998. See also transcript of Radio 4 'PM News,' 28th February 2000

meeting ground known as 'enchanted forest'. On one occasion on our way back from the Ice Palace at seven in the morning, there were these four men naked. We watched them. They just kind of reached out and grabbed us and drew us in." [188]

The Vietnam era witnessed a huge increase in recreational drug consumption among the younger generation. Justice Department figures reveal that the Drug Enforcement Agency confiscated 9,000 kilograms of cocaine in 1980, compared with 100,000 kilograms in 1990. And the National Institute on Drug Abuse also reported that 5,000,000 people were using nitrite inhalants at least once a week.[189] Readily available street narcotics, such as cocaine, heroin, amphetamines and the new nitrite inhalants, such as the party drug 'poppers', were now being used to heighten sexual pleasure. With the maximum of hard drug-taking, chronic antibiotic use and the minimum of consideration being given to the body's basic needs, such as a sensible diet and regular sleep patterns, Howard Rosenman, another active member of San Francisco's gay community, recalls similar days of reckless excess:

"Between 1972-1983, we had a group in California, about fifty of us, partying at Nando Scarffioti's house, production designer for The Last Emperor. At the beginning we would buy a gram of coke and split it between all of us for the entire weekend: just one little toot at the very beginning. By the time the parties were over we would be consuming 6oz of cocaine a weekend and every other drug known to man. Of those fifty there are six that are alive - everybody else is dead." [190]

During the 1970s and early 1980s, Gary Null spent a great number of hours interviewing literally hundreds of hetero- and homosexuals. He witnessed firsthand the effects of a relentless lifestyle:

"I went to the baths, to the night-clubs and I would hang out and interview people. I knew people who were partying ten hours a night, seven nights a week, for two or three years straight. There were two guys who lived nearby, and I spoke to

---

[188] **Kaiser, Charles**, *Gay Metropolis*, Phoenix Press, 1997
[189] **Duesberg, Peter H** "The Role of Drugs in the Origin of AIDS", *Biomed. & Pharmacotherapy*, Vol 46, 1992
[190] Kaiser, Charles, ibid.

them on a regular basis when I was out there. I watched them physically deteriorate. In less than six months, I saw them go from being really masculine and pumped-up bodybuilders, to just shells, emaciated... I found only two percent of people were doing it because they wanted to hurt themselves. Most of them just loved what they were doing. It was just like taking a kid and putting him in a candy shop. They wanted to eat everything in there, and the fact that they were going to get sick - well, you know '...the sickness will pass, let's keep gorging!'"[191]

From the outset, there were medical scientists who were seriously considering whether it was the accumulation of drugs, antibiotics, poor sleep and diet that was responsible for such fatal immune system depression.[192] Here Duesberg, writing in 1992, seeks to wrench the AIDS establishment back to reason:

"Hardly anybody can remember that only ten years ago AIDS was still considered by many scientists as a collection of diseases acquired by consumption of recreational drugs. Since nearly all early AIDS patients were either male homosexuals who were using nitrite and ethylchloride inhalants, cocaine, heroin, amphetamines, LSD and other drugs as sex stimulants, or were heterosexuals injecting cocaine and heroin intravenously, early AIDS researchers named these drugs as the causes of AIDS.[193] Drugs seemed to be the most plausible explanation for the near-perfect restriction of AIDS to these risk groups because drug consumption is their most specific, common denominator. This original drug-AIDS hypothesis is

---

[191] Null, Gary, *Zenger*, ibid.

[192] **Kaslow, R A, et al** "No Evidence for a Role of Alcohol or Other Psychoactive Drugs In Accelerating Immunodeficiency in HIV-1-Positive Individuals", *JAMA*, 261 (1989): pp.3424-3429; **Weiss, R and H Jaffe**, "Duesberg, HIV and AIDS", *Nature* (London), p.345 (1990)

[193] **Marmor, M. et al** "Risk Factors for Kaposi's Sarcoma in Homosexual Men," *Lancet,* i (1982): pp.1083-1087; **Jaffe, H W, et al** "National Case-Control Study of Kaposi's Sarcoma and *Pneumocystis Carinii* Pneumonia in Homosexual Men: Part 1, Epidemiological Results," *Ann. Intern. Med.*, 99 (1983) pp.145-151; **Haverkos, H W, et al** "Disease Manifestation Among Homosexual Men with AIDS: A Possible Role of Nitrites in Kaposi's Sarcoma," *Journal of Sex. Trans. Dis.*, 12 (1985) 203-208; **Newell, G R, et al** "Volatile Nitrites: Use and Adverse Effects Related to the Current Epidemic of the Acquired Immune Deficiency Syndrome," *Preventative Med.*, 14 (1985b): pp.81-91

called *the lifestyle hypothesis.*"[194] [195]

Duesberg explains that, with AIDS, the world is witnessing the long-term effects of drug abuse now becoming evident in those sections of the population which chronically abuse these substances:

> *"The key to the drug hypothesis is that only long-term consumption causes irreversible AIDS-defining diseases. Occasional or short-term recreational drug use causes reversible diseases or no diseases at all. Toxicity of drugs is first a function of how much is taken at any given time."*[196]

And this observation from Gary Null, interviewed in 1997 on the longer term effects of continual excess:

> *"There are consequences. Every action begets a reaction, and the reaction of a lot of the heterosexuals who participated in the revolution is that they are very sick today, just as the gays who participated in that revolution are very sick, unless they have detoxified and changed their lives. Then they're OK. But the majority have not done so, so they linger in this disease limbo. Nobody knows what they have or why they have it. But I've been on top of this a long time and that's how I see it."*[197]

Duesberg points out that no one has a problem accepting that it can take twenty years of smoking to acquire irreversible lung cancer or emphysema, or twenty years of hard drinking to acquire irreversible liver cirrhosis:

> *"Consider a grace period of about ten years to achieve the* [drug] *dosage needed to cause irreversible disease, and you can date the origin of AIDS in 1981 as a consequence of the drug use epidemic that started in America in the late 1960s during the Vietnam War.... Since 1987, AZT and other* [similar drugs] *have been added to the list of toxic drugs consumed by AIDS patients and those at risk from AIDS. AZT is now*

---

[194] **Oppenheimer, G M** "Causes, Cases, and Cohorts: The Role of Epidemiology in the Historical Construction of AIDS," *AIDS: The Making of a Chronic Disease*, Berkeley, Calif: University of California Press, 1992: pp.49-83

[195] Duesberg, Peter H, *Inventing...* ibid. pp.410-411

[196] Duesberg, Peter H, *Inventing...* ibid. pp.411-412

[197] Null, Gary, *Zenger*, ibid.

prescribed to about 200,000 HIV positives world-wide." [198]

The AIDS problem has been immeasurably worsened, Duesberg believes, by medical orthodoxy's dismissal of the abundant cumulative evidence which convincingly demonstrates that it can take about ten years of nitrites, heroin, amphetamines, or cocaine to develop AIDS through toxic load and potentially less than a year of the much more toxic drugs, such as AZT, to cause AIDS by prescription. [199]

> *"The untold price of frequent drug use is the cumulative toxicity that builds up over a lifetime, causing irreversible damage,"* Duesberg concludes. [200]

As mentioned, the idea that heavy recreational drug consumption could, in itself, be the cause of AIDS is not a new one and was originally held by the medical establishment prior to discarding it in favour of the more profitable advent of Gallo's 'virus' in 1984. [201] But the serious champions of the drug hypothesis, like Duesberg, have been consistent in publishing hard evidence in medical journals that cumulative drug toxicity, brought on by long-term drug consumption (either recreational or pharmaceutical), has been the obvious culprit with western AIDS all along. Although the dangers of drug overdoses are widely known, street narcotics have surprisingly been viewed by the orthodoxy as <u>illegal</u> rather than <u>toxic</u>, *Science* even stating *"...heroin is a blessedly untoxic drug"* provided that it is *"injected with a clean needle."* [202]

Alongside the huge increase in the use of drugs runs the corresponding and dramatic rise in drug-induced hospital admissions. In the US, cocaine-related admissions for instance stood at 3,296 cases in 1981, increasing to 80,355 cases in 1990 and to 119,843 admissions in 1992. Heroin-related emergencies doubled in just three

---

[198] Duesberg, Peter H, *Inventing...* ibid. p.420

[199] **Duesberg, Peter H** "How Much Longer Can We Afford the AIDS Virus Monopoly?" *AIDS: Virus or Drug-Induced?* Genetica: 1996

[200] Duesberg, Peter H, *Inventing...* ibid. pp.411-412

[201] **Kaslow, R A, et al** "No Evidence for a Role of Alcohol or Other Psychoactive Drugs In Accelerating Immunodeficiency in HIV-1-Positive Individuals", *JAMA*, 261 (1989): pp.3424-3429; **Weiss, R and H Jaffe**, "Duesberg, HIV and AIDS", *Nature* (London), p.345 (1990)

[202] **Cohen, J** "The Duesberg Phenomenon: Duesberg and Other Voices," *Science*, 266 (1994a): pp.1642-1649

years to 60,000 cases in 1993. [203] Nitrite consumption went from a handful of medical doses in the early seventies to millions of applications annually in the 1980s. Drug offenders are now by far the largest prison demographic, comprising 61% of the total, compared with 38% in 1986. In 1993, a survey concluded that between 60 – 80% of the 12 million prisoners in the United States had been on illegal drugs. [204]

Ten years after this toxic onslaught struck the western nations and institutionalised itself into the fabric of society, AIDS incidences (cases of chronic immune suppression) went from a few dozen cases in 1981 to about 100,000 in 1993. [205] It is interesting to note that the rise in AIDS cases exactly parallels the rise in cocaine and heroin-related hospital emergencies since 1981, according to official figures [206]. Since 1987, more toxicity has been admitted into society with the advent of AZT and its derivatives.

The AIDS establishment's dogmatic support of HIV and its unwillingness to investigate the drug/AIDS connection can be viewed either as markedly incompetent or calculatedly dismissive of the evidence. The great majority of American and European homosexuals today inhale nitrites on a regular basis, yet there exists *not one study* that measures the long-term effects of these substances either on animals or humans. 97% of all American AIDS patients consume recreational drugs, [207] yet four separate study applications to examine the link between recreational drugs and AIDS-related diseases filed with the National Institute on Drug Abuse (NIDA) between 1993 and 1995 were rejected with the notation: *"Not recommended for further consideration."* [208] Ironically both NIDA and the CDC, in view of the mounting evidence, have since reconsidered and now confirm the

---

[203] Duesberg, Peter H, *AIDS Acquired by Drug Consumption*, ibid. Also **Meddis, S V** "Heroin Use Said to Near Crisis Level", *USA Today*, 25th May 1994, 1, 3A

[204] Duesberg, Peter H, *Inventing…* pp.419-420

[205] Centers for Disease Control and Prevention, "US HIV and AIDS cases Reported Through June 1994", 1-27

[206] Duesberg, Peter H, *Inventing…* pp.194 & 420

[207] Duesberg, Peter H, *AIDS Acquired by Drug Consumption*, ibid.

[208] **Lang, S** "To Fund or not to Fund, That is the Question: Proposed Experiments on the Drug-AIDS Hypothesis. To Inform or not to Inform: That is Another Question," *AIDS: Infectious or Not?* Genetica, 1997

connection between Kaposi's Sarcoma and nitrite inhalation, advising against increased usage of these substances.[209] [210]

Duesberg's exhaustive supply of the evidence over ten years leads him to file the following dramatic conclusion:

> *"All AIDS diseases in America and Europe that exceed their long-established, normal backgrounds are caused by the long-term consumption of recreational drugs and by AZT and its analogs.[211] The correct hypothesis of AIDS must 1) explain why a [single] agent is a plausible cause of one or all of the thirty fatal AIDS diseases and 2) predict all clinical... aspects of AIDS. The drug hypothesis meets these criteria to the letter, but the HIV hypothesis does not."[212]*

Later in his report in the *New York Times*, Dr Friedman-Kein states that he had personally tested 9 of those initial 41 victims, remarking that in each case he had found *"...severe defects in their immunological systems, severe malfunction of the T and B cell lymphocytes which have important roles in fighting infections and cancer."[213]*

And it is towards the human immune system that most of this toxic and irreversible damage is directed. Dr Paul Brand introduces us to the importance of the immune system as our body's first line of defence against hostile microbiological invasion. In his book, *The Forever Feast*, he explores some of the amazing aspects of a human's in-built army of infection fighters:

> *"I must share just one facet of the skills of the T lymphocytes, because I get excited at the ingenuity that must have gone into their design, and because I'm so happy to have these little guys on my side when I am sick. My T lymphocytes*

---

[209] **Haverkos, H W, et al** *Health Hazards of Nitrite Inhalants,* NIDA Research Monograph 83, Dept of Health and Human Services: Washington DC, 1988; **Lauritsen, J** "NIH Reconsiders Nitrites' Link to AIDS," *Bio/Technology,* 12 (1994): pp.762-763

[210] **Haverkos, H W & D P Drotman** "Measuring Inhalant Nitrite Exposure" NIDA and CDC, 1995, pp.157-164

[211] **Duesberg, Peter H** "AIDS Epidemiology: Inconsistencies with Human Immunodeficiency Virus and with Infectious Disease," *Proc. Natl. Acad. Sci.,* USA 88 (1991)

[212] Duesberg, Peter H, *Inventing...* ibid. p.414

[213] *New York Times,* 3rd July 1981

concentrate in places where most germs try to get into the body. It is never very long before an invading germ meets a T lymphocyte.

The first wonderful thing is that the lymphocyte knows at once that this living cell is not 'one of us', it is an enemy. The next wonderful thing is what it does. It inspects the enemy cell and takes a template or pattern of its surface, noting especially the weak points. Then our friend runs back to the factory where new cells are made and announces the emergency: "An enemy has entered the body and is rapidly multiplying. We have to manufacture antibodies of exactly this shape, so that the enemy will be killed and no other cell will be harmed."

An older lymphocyte may hurry up at this point and tell the factory that the shape of the needed antibodies is exactly the size as was used a year ago, when there was a brief war in the body during the flu season. Therefore there is no need to repeat the time-consuming preparation of the prototype antibodies - we already have them. All that is needed is to rush into mass production. Thus before the virus has time to do any real harm, masses of specific antibodies are all over the body, overcoming every last virus, and restoring health and wholeness everywhere."[214]

Lennart Nilsson, author of *The Body Victorious,* writes:

"Suddenly the site of injury and infection, previously so peaceful is transformed into a battlefield on which the body's armed forces hurl themselves repeatedly at the encroaching micro-organisms, crushing and annihilating them. No one is pardoned, no prisoners are taken... All these events take place in a microscopic world where nothing, neither the body's cells nor the micro-organisms that assail them, measures more than a few thousandths of a millimetre across."[215]

So what was really happening to these men with their severely malfunctioning T and B cell lymphocytes? Were those men, diagnosed with AIDS-related symptoms, really suffering from a new and exotic

---

[214] **Brand, Paul** *The Forever Feast*, Monarch Publications, 1994
[215] **Nilsson, Lennart** *The Body Victorious*, Faber, 1987

killer virus? Would it not be more reasonable to propose that they were suffering the effects of destroying their personal little army of infection annihilators through persistent sexual infection, hard drugs, poor diet, little or no sleep and an enormous array of immuno-suppressant antibiotics? Had their annihilators quite literally been annihilated? They were certainly finding themselves unable to combat even the most minor of illnesses – illnesses that in normal circumstances should have posed no threat at all.

Some in the active gay scene were asking themselves the same questions and began calling for abstention from certain meeting places and certain forms of particularly dangerous sexual behaviour. Dan William, a prominent New York doctor and himself a homosexual, suggested that bathhouses be required to post warning signs about the epidemic and of the dangers of promiscuous sex. His suggestions were angrily rejected by most in the community, and William was accused of being *"a monogamist and a scare-monger."*[216]

Whilst there was a definite resistance to giving up a lifestyle that most gay men found both compulsory and necessary to their identity, there were also other reasons why calls for moderation in homosexual behaviour were rejected. Gallo's announcement brought relief to many in the gay communities. The new virus tag was readily accepted, and those previously advocating restraint in extreme sexual practices, indiscriminate drug-consumption and 'high-revving' lifestyles were now dismissed. Less focus on lifestyle was necessary, it was simply the virus. Joan Shenton again:

"Once HIV was accepted as the cause of AIDS by the majority of gay men, a certain sense of relief entered their lives. They had seen many of their lovers and closest friends waste away before their eyes. Now they could grieve for them, knowing that HIV, this strange novel virus said to come from Africa, had caused the death of their loved one, perhaps after one 'unlucky' sexual encounter. Nothing to do with the fact that the friend or loved one had probably been sniffing nitrites on the dance floor; or taking any one of fifty different 'recreational' chemical drugs night after night for years; might have had

---

[216] Shilts, Randy, ibid.

hundreds of sexual partners in a year; might have stopped eating and sleeping properly; and might have been taking antibiotics all year round for recurring syphilis, gonorrhoea and hepatitis. No, the friend or loved one had definitely died of HIV. Anyone challenging the accepted cause of death was deeply resented and quickly labeled homophobic."[217]

No mysterious, sexually spread virus is necessary to explain the catastrophic health failures being witnessed in these gay men. The link between marked ill-health and irresponsible lifestyle is obvious. In the debate on AIDS however, this common sense approach to cause and effect has been largely ignored. The fact that A (the ill health and/or death of a loved one) is believed to be the result of B, (the 'strange novel virus') whilst taking no account of other factors, C, is the curse that bedevils analytic thought in AIDS 'science' today. Commenting on the need for intellectual rigour when seeking to establish cause and effect, Geoff Watts, presenter of 'Medicine Now' says:

"Another trap for the unwary lies in the failure to distinguish between association and causation. The fact that two things repeatedly happen at the same time doesn't mean that one is necessarily the consequence of the other. Both may be the result of some third event of which the observer is unaware."[218]

That other factor 'C' or third event which coherently explains the immuno-deficient disorders seen in these men is excessive and toxic lifestyle.

Aside from uncritical thinking, there were also those in the gay community who were quite well aware of the 'third event' lifestyle factors contributing to their friends' ill-health and death. Joan Shenton again:

'[Leading gay figure] and cabaret singer Michael Callen told me that when HIV came on the map, many gay leaders, though largely persuaded of the multi-factorial risk hypothesis (repeated re-infections and a fast-track drug-associated lifestyle), took a conscious decision for political reasons to support the 'no-blame' AIDS-as-virus hypothesis."

---

[217] Shenton, Joan, ibid.

[218] **Watts, Geoff** *Pleasing The Patient*, Faber and Faber, 1992

The enthusiastic acceptance of the virus hypothesis as an excuse to continue a dangerous lifestyle was mirrored in the equally enthusiastic acceptance of the 'gay gene' some years later. In 1993, Dr Dean Hamer proposed a link between the 'X' chromosome and sexual orientation.[219] *The Wall Street Journal* immediately announced 'Research Points to Gay Gene'.[220] Overnight, the little known

Dr Dean Hamer

geneticist, who had previously restricted his experiments to mice, became a hero to gay activists. Thousands of T-shirts appeared bearing the slogan *"Thanks for the Genes, Mom"*. Hamer's homosexual gene theory progressed to become a major influence in the passing of much pro-gay legislation. Two years later, Hamer, himself openly homosexual, was under investigation by the Office of Research Integrity for selectively reporting his data, and for promoting the socio-political ramifications of his findings, rather than merely reporting the science.[221]

And so, the disturbing pattern of AIDS research is once again seen. Not unsurprisingly, no one to date has yet been able to reproduce Hamer's 'gay gene' or find any trace of it.

Readers may be interested to know that Hamer is currently attempting to isolate the gene suspected of influencing people to believe in God.[222] Hamer's interest in this particular sphere should come as no surprise to those with some understanding of the mind of a geneticist. Hamer's theories are merely a crude attempt to redesign the existing moral framework which inconveniently for Hamer et al. was never intended to encompass the woefully inadequate 'Man-is-God' ideology. Mark Almond, a lecturer in modern history at Oriel College, Oxford, has this to say:

---

[219] **Hamer, M** *Science*, "Linkage Between 'X' Chromosome and Male Sexuality," #261, July 1993

[220] *Wall St Journal*, 16th July 1993

[221] **Marshall, E** "Gay Gene Study Questioned," *Science*, #268, 1995

[222] *Today* program, BBC Radio 4 Interview with Sue McGregor, 4th May 2000. Credence contacted Hamer to confirm the God story, and learned that he is indeed soon to be releasing a book entitled *'The God Gene'*.

"In our age when 'Science' has achieved a God-like status, and many people are morally confused, nothing helps to sell a divergence from traditional ideas like the claim that it is scientifically justified. The official investigation into Hamer is not before time. We cannot allow the myth of the gay gene to continue, a gene which ominously suggests that science is the cause of moral behaviour." [223]

In his book *Homosexuality and the Politics of Truth*, Jeffrey Satinover argues against the genetics of homosexuality and in favour of a variety of *'nurture not nature'* factors. Satinover states:

"The desire to shift to a biological basis for explaining homosexuality appeals primarily to those who seek to undermine the vast amount of clinical evidence confirming that homosexuality is significantly changeable." [224]

Michael Callen, author of *Surviving AIDS* and now deceased, confessed to having had 2,000 sexual partners by the time he was 23. In his book, Callen wrote:

"Can researchers really comprehend the dynamics of urban gay male promiscuity? The commercialisation of promiscuity and the explosion of establishments such as bathhouses, bookstores and backrooms is unique in Western history." [225]

But urban promiscuity was by no means confined to the gay community. Immune system failure as a result of rampant self-abuse was occurring in promiscuous heterosexuals also. Gary Null again:

"In 1979-1980, I was doing research on heterosexuals who were coming down with a series of illnesses, chronic fatigue, thrush, herpes, hepatitis, chronic coughs and pneumonias – no matter what time of year. Their lifestyles included lots of unprotected sex with lots of partners, lots of drink and lots of drugs. Sometimes at swingers' parties, which were all the rage

---

[223] **Almond, Mark** *Mail on Sunday,* 9th July 1995

[224] **Satinover, J** *Homosexuality and the Politics of Truth*, Baker Books, 1996. See also **Whitehead, Neil,** *My Genes Made Me Do It. A Scientific Look at Sexual Orientation*, Huntingdon House Publishers, 1999. **Horgan, J** "Limitations of Genetic Research into Human Behaviour", *Scientific American*, June 1993, pp.123-31. See also www.narth.com, National Association for Research and Therapy of Homosexuality.

[225] **Callen, Michael** *Surviving AIDS*, Harper and Row, London: 1990

at the time, you might have 15 – 20 different partners a night. You might do this three or four times a week. And of course you drank a lot. You took amyl nitrite. Lots of lines of cocaine and smoking. These were both men and women.

The trouble is, no one wanted to hear that. We wanted to hear, we needed to hear that these people were not representative of society as a whole; that they were part of Sodom and Gomorrah, self-loathing, self-hating, self-destructive. By 1990, I had seen thousands of heterosexuals who had a virtually indistinguishable form of AIDS that had gone almost unnoticed. Nobody was looking at them, nobody was marking them as a risk factor... They're just part of the $1.3 trillion national medical bill each year. They're getting antibiotics and treatments for their individual conditions. They're virtually invisible." [226]

The findings of Null serve to reinforce the argument that in the early years, AIDS or immune system failure was not a homosexual plague, it was the plague of toxic excess, affecting all who indulged in irresponsible drug and sex lifestyles.

The rapid uptake on the idea that homosexuals were the harbingers of the dreaded AIDS in the US was no doubt influenced by the McCarthy *"queer witch-hunt"* years. In one particular political campaign in the late 1940's, thousands of leaflets were distributed to the electorate explaining that sexual perverts were perhaps as dangerous as communists. The message vigorously encouraged a campaign to rid the government of *"queers who had lodged themselves in the tissues of bureaucracy."* [227] Soon after, the US Senate responded to the inevitable public outcry and formed a special 'pervert' committee to investigate *"the corrosive influence that homosexuals tend to have upon fellow employees. One homosexual can pollute a government office."* [228]

---

[226] Null, Gary, ibid.

[227] **Von Hoffman, N** *Citizen Cohn. The Life and Times of Roy Cohn*, New York, Doubleday Press, 1988

[228] Von Hoffman, N, ibid.

It was attitudes such as these that were surely the more corrosive in influence. The prejudices that helped shape the homosexuality/AIDS connection have shrouded the more important issues of the irresponsible and damaging lifestyles indulged in by those of either sex or sexual preference. In conversation with Joan Shenton, AIDS victim Michael Callen unflinchingly admitted that it was not the effects of a supposed virus, but his lifestyle that was the cause of his illness, stating:

"It became impossible for me to pretend that the disease history was irrelevant to the fact that I was sick. It was sort of emotionally attractive to believe that it had nothing to do with any [lifestyle] choices I had made, that it was just bad luck – I'd accidentally slept with the wrong person. But once I was presented with a non-moralistic, calm, medical presentation of a multi-factorial mechanism which might account for my illness, I was never quite able to believe again that a disease of this complexity was ever going to have a single, simple [viral] cause."[229]

Countering the non-moralistic argument put forward by Callen and others, Mark Almond argues against certain human sexual behaviours, reminding us that:

"Human beings are distinguished [from animals] by their ability to act according to moral criteria. In fact most morality is about controlling natural impulses as well as unnatural ones. Morality and individual responsibility remain the basis for any civilised society."[230]

The queues at the bathhouses were not noticeably thinning. Yet all the while, increasing numbers of gay men were manifesting symptoms of AIDS. Despite intense political and media pressure to believe otherwise, there still remained a number of medical professionals who believed the root cause of AIDS was more attributable to lifestyle than virus. In an effort to look at ways of trying to stem the rapidly growing number of AIDS cases now being reported across California, a meeting was convened at a suburban San Francisco AIDS centre between concerned doctors and several of the owners of the notorious

---

[229] Shenton, Joan, ibid.
[230] Almond, Mark, ibid.

bathhouses:

"The bathhouse owners who attended were hostile. Some had only come because they felt pressured to attend. Other proprietors couldn't be bothered to attend and simply sent their attorneys. After Dr Abrams had finished speaking, the owner of one of the largest bathhouses took the doctors aside and tried to reason with them. "We're both in it for the same thing," he said. "Money. We make money at one end, when they come to the baths. You make money from the other end, when they come here." Volberding, Dr Abrams' colleague, was speechless. This guy wasn't talking civil liberties, he was talking greed. The bathhouses were open not because the owners did not understand they were spreading death – they understood that – but because they were still making money."[231]

A marked unwillingness to participate in any line of questioning which might threaten a lucrative income was an attitude of mind not solely confined to the bathhouses. Intolerance to reasonable debate has been a prevalent factor in the AIDS establishment's attitude from the outset, and is alive and well in all the major AIDS organisations today.

It is said that the last recourse of a cornered politician is fervent patriotism. And there can be no doubt that in the AIDS industry today, a particularly perverse form of patriotism exists. AIDS patriotism rears its fanatical head whenever one attempts to counter the high degree of intellectual dishonesty inhabiting the AIDS debate. On many occasions Credence researchers have posed simple questions to the AIDS scientists and assorted 'AIDS politicians' - questions which the latter do their best to avoid. After finding themselves cornered and seeing their inevitable entreaties to *'respect the worthiness of the AIDS calling'* falling on stony ground, these men and women resort to raising their AIDS patriotism like a shield before them - often the shield of ridicule or personal abuse directed towards those asking the legitimate questions. This experience is by no means unique. Medical correspondent Nicholas Regush has a regular health column with ABC News, entitled *Second Opinion*. He is one of a number of journalists

---

[231] Shilts, Randy, ibid.

who has discovered the secretive, closed-off world of 'AIDS science'. Says Regush:

> *"I have worked as a medical science reporter for 30 years. I began this career at age 22. I've interviewed thousands of scientists for newspaper and magazine stories, radio and television productions, and books. I've met many scientists who at least try to keep an open and fair mind on scientific issues. I have also met many propagandists who think they're scientists. In all the time I've worked as a journalist, I've never come across a nastier group of people to interview than those propagandists who work in HIV research."* [232]

Dr Kremer attempted to bring the truth about AIDS to the media as far back as 1984. He invited medical professionals and the media to his hospital to see for themselves the hepatitis patients who would test HIV+ due to blood test cross-reaction but who did not have AIDS. Stefan Lanka recounts Kremer's experience:

> *"Kremer informed the mass media, who went to his hospital to see for themselves in great detail. He told them all the evidence. And the very same journalists from talk shows and Der Spiegel, one of Germany's largest and most popular magazines, published just the opposite. So Kremer knew it was intentional from the very beginning. They played war. They all wanted to have a blood and sex plague contrary to the evidence he presented them. So AIDS was built upon misconceptions. He was dealing at the top political level. They told him off the record that they knew and they didn't care."* [233]

AIDS is big business, and any attempt to shed light on the lies of this deceitful and self-serving industry is met with fierce opposition, and all attempts necessary are made to avert the penetrating gaze of truth. Today, the facts clearly demonstrate that it is choice of a toxic lifestyle, coupled with the wholly misguided pressure to submit to inaccurate blood tests and the subsequent effects of ravaging 'anti-viral' drugs, that produce the phenomenon known as AIDS in the western world. This conforms exactly to the 'AIDS=Long-Term Drug

---

[232] **Regush, Nicholas,** *Second Opinion,* "The HIV Party Line", www.abcnews.go.com/sections/living/secondopinion, March 2000
[233] **Lanka, Stefan,** *Zenger,* "Challenging AIDS Views," December 1998

Abuse' model which explains why the syndrome is still chiefly restricted to its risk groups and has not spread exponentially through the general population as predicted.

What then do we make of the reports that AIDS is decimating Africa, Asia and other Third World regions? What of the millions dying of AIDS where lifestyle, expensive blood tests and toxic drugs cannot possibly be the primary cause? We start examining these issues in our next chapter. In so doing, we discover rational and straightforward medical reasons for 'AIDS' in these countries. But once again, nothing is quite as it seems in the AIDS story, as our investigations uncover new depths of man's inhumanity to man.

Dr Robert Gallo of the National Institutes of Health, who made the 1984 historic global announcement that HIV was the probable cause of AIDS

Peter H Duesberg, professor of molecular and cell biology at the University of California at Berkeley, has been at the heart of the 'dissident' movement, declaring the fraudulence of the HIV=AIDS hypothesis

Dr Luc Montagnier of the Pasteur Institute, Paris (above), and Dr Robert Gallo were the most high-profile and foremost exponents of 'viral' AIDS, an unproven notion that is used to terrify millions of men, women and children around the world.

Virologist **Dr Stefan Lanka** is an uncompromising scientific leader in the struggle against the HIV theory of AIDS. His published research in 1994 astounded many, declaring that HIV does not exist

Eddie, (deceased)
Eddie, a dancer, was prescribed AZT on being diagnosed 'HIV positive'. The above picture was taken at the point of his diagnosis and at the beginning of his chosen mission – to keep a photo-journal of his 'illness'. It was Eddie's wish that these images might serve in some way to educate a future generation, and call for more research into AIDS. Posthumously, Eddie's wish has been fulfilled.

Eddie, 13 months after beginning AZT. Experiencing malabsorption of food and a host of opportunistic infections, he died soon after, weighing just sixty pounds.

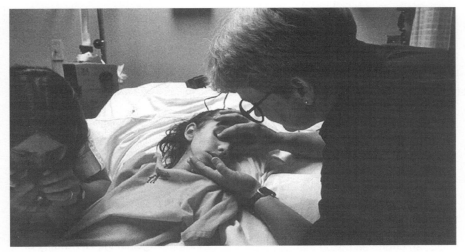

The death of a 12 year old girl. Establishment medicine says that she died of AIDS. More and more doctors and AIDS researchers however are stating that tragedies like these are being caused by the very drugs used to fight the elusive 'HIV'.

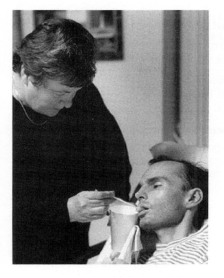

Deceased

- Danny -
Deceased

Loving Ministrations
must carry no condemnation

- Ida -
Deceased

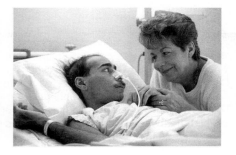

- Eddie -
Deceased

SIGMA

TOXIC
Toxic by inhalation, in contact with skin and if swallowed. Target organ(s): Blood Bone marrow. If you feel unwell, seek medical advice (show the label where possible). Wear suitable protective clothing.

3'-AZIDO-3'-DEOXY-THYMIDINE
(AZT; Azidothymidine)   *(30516-87-1)*

Desiccate
Store at less
than 0°C

$C_{10}H_{11}N_5O_1$ FW 267.2
Purity 99% (HPLC)
For laboratory use only. Not for drug, household or other uses.

AZT label. This label has appeared on bottles containing as little as 25 milligrams, a small fraction (1/20th – 1/50th) of a patient's daily described dose. (*Physicians Desk Reference*, 1994, p.324)

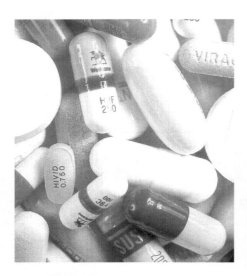

A selection of AIDS drugs including AZT, seen here bearing the Wellcome trademark. AZT was originally pioneered as a chemotherapy agent in the 1960s by Dr Richard Beltz, whose studies led him to shelve the drug as an unusable poison. This very same substance was brought out of retirement years later by Wellcome and patented as the new AIDS wonder drug

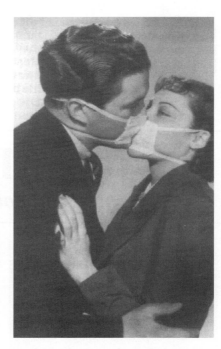

Everybody's at risk... A poignant illustration highlighting the hysteria the world has suffered at the hands of HIV propaganda

"Although no one knows what the long-term effects of protease inhibitors will be, I'm certainly pleased... my doctor prepared me for the common side effects – feeling weak or tired, vomiting, diarrhea, loss of appetite, abdominal pain, taste disturbance, numbness in the hands, feet or around the lips, headache and dizziness." – Abbott Laboratories advert for AIDS drug Ritonavir

HOW TO BE POSITIVE IN ONE COUNTRY AND NEGATIVE IN ANOTHER

WESTERN BLOT "VIRUS" PROTEINS		AFRICA	AUSTRALIA	UNITED KINGDOM	USA CDC 1	USA CDC 2	USA FDA	USA RED CROSS
ENV gene	p160 p120 p41	ANY TWO	ONE OR MORE	ONE OR MORE	p120/p160* &p41	p120/p160* OR p41	ONE OR MORE	ONE OR MORE
POL gene	p68 p53 p32	OPTIONAL	ANY THREE	p31**			p32	ANY ONE
GAG gene	p55 p40 p24 p18			p24		p24	p24	ANY ONE

Dr Roberto A Giraldo works at a laboratory of clinical immunology in one of the most prestigious university hospitals in New York. He has worked extensively with the ELISA, Western Blot and Viral Load tests. His disturbing conclusion is that everybody reacts positive on the ELISA when their *undiluted* serum is used - the standard medical practice for serological testing

One of many challenges to the AIDS establishment to furnish empirical proof for the existence of their virus, HIV. This advertisement is from the UK magazine *Continuum*, a publication long dedicated to exposing the scientific and medical frauds surrounding HIV and Acquired Immune Deficiency Syndrome (AIDS)

Stephen Rogers quit protease inhibitor 'combo cocktails' after recognising that the drugs were causing the very symptoms of AIDS

Author **Christine Maggiore** and son: *"I exercise my right to live in wellness without HIV treatments and without fear of AIDS."*

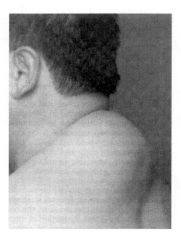

'Buffalo Humps', fatty deposits appearing around the base of the neck and across the shoulders. These are just one of the many side effects that can be experienced by those prescribed the 'exciting new range' of protease inhibitor drugs.

Huw Christie, editor of *Continuum* , was diagnosed HIV positive south of the Thames and HIV negative north of the river. Huw knows the truth, and as a result is alive and well today.

Part 2

'AFRICAN' AIDS

ON A MISSION

into the African AIDS jungle

"AIDS Turning Africa into Continent of Orphans." **Reuters, 27th June 1997**

The United Nations warned Africa was in danger of becoming a continent of orphans unless swift action was taken to control the spread of the deadly virus that leads to AIDS. Peter Piot, executive director of UNAIDS, the UN organization set up to fight AIDS, said "Millions of children are affected, infected or vulnerable to AIDS. Over 1,000 children are infected every day."

"Doctors Powerless as AIDS Rakes Africa." **New York Times, 8th June 1998**

"The majority of people in Africa have no idea if they are infected with HIV. Four million new cases were reported last year in the countries of sub-Saharan Africa...."

"AIDS in Africa: The Silent Stalker." **New York Times, 27th December 1998**

HIV probably first infected rural areas of Africa, slowly moving into the cities and around the world until it hit homosexual communities where conditions were sufficient for rapid transmission of the disease...."

"UN Agency Urges Action on Africa AIDS Spread." **Reuters, 8th May 1999**

"UNAIDS head Dr Peter Piot criticised African governments for not doing enough to prevent the spread of HIV in their countries. Speaking at a conference of African ministers of finance...."

"WHO Urges Africa to Declare AIDS Emergency." **Reuters, 23rd June 1999**

"Officials from the World Health Organization are urging African nations to declare the AIDS epidemic an emergency. The WHO hopes that the formal declaration will focus attention on the problem in Africa and help bring in additional international resources."

Broken Landscape - Pictures of the Year, December 1999
"AIDS in Africa is an invisible, slow-burning tragedy on a monumental scale. WHO estimates there are nearly 30 million people infected with HIV in the world today...."

* * * * *

'A continent of orphans!' 'Doctors powerless!' 'AIDS - the silent stalker!' 'A slow-burning tragedy.' 'Africa is not doing enough, we must all work together to turn around this broken landscape.'

There's an old African saying which goes: *'The African race is like a rubber ball: the harder you dash it to the ground, the higher it will rise.'* And for one reason or another, it seems at this point in history that Africa is indeed being dashed to the ground - almost mercilessly so. Can it bounce back from this present curse of AIDS?

Thankfully, the 'AIDS in Africa' situation is more about perception than reality. As we begin to unravel the vivid mythology surrounding AIDS, Africa and the Third World, we realise once again that our understanding of the situation has been shaped by knowledge claims that are considerably more than just 'neutral'. We must focus on who exactly is reporting the African 'facts' to us, and their reasons for so doing. Why anybody would purposely be instigating and then orchestrating a tidal wave of depressingly bad news and all of it false, seems totally incomprehensible to the rational, enquiring mind. But orchestrated and false it is, as we shall discover. No one could argue that our story so far fulfils the criteria for truth being stranger than fiction. And the 'AIDS in Africa' story is no different. Establishing the truth and identifying the perpetrators can only help to put the bounce back into Africa, and into the other nations equally ravaged by the myth of HIV and viral AIDS.

* * * *

When people discuss the general perception of the Third World AIDS crisis, a common theme seems to be one of resigned acceptance: *'Yes, it's a real tragedy taking place over there.... but with so many people in the world, could this perhaps be Nature's way of evening out the populations of these vastly inhabited and under-resourced regions?'*

In their book *AIDS, Africa and Racism*, Rosalind Harrison and Richard Chirimuuta examine what 'in-built' social and psychological factors there might be that help make it easier for us 'over here' to believe and accept what is going on 'over there'. Quite uncomfortably, one of the key factors examined is 'inherent' racism.

Pliny the Elder was one of the first historians to describe Africa and its inhabitants. His 1st century *Summary of the Antiquities and Wonders of the World* brought some extraordinary ideas to the attention of a wide audience:

> *"Of the Ethiopians there are some that have neither nose nor nostrils, but the face all full. There are some called the Syrbote that are eight foot high and live with the chase of elephants. In a part of Affrike be people called Ptoemphane, for their king they have a dog, at whose fancy they are governed. Towards the west, the Arimaspi, a people that hath one eye in their foreheads. The Cinamolgie, their heads are like the heads of dogs... Grammantes make no marriage, but all their women are common.... Gamphasantes go all naked. Blemmy is a people who have no head at all. And others that walk more by training of their hands than with their feet."*[234]

Pliny's fanciful imaginings confirm only the fact that in his life he had never really ventured any further than Germany. More accurate world history documents Africa as a culturally sophisticated and thriving continent, rich in mineral deposits and other precious commodities.[235] Between 1509 and 1513, a certain Leo Africanus kept an account of his journeys in Africa. Here he describes one of the regions widely believed to be populated by Pliny's monsters.

> *"...I myself saw fifteen kingdoms of the Negroes.... In Tombuto (Timbuktu) there are many shops and merchants and especially of such as weave linen and cotton cloth. And hither do the Barbarie (Barbary) merchants bring cloth of Europe...*

---

[234] **Reader, John** *Africa – A Biography of a Continent*, Hamish Hamilton, 1997

[235] **Brown, Michael** *Africa's Choices*, Penguin, 1995. Brown notes that Francis Bacon, the founder of modern European science, had to go to Morocco to learn mathematics.

127

Corn, cattle, milk and butter this region yieldeth in great abundance.... Here are great store of doctors, judges, priests and other learned men that are bountifully maintained at the King's court and charges..." [236]

Interspersed with warring of course, Africa enjoyed many centuries of successful trading with other continents. But then, Africa was 'discovered' and the slave trade began. In 1748, British philosopher David Hume, a leading figure and influential shaper of public attitude, wrote:

" I am apt to suspect the Negroes, and in general all the other species of men (for there are four or five different kinds) to be naturally inferior to the whites. There never was a civilised nation of any other complexion than white.... No ingenious manufacture amongst them, no arts, no sciences... Such a uniform and constant difference could not happen, in so many countries and ages, if nature had not made an original distinction betwixt these breeds of men." [237]

Thomas Atwood, chief British judge of Dominica and later of the Bahamas, stated:

"Negroes are in general much addicted to drunkenness, thievery, promiscuity, and idleness... Idleness is so very predominant in Negroes, and their dislike of labour is so great, that it is very difficult to make them work; sometimes it is necessary to have recourse to measures that appear cruel, in order to oblige them to labour." [238]

With the Victorian era came many bloodthirsty battles contesting African soil. In his book, the self-explanatory *Marching over Africa*, Frank Emery has collated numerous letters written by British servicemen serving in Africa between 1868 and 1898. Included is the following:

"My darling Mother, we had a great fight yesterday, and you will be glad to know I am all right.... The Egyptian dead and wounded looked ghastly as we passed them in our advance,

---

[236] **Africanus, Leo** *A Geographical Historie of Africa*, 1600
[237] **Fryer P** *Staying Power: The History of Black People in Britain*, Pluto Press, London and Sydney: 1987
[238] Fryer P, ibid.

their dusky faces upturned in the blazing sun.... One fellow ran right along in front of the whole line. I should think he ran 600 yards, and it certainly took 30 or 40 shots before he was hit. I felt quite sorry for the poor beggar. It was really quite like rabbit shooting.... I think the big fight to take Tel-el-Kebir will be the day after tomorrow. Goodbye now, dearest Mumseh. With best love to all at home and the Park - Marling." [239]

Equatorial explorer Joseph Conrad spent many years working and travelling throughout inner Africa. Conrad's most famous work, a 1901 novel entitled *Heart of Darkness*, tells of a steamer voyage into the unexplored heart of Congo Land, and follows able seaman Charles Marlow on his quest to track down a Mr Kurtz, an ivory dealer, living somewhere in the jungle and reported to be dangerously insane. Conrad's book was later to become the chief inspiration for Oliver Stone's Vietnam war epic *Apocalypse Now*, where, in a similar river expedition, a Captain Willard is assigned to track down and eliminate the bloodthirsty and insane Colonel Kurtz. And as our journey continues, we will be hearing from Conrad and Willard from time to time, the parallels between their journey into the heart of darkness and ours into African AIDS becoming ever more apparent the further up-river we travel. Conrad's *Heart of Darkness* was widely read and served as an early 'Africa tourist guide' for the western masses. In the following text Conrad brings a bulletin from the front:

"We penetrated deeper and deeper into the heart of darkness.... We were wanderers on prehistoric earth, on an earth that wore the aspect of an unknown planet.... Suddenly, as we struggled round a bend, there would be a glimpse of rush walls, of peaked grass-roofs, a burst of yells, a whirl of black limbs, a mass of hands clapping, of feet stamping, of bodies swaying, of eyes rolling, under the droop of heavy and motionless foliage. The steamer toiled along slowly on the edge of a black and incomprehensible frenzy. The prehistoric man was cursing us, praying to us, welcoming us - who could tell? We were cut off from the comprehension of our surroundings; we glided past as phantoms, wondering and secretly appalled, as sane men would be before an enthusiastic outbreak in a madhouse.... No, they were not

[239] **Emery, Frank** *Marching over Africa*, Hodder and Stoughton, 1986

inhuman. Well, you know, that was the worst of it - this suspicion of their not being inhuman. It would come slowly to one. They howled and leaped, and spun, and made horrid faces; but what thrilled you was just the thought of their wild humanity - like yours - the thought of your remote kinship with this wild and passionate uproar."[240]

One can quite confidently predict that with reports such as these being brought back to English shores, a 'sophisticated Africa' did not immediately spring into the minds of the spellbound readers. And like some sort of intangible heirloom, the perceptions of a dark continent have been passed down through the generations and are with us today.[241]

All local authorities now have a 'racism in schools' policy. The highlighted sentence in the leaflets is always 'Racism has no place in our schools'. But the policy exists because unfortunately racism does have its place in our schools. And in the workplace. A recent racial harassment trial, one of many in the UK, heard evidence of racist taunts directed towards a competent £50,000 p.a. black employee. Among the many taunts was: *"You lot don't bother getting married, you just have kids all over the place."*[242]

At the 10th International AIDS Conference in Yokohama in August 1994, Dr Yuichi Shiokawa said the African AIDS epidemic could be brought under control only if Africans restrained their sexual cravings. Professor Nathan Clumeck of the Universite Libre in Brussels is skeptical that Africans will ever do so. In an interview with French newspaper *Le Monde*, Clumeck quite nonchalantly claimed:

> *"Sex, love and disease do not mean the same thing to Africans as they do to West Europeans, because the notion of guilt doesn't exist in the same way as it does in the Judeo-Christian culture of the West."*[243]

---

[240] **Conrad, Joseph** *Heart of Darkness*, Penguin, 1994
[241] See also **Said, Edward** *Orientalism. A historical Perspective of Cultural Imperialism in the West*, Vintage Books, 1979
[242] *Daily Mail*, 7th January 2000
[243] *Sacremento Bee*, 30th October 1994

Rosalind Harrison goes on to define the West's general perception of Africa and its inhabitants:

> Africans are primitive peoples living in isolated tribes cut off from civilization, so they could have harbored diseases for centuries before they spread to the rest of the world.

> They are evolutionarily closer to monkeys, thus could more readily acquire monkey diseases, perhaps by having sexual relations with monkeys or at least involving them in their sexual practices.

> They are sexually unrestrained, and a sexually transmitted disease would therefore spread more rapidly amongst them than any other people.

> Their intelligence is limited and they cannot understand the complexity of a syndrome such as AIDS.

The notion that AIDS originated from monkeys was proposed chiefly by Max Essex, a colleague of Robert Gallo. Declaring to the world that he had isolated a Zairian strain of HIV dating back to 1959, Essex sent his samples to three different laboratories for verification. The three labs, one at the CDC, the second Gallo's, and the third Abbott Laboratories (the multi-million dollar manufacturer of the ELISA blood test), quite unsurprisingly confirmed the Essex findings. Equally unsurprising is that when sent for *impartial* and *independent* assessment, a virus could not be found. [244] This did not stop Gallo from using the Essex findings to make the completely false assertion that 60% of Ugandan children had been infected with HIV by the early 1970s.[245] Gallo's monkey proposals, coupled with the western world's rampant promiscuity, prompted Dr David Benoni of Gabon to ask: *"Why do they not look for a monkey in the US? AIDS started there and could equally well have been brought to Zaire by wealthy homosexuals."* [246]

[244] *The Lancet*, "Evidence for HTLVIII in Central Africa in 1959," 31st May 1986

[245] **Gallo, RC** *Science*, "Evidence for Exposure to HTLVIII in Uganda Before 1973," #227, 1995

[246] *New Scientist*, "Scientists Attack AIDS Slur on Africa," 28th November 1985

As a point of interest, Rosalind Harrison details a Dr Serge Voronoff who, in the 1920s, declared he had discovered the cure for ageing. Thousands of European men underwent an operation involving the surgical pairing of 'live' chimpanzee testicles with their own. Having no effect on longevity, or on the birth of AIDS, it does however speak volumes about limited intelligence in exalted positions. [247]

Responding to the great swathe of unscientific and prejudiced statements surrounding AIDS and Africa, science and health correspondent Yinka Adeyemi, stated:

> *"To the average European researcher in virus cancers, the notion that the Acquired Immune Deficiency Syndrome (AIDS) had its origin in Africa is now a scientific fact... Yet, arguments by such scientists, whose minds are made up about the African connection, are replete with fundamental loopholes and illogicalities that render them not plausible...."* [248]

And there is little evidence to support Shiokawa's earlier accusations of uncontrollable sexual cravings, a favourite perception shared in the West. In countering the 'African as Frenzied Sexual Being', the *Sacramento Bee* tells us:

> *"Widespread modesty codes for women, whose sexuality is considered a gift to be used for procreation, make many African societies seem chaste compared to the West. The Somalis, Afars, Oromos and Amharas of North-East Africa think that public displays of sexual feelings demean a woman's 'gift', so that sexual contacts are restricted to ceremonial touching or dancing. Initial sexual relationships are geared to the beginnings of making a family. The notion of 'boyfriends' and 'girlfriends', virtually universal in the West, has no parallel in most traditional African cultures."* [249]

This is not to say that there is nothing untoward to report with regard to African sexual customs. There are indeed some highly

---

[247] **Harrison, Rosalind** *"Western Medicine as Contested Knowledge,"* Rethinking AIDS Homepage, 1999

[248] *Nigerian Concord*, July 1985

[249] *Sacramento Bee*, 30th October 1994

questionable sexual practices taking place in Africa and the Third World. But however extreme or culturally 'exotic' these practices might be, they are no more so than their western counterparts. And in the light of what we have learned in previous chapters, what world-wide lurid commentaries might we be reading on the sexual habits of westerners, were the power of the 'global pen' to rest in African hands? Western reporting blames much of African AIDS on promiscuity. Richard Chirimuuta wryly comments that, for there to be such a high number of supposedly infected adults in central Africa, *"life must be one non-stop orgy."*

In contrast, a Western sexual activity survey carried out in 1998 by Durex (who else?) *"...demolishes the myth that young British males are more interested in beer and football."* [250] The British lead at 133 times a year, 128 for the US, 106 for the French and 99 times for the Germans. The report also stated that on average, the sexually active Briton will have had 8 partners by the age of 21, compared with the global average of 4.1. Youthful exaggeration allowed for across the study group, when it comes to errant sexual behaviour, we in the West appear to be in no position to cast the first stone.

So what is everyday life like for the vast majority of Africans? Jeremy Harding has spent many years travelling the troubled regions of Africa. In his book, *Small Wars, Small Mercies*, he documents some of the hardships facing Africa today. Harding reminds us that beyond the often misplaced negative perceptions, Africans do have a number of distressing issues with which they contend on a daily basis.

"I am alert to the negative images of Africa, and the generalities that go with them; that every African country is in chaos, that every African statesman is corrupt or incompetent, that every cubic centimetre of African blood, whether stored, shed or still in circulation, is [HIV] sero-positive, and that the staple diet of 640 million Africans is dust.

Yet it is disingenuous to accuse the media of crying wolf on a continent where so many wolves are at the door. Populous states like South Africa, Zaire, Nigeria and Egypt are in

---

[250] *Foundation News,* September 1999

dangerous disarray, whilst large numbers of Africans in Sudan, Liberia, the Horn and parts of Southern Africa are among the most jeopardised people in the world. It is largely from them that we derive our sense of Africa as a vast Laocoon,[251] caught in the coils of debt, hunger, war, disease and ethnic rivalry."[252]

Misconceptions of HIV aside, there are indeed many wolves at Africa's door which are all too real in nature. As Harding's introduction states: *"Across the lives of the African people lie the shadows of larger forces – global rivalries, massive arms flows into underdeveloped states and the glib experiments of the IMF."* [253]

'Glib experiments' and 'shadows of larger forces' are central to the 'AIDS in Africa' story, and will be examined in more detail shortly. With regard to general living conditions in Africa, the following testimonies will convey to the reader the struggles the great majority of Africans face on a daily basis.

"My name is Catherine Nyirenda. I come from Zambia. I live in Lusaka, the capital, a city of about one million people. Within the city, I live in Mutendere, a crowded residential area. My country is very poor. The annual income per person in Zambia is the equivalent of $300 a year. 70% of people live below the poverty line. This means that they spend most of their total income on basic food alone. I am a typical urban person. I earn about 50,000 kwacha a month, which is worth US$50.

This is how I spend my monthly earnings. My rent is $25 per month. If I don't pay for two months, I will be thrown out. I spend the next $11 on maize meal, our staple food. I have about $14 left for everything else. There's charcoal to cook on, cooking oil and vegetables each costing $12 in a month. This leaves $2 for the month to buy sugar, soap, baby requirements, my own clothes, transport, health needs and medical services. We have seen a steady increase in child malnutrition since

---

[251] The Laocoon is one of the most well known works of Roman art. It presents Laocoon, the priest of Apollo, and his two sons being overcome by two large snakes.

[252] **Harding, Jeremy** *Small Wars, Small Mercies*, Viking Press, 1993

[253] Harding, Jeremy, ibid. IMF: International Monetary Fund

1992. Chronic malnutrition now affects 44% of urban children, and 60% of rural children. My impression is that the western world is sick of poverty and death in Africa – this is all that gets attention in your news. Many may think that suffering is normal for us - but it isn't. We hurt and grieve and hunger as much as you would, and we hate disease, poverty, poor medical services and poor schooling."[254]

Joan Shenton recounts the following story:

"….We stopped off at the town of Rakai. We went to inspect the local water supply, a foul smelling pool next to the effluent from the town drain. When it rained, the water became even more contaminated. Many people did not have the energy or the fuel to boil the water before drinking it. We watched children dipping their plastic containers into the water and carrying them off, gracefully balanced on their heads. But these waters were more dangerous than any supposed virus. These waters carried infections and parasites that could gradually destroy even the strongest man's immune system. Before leaving Rakai village, we drove up to its small rural hospital on the hill. It was completely deserted – no patients, no staff and a large empty ward with dismantled beds leaning against the walls."[255]

And Jeremy Harding on life in everyday Mozambique:

"Mateus and his wife Catarina were urban Mozambicans. Mateus was a private in the Mozambique army, earning 11,900 meticais a month (700 meticais = 1 US dollar). Catarina had four children to feed and she calculated the family's basic maize consumption at 30kgs per month. Catarina was not from Maputo and, upon arriving in the capital, had qualified for a number of benefits, many of which had since lapsed. Two of the children were suffering from worms, but the cost of a remedy was prohibitive. Yet like most of the people, Mateus and Catarina had a system. Mateus handed over his salary to Catarina, who then bought subsidised food and resold it for a profit… Her way of life simply kept the family ticking over. She

---

[254] Personal testimony given at a plenary session of the Lusaka AIDS Conference
[255] Shenton, Joan, ibid.

would get up at 5am and then hustle for flour or rice or sugar. She would get back by 7:30am to cook for the children, leaving them in the care of her sister as she set off again to trade until dusk. For many people in Maputo, life was even harder... Like tens of thousands in Maputo, [256] *Catarina cherished the thought of going home."* [257]

Charles Geshekter teaches African History at California State University, Chico. He has spent much of his time studying African health issues. He notes that the many hardships facing Africans render it inevitable that millions will be suffering from weight loss, chronic diarrhoea, fever and the persistent cough of tuberculosis. Says Geshekter:

"The real threats to African lives are famine, rural poverty, migratory labour systems, urban crowding, the collapse of state structure and the sadistic violence of civil wars. When essential services for water, power or transport break down, public sanitation deteriorates and tuberculosis, dysentery and respiratory infections increase." [258]

Philippe Krynen is director of 'Partage', an organisation dedicated to supporting sick and displaced families (and especially children) in Tanzania. Krynen was the author of *Voyage des Krynen en Tanzanie,* an account of his experiences in a country he dramatically described as 'AIDS-devastated northern Tanzania'. His story was picked up by the media globally and used to shape Western impressions of a viral AIDS epidemic in Africa that was out of control.

Originally believing HIV to be the cause of AIDS, Krynen then began to note certain anomalies in the AIDS patients he was treating. Over half of them tested negative for the virus. Prostitutes were surviving when their clients were dying. And all those empty houses and huts where the UN said the Tanzanian AIDS victims had once lived? These turned out to be additional homes Tanzanians had owned

---

[256] Those hardships have now been dramatically increased by severe flooding, rendering thousands homeless in Mozambique, especially around Maputo. BBC News, 7th February 2000

[257] Harding, Jeremy, ibid.

[258] **Geshekter, Charles** "The Epidemic of African AIDS Hysteria": www.thememoryhole.com

who had moved to the city. This and other evidence caused Krynen to rethink his beliefs about AIDS:

"There is no [viral] *AIDS," Krynen now states unequivocally. "It is something that has been invented. There are no epidemiological grounds for it. It doesn't exist for us."* [259]

The real problem, Krynen states, has nothing to do with a doomsday virus and everything to do with the standard ills from which Africa has always suffered. In an article on his work featured in *Continuum* magazine, he highlights the gradual decline of Tanzanian lifestyle through poverty, malnutrition, inaccessibility to basic medicines and a growing use amongst the younger generation of marijuana and amphetamines:

"For the Africa of tomorrow, the most successful triple therapy we can give the children is food, water and education. Give them these and you can forget about AZT." [260]

Part of Krynen's work is building shattered confidence:

"How can you ask people who believe they are going to die tomorrow, how can you ask them to look to the future which are the children. They give up. They don't invest." [261]

Lucy was one such shattered individual. She had been orphaned, and now at 18 or 19 years of age, she was regularly ill with repeated infections. She had lost over 20lbs in weight. Most people believed she was HIV positive, and Philippe Krynen duly discovered that Lucy had been diagnosed as such during one unconfirmed screening. Krynen and his wife decided to support Lucy and help her try to regain her position in the community. They moved her out of her hut and built a small house for her. Within a few months, Lucy began to get better. With regular nutritious food, supplemented with vitamins, Lucy began to put on weight and her skin diseases disappeared. *"Because we didn't support the AIDS tag on her,"* said Krynen, *"she recovered and was proof to the community that you recover from such episodes."*

---

[259] **Hodgkinson, N** *Sunday Times of London*, "African AIDS Plague a Myth," 3rd October 1993; also **Hodgkinson, N** *Sunday Times of London*, "The Plague That Never Was," 3rd October 1993

[260] *Continuum*, Vol 5, No 2, Winter 1998

[261] *Continuum*, ibid.

Says Lucy: *"I am strong and I am back to my old weight. I can do any work I'm faced with. I hope to have children."*[262]

Lucy is one of many such success stories (see photo section). With Philippe Krynen's care and their simple 'triple therapy' of food, water and education, Lucy, Julia, Deus, Seledina, Bernadetta and countless others have risen from the 'death curse' of AIDS. How many more Lucys and Julias are there across 'AIDS-ravaged' Africa?

Lucy had been orphaned, and she was a genuine orphan. There is actually a certain relevance to the term 'genuine orphan', as Joan Shenton intriguingly discovered. On her travels through Africa, she gained valuable insight into the true nature of the WHO's much reported 'orphan crisis':

> *"We heard that whenever* [western] *visitors arrived in this area, a carefully orchestrated show was put on. All the children were brought together and encouraged to put their hands up when they were asked if they were orphans. In Uganda a child is called an orphan if one parent has died. Many would put up their hands who were real orphans, part-orphans and not orphans at all, for instance if parents had migrated to find work, leaving them with grandparents."*[263]

Dr Christian Fiala, author of *Do We Live Dangerously? A Doctor in Search of the Facts and Background to AIDS*, has called the AIDS orphan story *"...one of the most cynical since the 'discovery' of HIV"*, stating:

> *"It sheds a characteristic light on the nature about the reporting of AIDS: obviously everything is allowed, without reservation, that makes people feel threatened... even European countries would have a large number of 'orphans' if one applied the Ugandan definition."*[264]

Local town official Badru Ssemanda is unhappy about the way in which some local entrepreneurs are juggling the statistics and adding to the problem:

---

[262] *AIDS and Africa,* Meditel transcript. Dispatches. Channel 4, 1993, ibid.
[263] Shenton, Joan, ibid.
[264] **Fiala, Christian** "The Ugandan Example", Rethinking AIDS 1999

"People are trying to make a living out of this AIDS. They think that if they publicise it and exaggerate it, they might win sympathy from the international community and will get assistance. We need assistance, but not through bluffing people and saying that people are dying at a rate which is not true."[265]

Krynen has been outspoken at the cynical manipulation of such a serious issue. Quoted in the UK *Sunday Times*, 3rd October 1993, he states:

"...if you ask how the parents died they will say AIDS. It is fashionable nowadays to say that, because it brings money and support. If you say your father has died in a car accident it is bad luck, but if he has died from AIDS there is an agency to help you. The local people have seen so many agencies coming, called AIDS support programs, that they want to join this group of victims. Everybody claims to be a victim of AIDS nowadays. And local people working for AIDS agencies have become rich. They have built homes in Dar es Salaam, they have their motorbikes; they have benefited a lot....

We have everybody coming here now, the World Bank, the churches, the Red Cross, the UN Development Program, the African Medical Research Foundation, about 17 organizations reportedly doing something for AIDS in Kagera. It brings jobs, cars; the day there is no more AIDS, a lot of development is going to go away...."

And there is abundant proof that some African doctors have taken part in propagating the 'AIDS in Africa' myth for similarly unscrupulous reasons, as *Spin* reporter Celia Farber discovered for herself whilst in Africa:

"Many believe that the statistics have been inflated because AIDS generates far more money in the Third World from Western organizations than any other infectious disease. This was clear to us when we were there: Where there was 'AIDS' there was money – a brand new clinic, a new Mercedes parked outside, modern testing facilities, high-paying jobs,

---

[265] *AIDS and Africa*, ibid.

international conferences. A leading African physician... *warned us not to get our hopes up about this trip. 'You have no idea what you have taken on,' he said on the eve of our departure. 'You will never get these doctors to tell you the truth. When they get sent to those AIDS conferences around the world, the money they receive is equal to what they earn in a whole year at home.'*

In Uganda, for example, the World Health Organization allotted $6 million for a single year, 1992-3, whereas all other infectious diseases combined – barring TB and AIDS – received a mere $57,000." [266]

* * * * *

Meanwhile, 5,000 miles away at 1818 H St, Washington DC, World Bank Headquarters, one of many letters has been circulated to all bank staff and its supporters (UN, USAID, UNFPA and other closely linked affiliates). This one is dated 2nd June 1999. Condensed, it reads as follows:

Friends and Colleagues,

A wildfire is raging across Africa. HIV/AIDS has spread with ferocious speed. By any measure, its impact is simply staggering. The arithmetic of risk is horrific. A child born in Zambia or Zimbabwe tonight is more likely than not to die of AIDS. In many other African countries, the lifetime risk of dying of AIDS is greater than one in three. This fire is spreading. The global death toll will soon surpass the worst epidemics of recorded history. Combustion is fearfully fast.

To date, two forces have helped feed the flames: ignorance and inaction. Ignorance is rapidly vanishing, largely extinguished by the pandemic itself. AIDS is everywhere evident in Africa. Inaction, unfortunately, remains common. And we must be honest with ourselves: We in the Bank have not done our full part. True, many country and task teams have done excellent work on AIDS. The Bank has published some of the leading analytical work on the subject. The

---

[266] **Farber, C** *Spin*, "Out of Africa, Part 1", March 1993, pp.61-63, pp.86-7

Human Development family in particular has built strong projects and partnerships, and helped bring the scope of the crisis to light. But as an institution, we have failed to bring to bear the full weight of our collective instruments, intellect and influence. As Africa is the hardest hit, we in this Region bear the primary responsibility to lead. It is time we met that responsibility. We announce today ACTafrica. By its terms, we will now put HIV/AIDS at the center of our development agenda. ACTafrica's work will provide several specific services, including:

Equipping and supporting country teams to mobilize African leaders, civil society and the private sector to intensify action against AIDS.

Supporting country teams, sector families and task teams in integrating AIDS into their portfolios and country programs.

Collecting and disseminating information on the progress of the epidemic, country by country statistics, and best practices.

Strengthening and expanding our partnership with UNAIDS and its co-sponsors, as well as with key agencies, NGOs [non-Governmental Organizations] and interested bilaterals.

ACTafrica begins its work immediately. Those who look back on this era will judge our institution in large measure by whether we recognized this threat for what it was and did our utmost to put out the fire. They will be right to do so. Let's get to work.

Callisto Gadavo. [267]

Can we even begin to comprehend the true enormity of power wielded by this institute and its affiliates? *"Equipping and supporting country teams to mobilize African leaders"* is not the language of the hired hand. The World Bank, The International Monetary Fund, The United Nations, USAID, UNAIDS and other institutions have formally taken up residence in Africa. Invited or not, and bringing to bear the full

---

[267] World Bank memo. *The New AIDS in Africa Initiative.* 2nd June 1999. Full text can be found at www.IAEN.com

weight of their collective instruments, these agencies have begun the task of mobilising African leaders to put AIDS at the centre of their development plans.

In reality, what we are witnessing are the world's most powerful organisations preparing for an all-out, multi-billion-dollar assault on a virus that has never even been proven to exist. Country after country is being instructed to integrate the HIV=AIDS myth into their development programs. Why? These global corporations are far from obtuse. They are quite well aware of the glaring inconsistencies in the AIDS debate. Yet decisions have been made wilfully for those inconsistencies to be ignored. *Why?*

And what about the ideas put forward by Philippe Krynen, Charles Geshekter, or the many other health professionals besides, who have identified what is really needed at ground level for the betterment of Africa and her people? Their suggestions are sensible. They target root causes of poverty and disease. Their goals are simple, and with the right level of support, they are achievable. Indeed, it was a UN official who declared:

> *"African farmers are among the best farmers in the world, you know.... I'm a farmer myself and I'll tell you, under the conditions they work in, they are tremendous farmers. All they need is a little support and they'll be able to feed themselves. Africa can feed itself - it used to do so."* [268]

In *The Resourceful Earth*, agricultural economist Roger Revelle estimates that, with the right management, the continent of Africa alone is capable of feeding 10 billion people. [269] And in his book *The Greening of Africa*, Paul Harrison tells us of the two million tonnes of maize harvested in Zimbabwe in 1985. More than twice their need, it was the result of farmers working together with simple tools, and avoiding the debt-burdening mechanisation programs. Says Harrison:

> *"If small-holders can be helped, the problems of insufficient food production, malnutrition, and widespread*

---

[268] **Brown, Michael** *Africa's Choices After 30 Years of the World Bank*, Penguin 1995. A penetrating look at the calamitous results of western capitalistic interference in Africa.
[269] **Revelle, Roger** *The World Supply of Agricultural Land*, Blackwell, 1984

poverty are attacked simultaneously." [270]

Common sense tells us that adequate nutrition is a key factor in the battle against the widespread immuno-deficiency illnesses currently ravaging Africa. A recent article penned by long-standing HIV critic Celia Farber reads as follows:

> *"I asked Dr Sam Mhlongo* [the South African government's chief pediatrician] *what I would see if I went to a local hospital. "If you don't see poverty and malnutrition as the number-one cause of death in South Africa, I am prepared to close my bank account and give you all my money." I asked him how could there be all these media reports about the millions dying of AIDS in Africa? It can't be a wholesale fabrication, can it? Don't they say that AIDS affects the middle and upper classes, not just the poor?*

> *"There are no death certificates whatsoever. We have no references for anything. All you have is the media, with television, radio and newspapers, agreeing on this. That stuff about the upper classes being affected by AIDS is really rubbish. I am one of the so-called bourgeois, and I don't see any of this among the middle classes. It's the poverty-stricken, unemployed, black South Africans who are dying, because of diseases related to poverty."* [271]

But the major banks and affiliated AIDS agencies are incorporating few of these necessary and common sense malnutrition-combating suggestions into their plans. [272] Their focus is AIDS, AIDS and AIDS:

UNAIDS 1st December 1999. *"The new millennium dawns on a world facing an unprecedented human tragedy - the loss of millions of people to the AIDS epidemic…. Our call to action will include establishing widespread confidential counselling and voluntary testing for HIV. The benefits of such counselling include prevention of mother-*

---

[270] **Harrison, Paul,** *The Greening of Africa*, Paladin Grafton Books, 1990

[271] **Farber, Celia** *A Contrary Conference,* New York Press, 24-30th May, 2000

[272] *"Outsiders,"* writes Michael Brown, *"should stop offering answers to our perceptions of Africa's problems, and just listen to Africans for a change."* So begins *Africa's Choices, After Thirty Years of the World Bank.*

to-child-transmission, promotion of the rights of girls and women to make informed decisions and realization of the people's right to know their HIV status."[273]

How about *"...establishing a widespread network of support for the reintroduction of localised farming, supplying simple tools and tried and trusted irrigation programs"*? The outlay would be miniscule and the benefits incalculable. Charles Geshekter again:

> *"Yes, there is a measurable decline in African health and increases in African mortality. What is in dispute is whether the symptoms of such illnesses are caused by extraordinary patterns of sexual behaviour or whether the signs reflect the deterioration of life on the continent over the past 20 years. The breakdown and decline of public health and medical treatment across Africa is due largely if not entirely to domestic civil war, impossible levels of indebtedness and sharp declines in the prices paid for commodities produced by Africans. This is standard World Bank and IMF micro- and macro-analysis. Where's the mystery?"* [274]

And again, yet more AIDS-focused aid from the World Bank:

WASHINGTON, 10th January 2000. *"In an historic appearance today before the UN Security Council, World Bank President James Wolfensohn will call for a grand coalition, with Africans in the lead, to step up the fight against AIDS in Africa, which has already claimed 13 million African lives, and orphaned 10 million children."*[275]

The orphans we know about. What about the World Bank's thirteen million dead? The World Health Organization's own *Weekly Epidemiological Record,* dated 26th November 1999, states that a cumulative total of 794,444 cases of AIDS in Africa had been reported to Geneva since 1982. Thirteen million dead versus just under eight hundred thousand...are these super-powers actually talking to each other? An article in the *Sacramento Bee* discusses the part played by officialdom and the press in the reporting of AIDS, suggesting the

---

[273] www.unaids.org, 17th January 2000
[274] Farber, Celia, *A Contrary Conference,* ibid.
[275] www.worlbank.org, 11th January 2000

figures may well be a hoax. One Ghanaian doctor interviewed stated *"If tens of thousands are dying of AIDS in these countries, and Africans don't cremate their dead, then where are the graves?"*[276]

A hoax? The whole world being lied to? What's going on? A similar scenario befell able seaman Conrad and his crew when, at a certain point on their journey up-river, they suddenly found themselves cut off from the comprehension of their surroundings, with new and disturbingly different scenery closing in on them.

And likewise, it is at this point on our journey into the African AIDS story, that we suddenly realise we are now in very unfamiliar territory. A marked sense of unease now accompanies this mission. Are there coherent explanations for these eerie statistics, for the disturbing new scenery which appears to be closing in around us?

There are indeed. And as we glide onwards up-river, venturing deeper and deeper into the African AIDS jungle, the indistinct shadows of larger forces looming up ahead of us will soon begin to take definite shape. And as they do so, we will discover, to a much greater degree, the extent of man's inhumanity to fellow man.

> LUCAS: *"Captain, you heard of Colonel Walter E Kurtz?"*
> WILLARD: *"Yes, sir, I've heard the name."*
> LUCAS: *"He was brilliant and outstanding in every way, and he was a good man too. A humanitarian man, a man of wit, of humour. He joined the Special Forces. After that his ideas... methods have become unsound... unsound. Your mission is to proceed up-river. Pick up Colonel Kurtz's path, follow it, learn what you can along the way. When you find the Colonel, infiltrate his team by whatever means available and terminate the Colonel's command."*
> WILLARD: *"Terminate? Colonel Kurtz?"*
> CORMAN: *"He's out there operating without any decent restraint. Totally beyond the pale of any acceptable human conduct. And he is still in the field commanding his troops."*

From the film *Apocalypse Now.*

---

[276] *Sacramento Bee*, "The Myth of AIDS and Sex," 30th October 1994

145

CLOSING IN ON KURTZ

deeper into the African AIDS jungle

The approaching four-wheel drive creates billowing clouds of dust as it doggedly makes its way across the rough terrain towards the village. This Landcruiser could be flying any one of a number of flags. It is one of literally hundreds of USAID, UNAIDS, UNFPA, NACP, WHO and associated Non-Governmental Organization (NGO) all-terrain vehicles who, day and night, trundle back and forth, busily going about their work. In and around the townships or across the great plains they trek, busy, busy, busy across Africa. By the time the truck reaches the village, a crowd of inquisitive children has gathered, excitedly awaiting their official visitor. The driver, clipboard in hand, dismounts and takes stock of the scene. Village men and women, leaning or sitting in their doorways, peer at him curiously. He is now surrounded by a sea of little black faces. *"Orphans?"* he asks the assembled throng. A forest of hands. A quick count and an entry is made.

The village has no clean water supply. Food is scarce, and there are a number of pretty thin individuals. One young woman is persistently coughing. It hasn't really registered with her that a visitor has arrived. She's too weak to notice. She has propped herself up against a wall, and she just sits there listlessly in the shade. She's been ill for some time now. No-one really goes near her. The village thinks she might have AIDS. Our man approaches her. He has no ELISA blood test kits in the back of his truck to confirm the villagers' suspicions. The ELISA tests are too expensive. He could carry out a urine test if he wanted to.[277] It has been shown that a urine test for HIV is as 'accurate' as the blood test, but he doesn't opt for this measure either.[278] Instead, with the shortage of time always a real problem, the

---

[277] *Sexually Transmitted Diseases*, "Uganda Studies in Urine and HIV," November 1999

[278] A 1994 study in *The Journal of Infectious Diseases* entitled "HIV Tests are Notoriously Unreliable in Central Africa" concluded that HIV tests were useless in that region since the microbes responsible for tuberculosis, malaria and leprosy were so prevalent that they registered over 70% false positive results. Geshekter, ibid.

visiting official conducts the now widely employed World Health Organization's standard 'visual only' diagnosis.[279]

According to WHO guidelines, an AIDS diagnosis can now be confirmed by the simple observation of clinical symptoms such as persistent coughing, high fever, 10% weight loss and generalised itching.[280] Health reporter Richard Rath:

"The criteria for AIDS diagnosis in Africa overlap considerably with the symptoms of endemic diseases such as dysentery, tuberculosis, cholera and malaria. This is why a growing number of African scientists and researchers have criticized the WHO premise and insist that addressing structural poverty and unhealthy living conditions – not behaviour modification programs – constitutes an appropriate patient-centred approach to achieving better health care". [281]

The necessary medicines and water purification treatments, which would help prevent and treat these diseases, are not in the back of the truck parked in the village. But these are in existence and, subject to political will, could be made readily available. Nurse Namuburu Maxensia gave Joan Shenton a guided tour of her medicine cabinet:

"....she unlocked a large wooden cupboard and showed us a stock of drugs supplied free by the WHO's Essential Drugs Programme. These medicines used to be supplied free to the villagers but, under a new plan, a reduced fixed rate was being charged - as if anyone in the village could afford it.... Nurse Maxensia told us that before the new plan, the hospital was full and there were sometimes 50 outpatients. "But now we get so few," she said ruefully, "because they can't afford to pay."[282]

But even when western medicines are made available, there can be hazards. African historian David Lamb recounts the following:

"Foreign drug companies have discovered a bonanza in

---

[279] WHO Global Program on AIDS; Provisional WHO clinical case definition for AIDS, *Wkly Epidemiol Rec*, 1986; 7th March; No.10: pp.72-3

[280] Shenton, Joan, ibid. Maggiore, Christine, ibid. See also **Tamarit Tamarit, Brauli** *Health and Life Magazine*, freenews.dragonfire.net

[281] DISS/cuss, News Flash, 8th December 1997

[282] Shenton, Joan, ibid.

black Africa, which they have turned into a dumping ground for their pills, by capitalising on the absence of consumer protection laws and advertising standards. Everywhere, there are billboards which in the main are advertising downright lies. Aminopyrine and Ipyrine were virtually withdrawn from US and UK markets after discovering these drugs halted the production of white blood cells in bone marrow. A study of African MIMS revealed no less than 31 preparations containing these drugs were being prescribed for minor conditions. And in the same publication, anabolic steroids which can lead to stunted growth, changes in external genitalia and liver tumours were being promoted as treatment for malnutrition, weight loss and excessive fatigue in school children. And methadone is included as a cough repressant." [283]

According to Philippe Krynen, it costs little more than £5 per week to support a child and meet all his/her care, nutritional and sensible medical needs. Readers wishing to support Philippe Krynen's work can find further details at the back of this book.

Meanwhile our visiting official has conducted his visual diagnosis of the sick woman. And for the pathetic figure sprawled out on the floor before him, there's only the one disease that makes sense to him. It isn't malnutrition, it isn't tuberculosis, it isn't cholera or dysentery. Philippe Krynen's triple therapy of water, food and education is not the priority here. The victim's weight loss and persistent cough fulfil the WHO criteria. The villagers' suspicions have been confirmed. She has AIDS. Another entry is made.

The official learns that someone else in the village is suffering from a persistent cough, and also that others in the village are quite ill but insist they're feeling OK. They lead him to the home of an elderly man. He became ill two months ago, but has refused to visit a doctor. While in Uganda, Joan Shenton met with journalist Sam Mulondo to discuss the very real fears Africans now have of going to the doctor and then being diagnosed as an AIDS victim. Mulondo told her that when people developed diarrhoea, they would be so terrified it could be AIDS that they got worse and often died.

---

[283] **Lamb, David** *Africans*, Methuen, 1985

"People are dying psychologically.... Somebody gets simple malaria, they fear to go to the doctor because they will be branded as a clinical case of AIDS. People are just left at home. They don't go for any treatment whatsoever." [284]

The visual diagnosis carried out on the elderly man has 'confirmed' another case of AIDS. Another entry is made and another village it seems is teetering on the edge of an AIDS epidemic. Winifred Mwebe lived in Uganda for thirty years, and worked as a volunteer for several Ugandan organisations. Winifred says:

"I have never seen or heard of any Ugandan, young or old, dying of any illness other than so-called HIV-related illnesses. Whenever you ask what happened if someone died, the answer is "What else?" I think that shows how ignorant our community is about these controversial issues. Ignorance kills. It will not stop unless we educate our people. And education is never widespread when there is big money and politics involved. Many Africans still think the white man is superior and that they do not make mistakes." [285]

Another ominous twist in WHO diagnostic techniques is the announcement of a new medical 'law' which can be found in their 'Global Program on AIDS'.

"More than 12 million people are thought to have latent TB infections. If they become infected with HIV, TB can quickly develop." [286]

According to the World Health Organization's convoluted wisdom, TB is no longer just TB. It appears that WHO are suggesting that the main agent behind a patient's quickly developing tuberculosis is HIV. Therefore TB = HIV. <u>Therefore also, the millions of cases of TB reported across the Third World can now be catalogued by these agencies as HIV infection.</u>

Our AIDS official has finished his visit to the village. He has gathered his statistics and departs. Within a few hours the World Bank

---

[284] Shenton, Joan, Ibid.

[285] **Mwebe, Winifred** *Continuum*, "London's Timid Africans," Vol 5, No 2, 1998

[286] *Facing Up To AIDS: The Socio-Economic Impact in Southern Africa*, Sholto Cross, Alan Whiteside (Editor) Hardcover 1993, Macmillan Press, 1996

in Washington and UNAIDS in Geneva will have been informed that another Ugandan village can now be included in the growing pandemic. In turn, the World Bank and UNAIDS will relay to Reuters, the *New York Times*, Associated Press and other world news agencies that *"the fire is spreading."*

AIDS SPREADING RAPIDLY IN AFRICA DESPITE MEASURES. CNN Online, 13th September 1999.

"Researchers asserted Monday that the AIDS epidemic continues to expand in sub-Saharan Africa, despite efforts to stem HIV's spread. At least 11 million Africans have died from AIDS and another 22 million have contracted HIV...."

It is not the fire of AIDS that is spreading across the continent of Africa, but the inferno of data-stretching, misdiagnosis, disinformation and deceit. Ironically, the World Bank has a link on its web page entitled 'Reporting Fraud'. Credence Publications used this facility to report the 'orphan count', the visual diagnoses and the World Bank's refusal to look at the overwhelming evidence against the HIV hypothesis. To date no reply has been received. In all, fourteen requests for information and clarification on certain issues have been posted to The World Bank and UNAIDS. All of these requests have remained unanswered.

* * * * *

A little while later, more clouds of dust appear on the horizon. Another vehicle is approaching the village. This time it's UNFPA. It's distribution time for the villagers. The driver unpins the tailgate and begins unloading an assortment of supplies to be distributed throughout the village free of charge. But the locals aren't exactly rushing forward for these free handouts. They know what's on offer. It's not medicine. No simple malarial treatments,[287] nothing for diarrhoea, nothing for cholera, no water purification tablets. The UNFPA truck is carrying condoms and safe-sex pamphlets. The locals can also try on the safe-sex T-shirts. There are also sterilisation and abortion pamphlets, foil strips of the Yuzpe 'morning after' pill[288] and

---

[287] *"Malaria accounts for 32% of deaths in Tanzania and 36% of hospital admissions."* Personal correspondence. Philippe Krynen, Partage, Tanzania.
[288] Emergency oral contraceptive, to be taken within 72 hours of sexual intercourse to

instructions on inserting IUDs. And sometimes even, safe sex videos. Charles Geshekter again:

> *"While health officials fixate on condom distribution or make evangelistic demands for behaviour modification, approximately 55% of Sub-Saharan Africans lack access to safe water, 60% have no proper sanitation and over 50 million pre-school children are malnourished."* [289]

In essence, the UNFPA truck contains everything to do with stopping life, but nothing to do with preserving it. And that is because UNFPA or United Nations Fund for Population Activities exists to enforce one ideology, and one ideology alone - that of population control. And they are very busy doing so, not just in Africa, but the world over, delivering birth control items to people who really only need food, clean water, medicine and shelter. Wherever disaster is unfolding and there is real human need, there also you will invariably find the UN Fund for Population Affairs agents handing out their condoms, safe-sex leaflets and other related paraphernalia.

Kosovo, 1998: Announcing that systematic rape and general promiscuity were taking place in the refugee camps, UNFPA dispatched a crisis intervention team to the area, with 'desperately needed' reproductive health kits, including sterilisation equipment and emergency contraceptives. The refugees' response to UNFPA's assortment of condoms, IUDs and vacuum aspirators[290] was of course negligible. In an effort to 'crack the camps', UNFPA approached Sjedullah Hoxha, head gynaecologist on the maternity ward at the Pristina Hospital in Kosovo, and promised him necessary medical equipment and health supplies on condition he publicly supported UNFPA's 'reproductive health' campaign. With death rates of premature babies at 50% due to lack of incubators and basic medicines, Hoxha agreed. Neither his incubators nor any of the promised health supplies ever arrived, UNFPA offering sterilisation and abortion services only.

---

terminate any pregnancy.

[289] Geshekter, Charles, ibid.

[290] Used to perform abortions. Having been anaesthetised, the woman's cervix is stretched open and the contents of the womb sucked out.

Interviews with Kosovar refugees revealed that there was no interest whatsoever in UNFPA aid and that the rumours of widespread rape were unfounded. On the 'rampant promiscuity' in the camps, an assistant at the Don Bosco camp in Tirana, Barbara Molinario *"...could only laugh. 'The Kosovar women are very conservative. They wear long skirts and demonstrate a highly cultured sense of modesty.'"* [291]

HURRICANE MITCH PR Newswire, 25th May 1999

WORLD LIFE LEAGUE DENOUNCES UNFPA: AID TO CENTRAL AMERICA INCLUDES BLACKMAIL. *"The World Life League issued a 'population reduction' warning to the Central American nations affected by the hurricane. WLL leader Robert Sassone is cautioning Central American leaders to beware of the humanitarian aid and debt relief totalling $6.2 billion, which is being offered by the IMF, World Bank and Inter-American Development Bank, the organisations collectively forming the Consultative Group for the Reconstruction and Transformation of Central America. UNDP Caribbean Regional Director Fernando Zumbado was quoted as saying, "When you visit people after a disaster like this, the striking thing is the size of their families. These are the roots that cause the problems and they are still there." Says Sassone, 'Basically, the attitude of the UNDP and UNFPA seems to be that if Central Americans had fewer children, fewer people would have died and fewer would need care. The utter lack of logic in such a statement exceeds my greatest attempt to understand it and should probably replace the old definition of 'cruelty' in the dictionary.'"* [292]

UNFPA PRESS RELEASE, New York, 13th January 2000
VENEZUELA FLOOD RELIEF – *"The United Nations Population Fund has sent supplies to Venezuela to meet the reproductive health needs of pregnant women and others displaced by last month's devastating floods and mudslides."*

United Nations Press Release, New York, 10th April 2000 – *"The United Nations Population Fund (UNFPA) is airlifting about two tonnes of life-saving emergency safe motherhood and reproductive*

---

[291] Population Research Institute, 'The Kosovo File,' January 2000, www.pop.org
[292] PRI, ibid.

health supplies in the first of two shipments to Madagascar to help victims of cyclone Hudah, which last week hit the eastern African country still suffering from the effects of the earlier cyclone Eline and tropical storm Gloria."

UNFPA supplies dispatched to Venezuela and Madagascar include HIV testing kits, condoms, hormonal contraceptives and intra-uterine devices (IUDs). In itself of course, sensible family planning is not inherently sinister. But the notion that western powers can have the final say regarding global choice of contraception and family size, must surely be a little galling for those on the receiving end of such 'family planning' advice.[293] Winifred Mwebe reminds us that reality often conflicts starkly with the idealistic morals of the teacher:

"The government is busy in Uganda negotiating with the West so that it can get AZT and other so called AIDS drugs. The NGOs [Non-Governmental Organizations] are very busy as well, preaching the AIDS hypothesis and all they do is give out condoms and leaflets. All they have in their trucks is an organised program that suits their interests. While all this is going on, some of the NGOs are enjoying passionate nights with Ugandan prostitutes. And the prostitutes are surprised that these same people who are preaching the AIDS scare are not protecting themselves. They don't use condoms and they don't like them. And these NGOs are not dying of AIDS. You wonder why, if what they preach is true. But no-one really cares as long as the money keeps coming in."[294]

And an article alerting people to the more extreme family planning measures linked to UNFPA aid appeared in the *Washington Times.*

DON'T FUND UNFPA POPULATION CONTROL: 9th May 1999

"For at least 30 years the UNFPA has been a complicit partner in some of the most unspeakably brutal population control programs

---

[293] *"We reject the cultural imperialism involved in saying to poorer countries that you must accept the limits on births in your country which we think are good for you. The poorer countries have a right to decide for themselves the size of their families."* **Tully, Paul** Society for the Protection of the Unborn Child, speaking at the International Conference on Population and Development (ICPD), Cairo 1994

[294] **Mwebe, Winifred**, Credence Publications correspondence, 6th February 2000

around the globe. Congress still allocates almost $300 million a year to international population control - or what is euphemistically described these days as 'family planning'. UNFPA has had a particularly demon-like presence in developing nations, this organization once giving an award to the Chinese government for the effectiveness of its genocidal one child per couple policy. To this day no one knows precisely how many babies and women have died at the hands of the population control fanatics in China. What we do know is that this program will go down in history as one of the greatest abuses of human rights in the 20th century.

Last year the US Senate Committee on Human Rights heard from witnesses of the China population program, how rural women are forcibly strapped to steel tables in 'hospitals' and their babies aborted, in some cases in the 7th, 8th and 9th month of pregnancy. UNFPA still spends millions each year on population control programs in China. There are many Third World hospitals that lack bandages, needles and basic medicines, but are filled to the brim with boxes of condoms stamped UNFPA or USAID. The cause of world hunger and environmental disasters in the world today is not too many people. It is too much statism." Stephen Moore, CATO Institute.

Professor H Miller of The Stanford University Institute of International Studies writes:

"Say hello to the bio-cops. Backed by bloated and inefficient bureaucracies, and undeterred by their own meagre scientific expertise, UN officials are now jostling to become international environmental super-regulators." [295] [296]

These UN super-regulators may not be the experts, but they are in power. And power always has aims and objectives. And it is at this point that we must remind ourselves once again that *"science and research must be studied in the context of all the interested parties involved…. one should always ask what social, institutional, political and philosophical interests lie behind often apparently 'neutral' knowledge claims."* For inextricably woven into much of this seemingly

---

[295] For a list of UN and affiliated organisations relevant to this subject, please refer to the section entitled *Acronyms*
[296] *Wall Street Journal*, 24th October 1995

neutral and benign global activity, there is undeniably an agenda at work - that of population control. As we shall discover, The World Bank, IMF, UNDP, USAID and UNFPA, all key players in the AIDS program, adhere fanatically to the philosophy of population control in many of their major agendas, especially AIDS 'care'.

CORMAN: *"Well, you see Willard, in this war, things get confused out there, power, ideals, the old morality, and practical military necessity. Out there with these natives it must be a temptation to be god, because there's a conflict in every human heart between the rational and the irrational, between good and evil. The good does not always triumph. Sometimes the dark side overcomes what Lincoln called the better angels of our nature. Every man has a breaking point. You have, and I have. Colonel Kurtz has reached his. And very obviously, he has gone insane."*
WILLARD: *"Yes sir. Very much so, sir. Obviously insane."*

INSIDE THE MIND OF KURTZ

'icpd+5' and other documents

The present-day belief that a growing world population might soon become a serious issue owes its origins chiefly to the work of statesman Henry Kissinger. On 10th December 1974, a classified memorandum was completed by the American National Security Council under National Security Advisor Kissinger. Its official title read: *'Implications of Worldwide Population Growth for US Security and Overseas Interests.'* This National Security Study Memorandum 200 (NSSM 200) asserted that population growth in the so-named Lesser Developed Countries (LDCs) posed a threat to American national security. Kissinger had drawn on the findings of the Royal Commission on Population, initiated by Britain's King George VI in 1944, *"...to consider what measures should be taken to influence the future trend of population."* [297] The Royal Commission reported that Britain was gravely threatened by continued population growth in its colonies and that *"...a populous country has decided advantages over a sparsely-populated one for industrial production."* And it was British eugenicist[298] Sir Julian Huxley who was famed for declaring that *"...overpopulation is, in my opinion, the most serious threat to the future of our species."*[299]

---

[297] The Royal Commission on Population, London 1944, involved studies that attempted to forecast the future population impact of millions of servicemen returning home after World War 2 to lonely females.

[298] Eugenics is the study of how to improve a race by judicious mating and/or destroying the undesirable genetic stock of the subject race. This racist philosophy was to reach a tragic climax with SS leader Heinrich Himmler's sanctioned eugenics program under Dr Josef Mengele in Auschwitz concentration camp during World War 2. Eugenic philosophies were not the sole prerogative of the Nazis however. Many British and American politicians, steeped in Darwinian evolution espousing 'survival of the fittest' sentiments, were active during the late 19th and early 20th centuries in supporting the idea of racially purifying human stock and doing away with the 'useless eaters'.

[299] Sir Julian Huxley, the devout eugenicist and social Darwinist, served as the founding Director-General of the United Nations Education, Scientific, and Cultural Organisation. In 1947 Huxley wrote that among UNESCO's most urgent tasks was *"...to see that the eugenic problem is examined with the greatest care, and that the public mind is informed of the issues at stake so that much that now is unthinkable may at least become thinkable."* Accordingly, it is appropriate that the International Union for the Conservation of Nature which Huxley co-founded produced the United Nation's Global Biodiversity Assessment, which suggests that the human population should be reduced to one billion

The language of NSSM 200 was dressed in the philanthropic clothing of 'concern for the planet'. Kissinger requested that special attention be paid to the following questions:

> What new initiatives by the United States are needed to focus international attention on the global population problem?
> Can technological innovations or development reduce population growth?
> Could the United States improve its assistance in the population field and if so, in what form and through which agencies?

The NSSM 200 recommendations that followed were to limit population growth in the target nations through birth control, and covertly through war and contrived famine.[300] These measures were adopted as official foreign policy under the Ford presidency in November 1975. Brent Scowcroft, who had replaced Kissinger as National Security Advisor, was placed in charge of the initiative and CIA Director George Bush was ordered to assist Scowcroft in bringing the measures into effect, along with the secretaries of State, Treasury, Defense and Agriculture.[301] The emerging problems of famine, genocidal war and economic failure were to be addressed through strategically placed western-led government agencies, with the promise of food and economic aid to be used as a bargaining tool, in order to persuade the target nations to adopt the population control strategies presented to them. Especially earmarked for attention were the countries of India, Bangladesh, Pakistan, Indonesia, Thailand, the Philippines, Turkey, Nigeria, Egypt, Ethiopia, Mexico, Brazil and Columbia. Population growth in these nations was regarded as

---

and huge areas be rendered devoid of human presence. (The New American, www.newamerican.com)

[300] Population Research Institute, PO Box 1559, Front Royal, VA 22630. Text for NSSM 200 is displayed at www.pop.org and www.Africa2000.com.

[301] **Cooper, William** *Behold a Pale Horse*, Lite Technology Publishing, 1991. Author Cooper worked for many years within America's covert Office of Naval Intelligence as an encryptions technician. In this capacity, he was privy to a great many sensitive documents. His controversial and at times unlikely book reportedly blows the whistle on the covert activities of the military and political infrastructures that formerly employed him. Cooper's book on its own has been discounted by sceptics, yet other works written on the subject of population control essentially agree with Cooper's information on main details.

'worrisome' since these larger populations would supposedly increase relative political, economic and military threat to the US.[302]

Susan George, author of *How the Other Half Dies,* is one of many socio-political commentators who reminds us that it is the exploitative actions of key élite agencies which are largely to blame for world hunger and poverty. She comments: *"We all have the physical and technical resources to feed the world. World hunger and poverty is a scandal, not a scourge."*[303]

Largely as a result of NSSM 200, and by a process of gradualism, over-population is now perceived as a very serious issue. Following the Cairo 'population summit meeting' in 1994, global headlines such as *'time-bomb', 'crisis'* and *'spaceship running out of oxygen'* began appearing regularly.[304] Chief in attendance at the UN-inspired Cairo conference were all the familiar names in the AIDS debate, including The World Bank, IMF, UNFPA and UNDP. To the trained eye, even a cursory glance at the literature and web pages of these institutions reveals an unwavering commitment to NSSM 200 and consequently, an all-consuming interest in reducing the number of people on this planet.

The belief that the world's population is spiralling 'out of control' is in actual fact a false belief, but is now embedded in the public psyche almost as deeply as the belief in the existence of HIV. Whilst the remit of this book does not allow for a complete examination of the history of population control, or of the forces at work who seek to implement these multi-faceted Malthusian measures[305], a condensed coverage of

---

[302] Cooper, William, ibid.

[303] **George, Susan** *How The Other Half Dies*, Rowman & Littlefield, 1984. See also Kasun, J, ibid.

[304] **Chapman, Howard** *Too Many Stars in the Sky,* Image National Conference manual, 1994

[305] **Wood, John** *Thomas Robert Malthus. A Critical Assessment*, Croon Helm, 1986. Thomas Malthus (1766-1834) - a political economist who was concerned about what he saw as the decline of living conditions in 19th century England. He blamed this decline on three elements: The overproduction of young; the inability of resources to keep up with the rising human population; and the irresponsibility of the lower classes. To combat this, Malthus suggested the family size of the lower class be regulated so that poor families did not produce more children than they could support. Malthus' view that poverty and famine were natural outcomes of population growth and food supply was not popular among social reformers, who believed that, with proper social structures, all ills of man could be

158

this topic is necessary if we are to remain true to detailing the forces at work in Africa and the Third World, operating out there in the name of 'AIDS Care'.[306]

It is interesting to note that the entire world population could quite comfortably fit into an area the size of Texas. By converting the land mass of Texas (approximately 262,000 square miles) into square feet and dividing this area by the latest estimate of six billion, a family of five could thus occupy approximately 6,300 square feet of living space - a mansion by any means - leaving the rest of the planet completely empty and available for all mankind's agricultural, manufacturing, educational and recreational activities! Idealism aside, no one in the near future is likely to fall off the edge.[307]

In the book *War Against Population*, a critique of population control policy, author Jacqueline Kasun includes quotations from World Bank policymakers who have used the word 'assume' in their reports on the perceived threat of population growth. Says Kasun:

> *"The astonishing fact is that these assumptions have neither been verified nor questioned by official policymakers: they have simply been taken on faith, with no resort to the means for testing them, which have been and are readily available. One would suppose that a major policy of the US and the international lending agencies such as the World Bank – a policy extending over many years, costing billions of dollars and involving significant risks in terms of economic welfare and international goodwill – would be based on thorough investigation of the relevant facts. Population policy however has not."* [308]

---

eradicated. *"Here then at last, I had a theory by which to work."* Charles Darwin on Malthus' *'Essay on the Principle of Population'* **Milner, Richard** *Encyclopedia of Evolution*, King Holt and Co. 1990

[306] There are several books available which competently expose the fallacy of overpopulation and its purported dangers: not least **Kasun, Jacqueline** *The War Against Population*, Ignatius Press 1998 *"One of the best kept secrets in the world is the evil nature of the population control movement. This is the best and most important book on the subject."* Rice, E Charles, Professor of Law, University of Notre Dame.

[307] Chapman, Howard, ibid

[308] Kasun, Jacqueline, ibid.

In his essay entitled "The Myth of Over-Population", Mark Leonard makes the humanitarian point that *"...we have to recognise that in an inter-dependent world, it is in all our interests to give the six billionth member of the human race a world worth living in."*[309]

But UNFPA has other plans, it seems. *'Six Billion. A Time For Choices'* reads UNFPA's Internet home page. Yet for the vast majority of the hungry people submitting to these global population programs, choices are not on the menu. To gain a balanced understanding of the global handling of the African 'AIDS Crisis', it will serve us now to examine the moral code under which these multi-national agencies operate.

Whether we care to accept it or not, population control programs have been, and are being routinely 'integrated into country portfolios' by governments on a scale that is breathtaking. And these measures are being enforced by any and all means necessary. The US Office of Population Affairs (OPA) has pioneered several unsavoury political and military means of population control in countries deemed by western powers as 'most at risk' from over-population and the stripping of their natural assets. These nations were Nicaragua, El Salvador, Cambodia, Laos, Vietnam, Columbia and most developing Third World nations on the African, Asian and South American continents. Thomas Ferguson, case officer for the OPA's Latin American desk, gave a valuable insight into his department's attitudes towards its work when he remarked: *"There is a single theme behind all our work: we must reduce population levels. Either they do it our way, through nice clean methods, or they will get the kind of mess we have in El Salvador, or in Iran, or Beirut. Population is a political problem. Once population is out of control, it requires authoritarian government, even fascism, to reduce it..."*[310]

---

[309] **Leonard, Mark** *New Statesman,* "The Myth of Over-Population," 11th October 1999

[310] **Cooper, M William** *Behold a Pale Horse,* ibid. See also OPA's home-page at http://www.hhs.gov/progorg/opa/ For further research on population control, please refer to **Mullins, Eustace** *Murder by Injection,* Iconoclast Books, Ketchum, ID USA (Barnes & Noble); **Willner, Dr Robert** *Deadly Deception,* Peltec Publishing Co, Boca Raton, FL (800)214-3645; **Ehrlich, Dr Paul R** *The Population Bomb,* Club of Rome Publications; ; **Peccei, Dr Aurelio** *The Limits of Growth, A Report for the Club of Rome's Project on the Predicament of Mankind,* Club of Rome Publications and **United Nations Publications** *Global Outlook 2000,* 1990

Philippe Krynen, with some of his precious charges. Readers wishing to contribute to the valuable work at Partage Tanzanie will find details at the back of this book.

A TALE OF TWO LUCYS

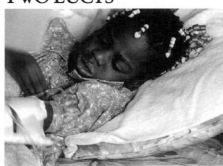

Lucy from Africa (left), diagnosed and left for dead in 1992, was cared for by Krynen who refused to interpret her condition as 'terminal'. Pictured here in March 2000, today she is the healthy mother of son **Joseph**. **Luci** (above) has just celebrated her 16th birthday. She is currently receiving conventional AIDS medications from her loving and dedicated carers who now have their own doubts about the medications. A copy of this book has been sent to Luci's home in the hope that she will celebrate many more birthdays.

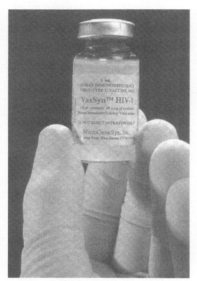

One of many AIDS vaccines now making its way towards Africa. These products are largely a mystery in their chemical make-up. What are the long-term effects of these mostly untested vaccines? How exactly are they supposed to combat a virus that has never been isolated?

The terminator

Life expectancy at birth

Propagandising the HIV psycho-product: The notion that Africa is being 'devastated by AIDS' is a complete falsehood. Yet Third World nations that declare their countries 'AIDS Disaster Zones' are delighted to receive huge United Nations and foreign aid hand-outs. They are however largely unaware of the population control agenda simultaneously at work.

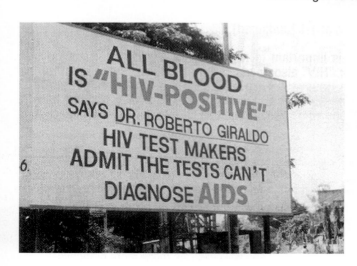

ALL BLOOD IS "HIV-POSITIVE" SAYS DR. ROBERTO GIRALDO HIV TEST MAKERS ADMIT THE TESTS CAN'T DIAGNOSE AIDS

Taking the Message on the Road: One wonders what the locals make of this unusual road-sign in Nagpur, India.

'AIDS-infested Africa' represents a commercial bonanza for First World drug companies to pioneer yet another vaccine. But what will the vaccine be based on? Protestors who recognise the track record of these companies are fearing the worst.

Spin reporter **Celia Farber** discovered one truth about AIDS during a visit to Africa: *"Where there was 'AIDS' there was money – a brand new clinic, a new Mercedes parked outside, modern testing facilities, high-paying jobs and international conferences."*

Children such as **Deus** and **Jovina**, diagnosed HIV positive from a very young age, thrive under the Krynen triple therapy regime of food, water and education. Millions of children just like these could survive and benefit from inexpensive help and care. Instead, African towns and villages are beset with UN aid meddling, corrupt national officials siphoning money from the agricultural development and health budgets and UNFPA's unsinkable truck convoys of condoms, 'reproductive aids' and safe-sex tee-shirts and videos.

Positively False author **Joan Shenton** found the fear of AIDS endemic in African villages because of western propaganda: *"People are dying psychologically.... Somebody gets simple malaria, they fear to go to the doctor because they will be branded as a clinical case of AIDS. People are just left at home. They don't go for any treatment whatsoever."*

What is devastating Africa? The same things that have always devastated Africa. Western meddling, malaria, tuberculosis, and contaminated water. 2 billion people around the world (a third of the world's population) do not have access to basic sanitation. Over 1 billion do not have a safe supply of water close to their homes. Every six seconds, one person dies from a water-contamination illness (see section entitled *Contacts!*). And yet these basic problems are largely overlooked by the global health agencies in their headlong rush to promote 'a killer AIDS epidemic'.

Hungry... Disturbing questions remain unanswered in the matter of Third World food aid. Is the phantom HIV really killing Africa, or is the real answer simpler and more unpalatable?

Western populations were told that millions were starving in Somalia because grain shipments sent by the West to feed the people were being pillaged by local warlord Mohammed Farah Aidid.

The US Marine Corps was duly sent to Somalia to stop Aidid but later reported that 'they couldn't find him'.

With a multi-billion-dollar satellite system that can read the words off a cigarette packet from 120 miles up, how was it that the US National Security Agency and the Marine Corps couldn't find one balding tin-horn rebel in Mogadishu to end the hold-up of grain shipments to the starving refugees? The press found him. They even gave him interviews. But Farah Aidid remains officially undiscovered. The grain shipments continue to get pillaged. Lots of black people die.

The following examples of 'African aid agency' support reveal the depths to which corporate 'aid' has sunk. Below is just one of many USAID 'population control' contracts awarded to various inter-related departments and Non-Government Organizations (NGOs).

Population Communications Services/Population Information Program
Center for Communication Programs, The Johns Hopkins University
936-3052 DPE-3052-A-00-0014-00
July 1990 - July 1995. $60,000,000. Worldwide.
Purpose: *... to initiate, implement, and sustain effective communication programs for population and family planning service delivery... and to inform ... professionals and policy-makers in developing countries ... Includes audience identification, message design, mix, production of materials, interpersonal communication, and evaluation.* [311]

The terms 'audience identification' and 'message design' are of particular interest to this study.

In November 1990, the World Bank launched a US $27 million population project for Ghana with the goal of cutting the size of the next generation of Ghanaians in half, from approximately 45 million to only 25 million by the year 2020. Aware of the fact that Ghanaians do not wish the size of their country to be manipulated by outsiders, the bank commissioned Opia Mensah Kumah, senior program officer for the US government's population communication campaign in Africa, to produce a 'procedural' report. The report stated that deeply held traditional beliefs and values would hinder population control efforts, making persuasion more difficult. Indeed, in many parts of the continent, cultural prohibitions exist against even counting one's children, believing them to be a blessing, not a curse. [312]

---

[311] USAID. Office of Population Department, 1996

[312] Sensible family planning is of course the responsibility of both partners. *"There's a lot of gender education saying "Set girls free, set women free." But what is the role of men? If men are seen as the ones who incapacitate women, then the men need to be educated alongside the women."* Gladys Mwiti from the Oasis Counselling Centre, Nairobi. Taken from *People Count* Tear Fund information brochure, 1995.

Based on Kumah's research, both the World Bank and USAID implemented programs designed to overcome resistance to population reduction and bring about drastic changes in public attitudes and personal conduct. Involving coercion and deception, their tactics conformed exactly to the tactics outlined by Colonel Michael Dewar in his book *The Art of Deception in Warfare*, a study on psychological warfare and covert actions. Dewar, with whom Phillip Day briefly worked in a commercial capacity, is a former army intelligence officer who now runs his own public relations agency in London. He outlines these six basic principles:

➢ The operation must be well planned and centrally co-ordinated, so as to be consistent and sustained.
➢ Preparation is essential. Those conducting the campaign must be thoroughly familiar with their audience, and be able to gauge its probable reaction to the campaign.
➢ False information must be made to appear absolutely logical, seeming neither out of harmony with current events nor in any way suspicious.
➢ The greater variety of sources that can be used to plant false information, the more believable it becomes.
➢ Timing is critical; people generally notice marked events, but are very poor at perceiving gradual change.
➢ The operation and its purpose must be concealed from the enemy.[313]

With almost military precision, the WHO population control strategy for Ghana incorporates each of these six principles:

➢ The activities of the World Bank, USAID and other donors are carefully co-ordinated, and strict monitoring procedures are in place to enforce the terms of the agreement at every stage.
➢ Extensive background research was carried out in Ghana. Surveys were conducted to determine how best to sell the idea of family planning, gradually exposing the populace to subtle messages, allowing new contraceptive ideology to take root slowly, without arousing suspicion.

---

[313] **Dewar, Michael** *The Art of Deception in Warfare*, David and Charles, 1989

162

➢ In all campaigns such as these, messages are discreet and shy away from the controversial. They are kept at a muted, persuasive level, repeated exposure to the message influencing the people to accept birth control to such an extent that they eventually identify with the message.

➢ WHO and relevant associates held approximately 80 special conferences and presentations during the first three years of operations in Ghana. These included presentations to traditional chiefs, private meetings with top government officials, dozens of seminars for journalists and government ministers, special briefings for private sector leaders, and a variety of special events. More than 100 pre-packaged radio broadcasts, numerous television productions and hundreds of propaganda packets were carefully prepared and distributed.

➢ Foreign policy had now been successfully incorporated into indigenous broadcasting systems. As such, the campaign had progressed from raising the level of awareness to influencing attitudes, opinions, and beliefs favourable towards WHO ideas on birth control, those ideas now being promoted within and by the targeted populace.

➢ The existence of this western orchestrated, western-led Ghanaian population control program remains largely unknown to the public. [314]

Where the World Health Organization, USAID and UNFPA do not have the time to carry out the above 'softening' procedures, they implement much swifter and blunter programs. James Miller, a correspondent for Human Life International, brings us the following report on population control measures covertly carried out in Tanzania, Nigeria, Nicaragua, Mexico and the Philippines - all executed in the name of humanitarian aid.

During the early 1990s, the World Health Organization conducted an extensive vaccination campaign against tetanus

---

[314] www.africa2000.com A comprehensive resource for information on population and demographic issues; race, class, and competitive fertility; international 'aid' & economic development; reproductive freedom v. control; covert activities & military strategy. Presents research and analysis by journalists from all over the world, as well as information from hundreds of formerly classified documents that are available from no other source.

in a number of countries. In October 1994, Human Life International became suspicious of the campaign protocols. They obtained several vials of the vaccine and had them analysed by chemists. Some of the vials were found to contain human chorionic gonadotrophin (hCG), a naturally occurring hormone essential for maintaining a pregnancy.

When introduced into the body coupled with a tetanus toxoid carrier, antibodies will be formed not only against tetanus but also against hCG. In this case the body fails to recognize hCG as a friend and will produce anti-hCG antibodies. The antibodies will attack subsequent pregnancies by killing the hCG which naturally sustains a pregnancy. When a woman has sufficient anti-hCG antibodies in her system, she is rendered incapable of maintaining a pregnancy.

HLI reported the sketchy facts regarding the Mexican tetanus vaccines to its affiliates in more than 60 countries. Soon additional reports of vaccines laced with hCG hormone were received from the Philippines, where more than 3.4 million women were recently vaccinated. Similar reports came from Nicaragua, which had conducted its own vaccination campaign in 1993.

The Known Facts concerning the WHO tetanus vaccination campaigns in Tanzania, Nigeria, Mexico and the Philippines.

Only women were vaccinated, and only women between the ages of 15 and 45. Why? Aren't men at least as likely as young women to come into contact with tetanus? And what of the children? Why were they excluded?

Human chorionic gonadotrophin (hCG) hormone was found in the vaccines. WHO has been actively involved for more than 20 years in the development of an anti-fertility vaccine utilizing hCG tied to tetanus toxoid as a carrier -- the exact same coupling as has been found in these vaccines.[315]

---

[315] More than twenty articles, many written by WHO researchers, document WHO's attempts to create an anti-fertility vaccine utilising tetanus toxoid as a carrier. Some leading articles include: "Vaccines for Fertility Regulation," Chapter 11, pp.177-198, Research in Human Reproduction, Biennial Report (1986-1987), WHO Special Programme of Research,

Allied with the WHO in the development of this particular anti-fertility vaccine have been UNFPA, the UN Development Program (UNDP), the World Bank, the Population Council, and the Rockefeller Foundation. The US National Institute of Child Health and Human Development was the supplier of the hCG hormone in some of the vaccine experiments.[316]

These incidents are by no means isolated. Covert population control measures have been carried out by these agencies for many years. Kasun details many disturbing cases of coercion being used to implement mass sterilisation. In a 20,000 persons per annum sterilisation program carried out in El Salvador and financed by USAID, there was little or no provision for informed consent. Similarly in Bangladesh, financial incentives were offered to individuals to go out and recruit candidates for sterilisation. Money was also offered to those being sterilised, but with a great many of those people not really understanding the nature of the operation. In that same country, sterilisation programs were also linked to oral re-hydration programs for children with diarrhoea. Since treatment usually meant life or death for the child, the mother was placed in a position of very little choice.[317]

And today, we have the Jubilee Campaign, in itself a thoroughly worthwhile global initiative to urge the financial institutions to cancel much third world debt. In the last year, many thousands of signatures have been collected from the general public in the UK, petitioning the World Bank, IMF and other financial institutions to write off the debts owed by HIPCs (Heavily Indebted Poor Countries[318]) and to examine sensible ways in which future monies could be spent wisely and above all, transparently. And the news

---

Development and Research Training in Human Reproduction (WHO, Geneva 1988). "Observations on the antigenicity and clinical effects of a candidate anti-pregnancy vaccine: B-sub unit of human chorionic gonadotrophin linked to tetanus toxoid," *Fertility and Sterility*, October 1980, pp.328-335

[316] Human Life International, www.hli.org, January 2000

[317] Kasun, J, ibid.

[318] Debts which have arisen largely as a result of western financial aid policies. See **Rich, Bruce** *Mortgaging the Earth*, Beacon Press, 1995. A critique of the policies the World Bank has imposed, bringing misery to the very people it was originally founded to help – the poor. *"For those who have long had their suspicions of the World Bank, 'Mortgaging the Earth' proves they were right."* New Statesman

recently concerning the Jubilee Campaign seems to be quite heartening. The banks appear to be listening and as a result, debt cancellation speeches are now being made by these institutions.

Sadly, but not unsurprisingly though, and despite the good work of Jubilee, there is another agenda at work behind these institutions' outward display of generosity. The vast majority of signatories to the Jubilee petitions have little or no idea that HIPCs are having their debts cancelled only on condition that these nations divert substantial funds into 'poverty reduction programs', a thinly veiled euphemism for 'child reduction' programs and other forms of population control.[319] The 'less children the better' policy is perfectly in keeping with Kissinger's NSSM 200, and mirrors UNDP's callous insights into the Hurricane Mitch disaster, i.e. less children in existence would have resulted in less people being affected by the disaster, therefore leading to less all-round poverty. It was former World Bank director Robert Macnamara who stated:

> *"More children means more expenditure on food, on shelter, on clothing, on health, on education, on every essential social service. And it means correspondingly less expenditure on investment to achieve the very economic growth required to finance these services... Nurturing children drains away resources that could otherwise be invested into industrial projects."*[320]

While Jubilee 2000 in no way aligns itself with the philosophy of population control (in fact their web-site reports on some of the less upright aspects of these global finance-house tactics[321]), the fact remains that the current Jubilee petition includes nothing which tells the reader of the unsavoury agendas at work. Contact details of the large financial institutions are included at the end of this book, so that readers may themselves directly campaign for a halt to these hidden and inhumane debt-relief conditions. As it currently stands, the Jubilee

---

[319] *"At the Annual Meeting of the World Bank and the IMF in September 1999, a new approach to poverty reduction was agreed. The strategies will set out how poverty will be tackled, and specify how resources, including savings from debt relief, will be spent."* DFID Background Briefing, October 1999

[320] Kasun, J, ibid.

[321] www.jubilee2000uk.org

petition allows no room for those signing to protest also against these enforced 'poverty reduction' measures.

Away from the public eye, the UK government is playing a substantial role in 'poverty reduction', not least via Clare Short's Department for International Development (DFID). While DFID is involved in a number of worthwhile overseas aid initiatives, it is also a generous sponsor of both UNDP and UNFPA. DFID has recently released a campaign brochure entitled *'Beyond ICPD + 5'*, a Third World sexual and reproductive health paper, which details governmental measures to tackle Third World 'poverty' issues. Included in the brochure, which now features prominently on the UNFPA web-site, are statements such as *"We believe WHO, UNFPA and UNAIDS have important roles as global champions... WHO's 'Make Pregnancy Safer' initiative is an example of the leadership needed... AIDS has now affected 50 million... DFID is supporting the social marketing of female condoms in Zimbabwe... DFID working intensively in more than 20 countries... Working in partnership with the World Bank..."* etc. etc.

As with many DFID health documents, population control measures are increasingly becoming clothed in emotive rhetoric championing women's rights. A deceptive outward appearance, pleasing to both the eye and the ear, but hiding the more distasteful inner workings, is a fairly typical industrial manoeuvre, again not dissimilar to the Windscale/Sellafield name change. Formally known as western meddling, cultural interference and mass family planning/sterilisation campaigns, population control has now been disarmingly dressed as 'choices and freedom for women'. While there are indeed many cultures oppressive towards females, it is interesting to note that out of the £140 million given by DFID to the UN's global activity fund last year, £45 million went to UNDP and UNFPA, whilst UNIFEM, the UN organisation supposedly fighting for a fairer world for women received just £1 million. [322] In many instances, when it comes to implementing population control, women's rights are simply the Trojan Horse to gain access to reticent countries.

---

[322] DFID spending statement 1998-2002

The translation of 'ICPD+5' is 'five years on from the International Conference on Population and Development' - the infamous population conference held in Cairo in 1994. Many Third World or 'developing' country representatives at that gathering were disappointed by the lack of discussion on development, finding instead that they were attending countless seminars focused almost entirely on overpopulation, and *"what are we all going to do about it?"* Objectives were agreed at these meetings and targets were set on population reduction. Undeniably, those targets are being worked on to this day. A spokesperson for DFID agreed that 'Beyond ICPD+5' does indeed detail policies for reducing the global populace. She believed also though, that whilst it would not have been straying from the truth to name their brochure *'DIFD's Population Control Measures',* this title would not have been entirely appropriate.[323]

The ruthlessness and recklessness with which WHO, USAID, UNFPA, UNDP and associates are applying population control across the globe, and especially Africa, is causing many African observers much consternation. Charles Geshekter again.

> *"The nebulous linkage of HIV to a complex of widespread symptoms has been greeted with justifiable skepticism by many Africans for another reason: they fear that the WHO claims of a pandemic will become an excuse for using Africa as a laboratory for unwarranted and unregulated vaccine trials or for testing powerful cytotoxic drugs, using Africans as guinea pigs.*[324]

As seen with their sterilisation programs, WHO and associates have also been conducting covert, unregulated vaccine trials all too frequently across the length and breadth of Africa, the Sub-Sahara and other Third World countries.[325] But what about the conventional, respected and regulated vaccination programs? Aren't these supposed to be effective?

---

[323] Steven Ransom telephone conversation with DFID spokesperson, 2nd February 2000

[324] DISS/cuss, News Flash, 8th December 1997

[325] **Douglas-Hulme, Ethel** *Pasteur Exposed. The False Foundation of Medicine*, Ennisfield Press, 1989.

Despite the widespread acceptance and use of vaccines, there are a growing number of people who now question the safety and ethical implications of such practices, and suggest that vaccinations can often be the cause of chronic health and mental problems.

HOUSE DEBATES VACCINE SAFETY 5th August 1999: *"We can no longer keep our heads buried in the sand like an ostrich pretending there is no problem," said Rep. Dan Burton, as he waved a sheath of documents he said showed thousands of casualties over the last year."* [326]

And a remarkably candid front-page headline in a recent edition of the UK's *Mail on Sunday* reads as follows:

MEASLES JAB: NEW LINK TO BRAIN DAMAGE. *"A Professor O'Leary, Director of Pathology at Coombe Women's Hospital in Dublin, provides compelling evidence of an association between infection by the measles virus and autism in children, many of whose parents said they developed the condition after they had been injected with Measles Mumps Rubella vaccine or MMR...."* [327]

Vaccines kill and maim regularly, yet very little is publicly known about vaccine methodology or the substance of what is actually injected into the human system during the inoculation. This is not altogether unsurprising. In the above case for example, Professor O'Leary was immediately instructed by his employers not to give any further information to the press. [328]

Hepatitis B vaccine contains mercury, aluminium and formaldehyde. The pertussus or whooping cough vaccine contains the same ingredients. Other components found in common vaccines include ethyl-glycol and carbolic acid. These vaccines are then grown and strained through cultures similar to those used in Gallo's laboratories. Cultures include monkey kidney, chicken embryo, embryonic guinea pig cells and, in the case of rubella, Hepatitis A and chicken pox, dissected organs of aborted foetuses. Says one concerned vaccine researcher, *"Would you mix this and feed it to your*

---

[326] Salon Health and Body. Vaccine Debate. www.salon.com
[327] *Mail on Sunday*, 9th April 2000
[328] *Mail on Sunday*, ibid.

child from a bottle? Yet the government requires it to be injected with a syringe directly into our children's bodies."[329]

To date, the US National Vaccine Injury Compensation Program or NVICP, established in 1986, has paid out in excess of $1 billion in injury awards to western vaccine-recipients. And there are quite literally thousands of cases pending. This despite the fact that the Health and Human Services Secretary Donna Shalala narrowed the definition of vaccine damage to such an extent that only immediate and severe reactions can now qualify. Seizures, disorders, brain damage, ataxia, paralysis, learning difficulties and deaths that occur many days or weeks following these vaccinations are now excluded. Added to this, doctors have little incentive to report themselves to the government's Vaccine Adverse Event Reporting System or VAERS, prompting former director of the FDA David Kessler to confess that *"...only 10% of vaccine injuries are ever reported."*[330] Lisa Jillani, of People Advocating Vaccine Education, has observed the growing number of children now suffering from 20th century behavioural disorders, and reports:

> *"So the injuries can even conservatively amount to tens of thousands of children, while doctors continue to diagnose and treat mysterious new illnesses and maintain the 'one in a million' adverse reaction myth taught in medical schools."*[331]

Vaccination is very big business. And wherever there is a great deal of money being made by powerful corporations, there will always be difficulties in bringing to light any hidden dangers existing within those industries. Whilst the remit of this book cannot extend to a full examination of the pros and cons of vaccination, readers are encouraged to research these matters for themselves, rather than rely on the much-promoted prevailing wisdom.[332]

Today, The World Health Organization confirms that more than twelve billion injections are performed every year, throughout the

---

[329] Global Vaccine Awareness League. Toxic Chemicals in Vaccines. GVAL homepage.

[330] *Dayton Daily News*, 25th May 1993

[331] **Boykin, Sam** *A Shot in the Dark*, 1998 www.creativeloafing.com

[332] Books available from Think Twice Global Vaccines Institute include **Miller, Neil Z** *Vaccination, Theory vs Reality.* **Coulter, Harris.** *A Shot in the Dark.* **Murphy, Jamie.** *What Every Parent Should Know About Childhood Immunisation.* www.thinktwice.com 'Vaccine Bookshelf'

world, and at least one third are not being carried out in a safe manner. In Africa, more than 80% of disposable syringes are used more than once. And an investigation carried out in Tanzania found syringes showing traces of blood from the previous patient.[333] Says Philippe Krynen:

> *"Since the IMF became responsible for the Health Budget, only vaccinations are free. Not only free, but hammered in... There are no roads, no disinfectant or sterilisation at the dispensary, no refrigerators for the vaccines on the way, but the magic EPI (Extended Program of Immunisation) like Superman is always on time. No matter how skinny, how feverish the buttocks – immunisation will not be missed."[334]*

Western vaccine magic is being performed in Africa on a breathtaking scale. Pressure to commence AIDS vaccine trials in Africa has also been mounting....

WORLD BANK BOOSTS SUPPORT FOR IMMUNIZATION, APRIL 1998 – *"Several key international players, including the World Bank, UNICEF, WHO, the Bill and Melinda Gates Children's Vaccine Program (Gates CVP) and the Rockefeller Foundation are pursuing a number of strategies to strengthen immunization delivery, accelerate vaccine introduction and stimulate new vaccine research and development...."[335]*

And from the leading press agencies...

PROMOTING AN AIDS VACCINE FOR DEVELOPING COUNTRIES, PRETORIA, Reuters 29th July, 1999 – *"Senior policymakers from South Africa and private sector representatives met to discuss speeding up the development of an AIDS vaccine. Representatives from the World Bank..."*

Leaving aside the general dangers of mass vaccination programs, there is surely no point at all in an AIDS vaccine. If vaccination theory is based on giving your immune system a taste of the foreign invader

---

[333] Fiala, Christian, ibid.
[334] *Continuum* Vol 5, No 2, December 1998
[335] World Bank press release. www.worldbank.org

and there is no HIV to begin with, what then is the nature of the chemical solutions being injected into African people? An injection of common sense into Africa's western dominated bureaucratic regime would seem a more appropriate approach. The uncomplicated issues of poverty, malnutrition, contaminated water and poor sanitation would then perhaps have a chance of being addressed.

But already AIDS vaccination has begun in Africa. Uganda is now in the process of having an AIDS vaccination campaign 'fully integrated into its country program'.[336] And now, the plan is to accelerate the vaccination schedule.

JANUARY 2000. **THE EUROPEAN UNION AND WORLD BANK** *have both launched institution-wide HIV/AIDS Vaccine Task teams to consider how each agency could help accelerate development and availability of an AIDS vaccine for developing countries.* [337]

And accelerated no doubt with generous donations such as these:

BILL & MELINDA GATES FOUNDATION ANNOUNCES $750 MILLION GIFT TO SPEED DELIVERY OF LIFE-SAVING VACCINES, 23TH NOVEMBER 1999, SEATTLE, WASHINGTON - *The Bill & Melinda Gates Foundation announced today a gift of $750 million over five years to help ensure that children in developing countries are immunized against major killer diseases in the new millennium. The fund will work closely with a partnership of international development and finance organizations, philanthropic groups, the pharmaceutical industry and others.*

BILL AND MELINDA GATES MAKE US $25 MILLION GRANT TO IAVA, THE INTERNATIONAL AIDS VACCINE INITIATIVE, 5TH JUNE 1999 - *"Bill and Melinda Gates' historic act of generosity will allow us to significantly accelerate the scientific effort," said Seth Berkley, MD., IAVI's president,. "With 16,000 new HIV infections a day, we have no time to spare." Wayne Koff, PhD., IAVI's Vice President*

---

[336] "AIDS Vaccine Being Tested in Africa for First Time," Associated Press, 9th February 1999
"The National Institutes of Health says the first test of a human AIDS vaccine in Africa has begun in Uganda…. AIDS has devastated Africa. In Uganda alone, it has killed nearly a half-million people and left 1 million children orphaned…." etc. etc.
[337] UNAIDS press release

for research and development, said "We are canvassing the globe for the best scientific opportunities." James D. Wolfensohn, President of the World Bank, said: "I am delighted the Gates Foundation has stepped in so generously."

UNFPA TODAY HAILED MICROSOFT CHAIRMAN BILL GATES AND HIS WIFE MELINDA FOR THEIR $2.2 BILLION DONATION TO A FAMILY FOUNDATION, THE HAGUE, 11TH FEBRUARY 1999 - *"News of the extraordinary donation has electrified the Hague Forum," says Nafis Sadik, UNFPA Executive Director. "Bill and Melinda have once again demonstrated their compassion for the world's poor." UNFPA assists developing countries to improve reproductive health services," etc. etc.*

While the full 'Gates interests' portfolio is unknown, Gates and Rhone Poulenc Rorer Inc., one of the planet's largest vaccine manufacturers, are reported to have direct interests in Chiro-Science (formerly Darwin Molecular), perhaps now the largest genome company in the world.[338] In basic terms, the cocooned world of genomics could be described as:

> *"...a number of incredibly rich people who have achieved almost everything material in life, who now wish to fund research into understanding the fundamental building blocks of life itself, the mapping of the human genome. Involved in this 'mapping' project are geneticists and researchers who intermittently construct various hexagonal and helical shaped theoretical models. These models or 'blueprints' are then converted into computer graphics and underscored with largely indecipherable but official-sounding and highly convincing scientific narrative. The end product is then given the Hollywood polish, heralded as 'a genetic breakthrough' and beamed out to millions of viewers across the globe, the relative worth of said breakthroughs going largely unquestioned."* [339]

---

[338] Leading Edge International Research Group. *Top Human Genome and Pharmaceutical Industries*, 1998

[339] Advocates of the 'golden future' genome program insist that the research could lead to cures for disease, and that familial traits and/or hereditary human characteristics perceived as weaknesses could be 'bred out'. Breeding out human defects however raises a wide range of ethical questions. A report in the *Washington Times* described the

Whilst the pursuit of knowledge is no bad thing, James Le Fanu, author of *The Rise and Fall of Modern Medicine*, is not impressed with the god-like status bestowed upon those who are constructing the latest genetic theory:

"By all accounts, 1st December was a momentous day in the history of science, with the publication in the journal 'Nature' of the first chapter of the 'Book of Man', snappily titled 'The DNA Sequence of Human Chromosome 22.' It is not however an easy read, its alphabet restricted to only four letters: a typical line reading TTTGAGCTGATTAGCC plus 35 million more of these same letters in the first chapter...

The information that is locked away in each and every cell is of such inscrutable complexity as to defy imagination... This is just one illustration of a recurring feature in genetic research – the yawning gap between the key to a golden future and the reality that in practical terms its benefits are scarcely detectable. It would be to overestimate considerably the collective intelligence of scientists to suggest they have even the vaguest idea of how this information begins to translate into "who we are". Geneticists must insist that what they are doing is important to guarantee the continuous flow of research funds. They endorse the image of the 'blueprint' because their claim to holding the key to deciphering this blueprint elevates their role in society to that of the shaman – the possessor of arcane knowledge that no-one else can understand. The reality is more prosaic. 'The DNA Sequence of Human Chromosome 22' is an extremely tedious document whose claims to profundity are unwarranted."[340]

Science correspondent for *The New Statesman*, Ziauddin Sardar has this to say:

---

case of an expectant couple who requested a diagnostic test from their Health Maintenance Organization to determine if their child would have a genetic abnormality. According to the report, they were told by officials that if they had the test done and a foetal defect was detected, they would be *obligated* to opt for abortion. If they refused, continued the report, *"...not only would the HMO not pay for the test or provide healthcare for the child, it would also cap the benefits for their already existing child."* Baobab Press Vol 4, No 5, 1995.

[340] **Le Fanu, James** "Stop all This Fuss About Our Genes," *New Statesman*, 13th December 1999

"Stephen Hawking has announced that we are ready to peep "into the mind of God". The Nobel prize-winning physicist Leon Lederman tells us that we are very close to discovering the ultimate elementary particle - "the God particle" – which orchestrates the cosmic symphony. This discovery will reduce the laws of physics to a single equation that could be printed on a T-shirt. Soon the human genome will be number crunched, and from conception to death, the biochemistry of everything we are will be stored in the computer. We are thus very near to a grand synthesis, a Theory of Everything.... This triumphalist picture reveals more about our ignorance than what we have learnt." [341]

Highlighting the lucrative nature of the booming gene therapy business, a recent article in the UK *Guardian* newspaper reported a 25% increase in the share value of Human Genome Sciences, a market leader in genetic research, after they had announced the 'discovery' of CCR5, the gene which supposedly acts as the docking point for HIV.

"Drug companies including Schering-Plough, Japanese firm Takeda and Britain's SmithKline Beecham have expressed interest in the gene, which could be crucial in the search for a cure to AIDS." [342]

Credence Publications contacted Human Genome Sciences to ask why the drawings of CCR5 had been misleadingly described as photographs in many of the press releases. Steve Ruben, head of research at HGS, candidly stated, *"There is nothing as representative as an actual photograph of CCR5. We've got it in a test-tube, but we can't look at it. This is molecular level science."* [343] Another virtual artefact from the world of gene therapy:

'The lucrative gene that cannot be seen...? Let us infer with fluorescent green.'

To HGS and its many shareholders of course, the existence of CCR5 is beyond dispute.

---

[341] **Sardar, Ziauddin** "All That We Don't Know," *New Statesman*, 6th March 2000

[342] UK *Guardian*, 17th February 2000

[343] Steven Ruben in conversation with Steven Ransom 16th March 2000

It is previous statements such as Koff's *"We are canvassing the globe for the best scientific opportunities"* that give Geshekter and others their 'human guinea-pig' concerns. José Esparza, William L Heyward and Saladin Osmanov are the authors of a WHO report on large-scale human testing of vaccines in Africa. Disarmingly entitled 'Phase III' trials, the authors note:

> *"Phase III trials will require extensive international collaboration and co-ordination, and it is likely that developing countries will play a major role in these trials. This is appropriate since some of the highest HIV incidence rates are found in developing countries..."* [344]

And another gift from Mr and Mrs Gates:

> **New York,** *4th April 2000* - **UN Population Fund Hails Gates Foundation's $57 Million Grant to Protect African Youth against HIV/AIDS** - Initiative Targets Botswana, Ghana, Tanzania and Uganda; Largest Private Donation Ever for HIV/AIDS Prevention Among Youth. *"This grant is a vital complement to the Bill & Melinda Gates Foundation's other assistance in the area of disease prevention, including its support for the development of an AIDS vaccine,"* stated Dr Nafis Sadik. *"<u>The funds will allow us to apply locally tested methods</u> for protecting young people against AIDS on a national scale. Other countries in the region will also be able to learn from these examples."* [345] (emphasis ours)

And 'the major role' these developing countries will play? Their inhabitants will innocently bare their upper arm, trusting that what is being locally tested and injected into their bloodstream is being done so for their own well-being and best interests. The large number of pharmaceutical industries wishing to conduct and monitor the effects of unproven vaccines will find in Africa and other 'far-away' regions ideal laboratory conditions. [346] So too will those organisations intent on 'mapping' the human genome.

---

[344] www.who.ch/lowband/document/vaccines/aids/8

[345] UNFPA press release, www.unfpa.org

[346] **The Associated Press; Thursday, 27th February, 1997.** Three South African researchers said they intend to continue their work despite criticism for violating accepted procedures in testing their experimental AIDS drug Virodene. The panel, the Medicines Control Council, accused the researchers of exposing AIDS patients to a toxic industrial

But dangerous vaccine and gene tampering programs are just the tip of the iceberg. AZT and its derivatives are also set for African shores. Entitled "Securing the Future", the following press release details Bristol-Myers Squibb's entry into the African arena.

Our Commitment. The Bristol-Myers Squibb Foundation will pledge US$100 million over the next five years to help South Africa, Botswana, Namibia, Lesotho and Swaziland find sustainable solutions for women, children and communities suffering from the HIV/AIDS epidemic in their countries. Our commitment to the AIDS battle has taken many forms over the years, always guided by the company's mission to extend and enhance human life. In 1991, we developed Videx, also known as ddI. In 1994, Zerit became the fourth anti-retroviral to be approved by the FDA. Zerit and Videx, along with other exciting classes of drugs including protease inhibitors, have dramatically slowed the progression of the disease. [347]

Since its inception in 1948, the World Health Organization has been responsible for setting the standards in development, manufacture, distribution and administration of essentially all pharmaceuticals used throughout the world. WHO has also been responsible for setting all the major research agendas, and is intimately involved in determining which drugs should be made or remain illegal.[348] And from that date, WHO has enjoyed absolute freedom to roam the globe with its programs. WHO is fully aware of the impurities in its vaccines, and it is fully aware of extreme side-effects produced by AZT and Bristol-Myers Squibb's 'exciting' ddI.[349] With full knowledge of the enormous destruction these drugs and vaccines mete out to their

---

solvent. It also said the researchers failed to obtain required permission from medical authorities to conduct experiments on humans. According to the report, the amount of toxic solvent in the drug used in the human trials was well above environmental exposure limits. It said also that the researchers bypassed all conventional funding and controlling bodies that normally scrutinise such applications.

[347] Bristol-Myers Squibb press release, 6th May 1999

[348] DOD Appropriations. Part 5. *R&D Test & Evaluation. US Army Printing Office,* Washington DC, 1969

[349] *"During testing, ddI was found capable of destroying nerves throughout the body and causing fatal damage to the pancreas, something not even AZT was reported to do. Doctors began experimenting with ddI, giving it to patients who were unable to tolerate AZT. Hundreds of patients inexplicably died during these unofficial trials."* (See section entitled *The AIDS Pharmacy*)

recipients, all treatment programs are nevertheless being fully implemented.[350]

The Durban 2000 AIDS conference, held on July 9-14th 2000, has the funding of fifteen sponsors, eleven of whom are pharmaceutical industries and/or organisations who have a direct interest in population control. That the Ford Foundation is one of the sponsors of Durban 2000 will come as little surprise to readers *au fait* with the population control 'league of friends'. They are billed on their web-site as *'providing grants and loans to projects that strengthen democratic values, reduce poverty and injustice, promote international co-operation, and advance human achievement.'* Whilst The Ford Foundation funds a number of worthwhile projects across the globe, it also funds various 'reproductive health' programs that do not best serve the interests of the recipient.[351] Also, the Ford Foundation's longstanding links with the Rockefeller Institute, coupled with its own history of CIA collaboration in Africa in the early 1970s, makes the purpose of the corporation's attendance at the Durban convention highly questionable.[352]

Given the source of sponsorship monies, what opportunities will there be at Durban 2000 to discuss the ethics of widespread untested vaccinations on men, women and children? Who will be there to inform the shareholders that Lucy, Deus, Julia, Seledina, Bernadetta and many others have all responded excellently to Philippe Krynen's 'food/water/education' therapy and that Lucy, written off for dead seven years ago, is now the proud mother of a healthy and beautiful four-year-old son?

---

[350] Project AIDS International's Fraud Investigation Team submitted a dossier to the United Nations Human Rights Commission in March 1993, detailing the deadly effects of AZT, the fraudulence of the HIV=AIDS hypothesis and the bogus nature of the 'AIDS test'. It sought especially to draw the Commission's attention to the routine practice of treating 'HIV positive' infants with known deadly poisons. Their brief was ignored.

[351] Kasun, J, ibid. Includes further detail on Ford Foundation population control spending.

[352] **Williams, MJ** US Department of State Bulletin, November 1973. Covert action in Sub-Saharan Africa. Operation PUSH. *People to Save Humanity*, comprising WHO, World Bank, Rockefeller Foundation, Ford Foundation, CDC, USAID and AFRICARE. Aims: Under the guise of humanitarian aid, covertly to install US intelligence agents in certain African countries, destabilise anti-US leaderships, and install US policy sympathisers.

Who will draw attention to the growing clinical evidence that conventional AIDS pharmaceuticals are highly carcinogenic, and that had Lucy been treated with these drugs, both she and her child might not be with us today? Who will catalogue the internal damage and deformities that AIDS drugs mete out to the recipient and especially to the unborn child? Who will openly denounce Durban 2000's all-consuming profit-driven Malthusian mentality? Who in actual fact will stand up and declare this whole gathering despicable?

WILLARD: I was going to the worst place in the world, and I didn't even know it yet. Kurtz was close. Real close. So close you could feel him.

CHIEF: My orders are, I'm not supposed to know where I'm taking this boat, so I don't.

WILLARD: We're going up-river about 75 klicks above the Do Lung bridge.

CHIEF: That's Cambodia, Captain.

WILLARD: That's classified.

THE POLITICS OF AIDS

confronting Kurtz

And just as Captain Willard nears his mission's end, his only co-ordinates 'somewhere up river', like him we are now deep into enemy territory. We are in a highly restricted zone. Looking for an exit - any exit. The whole mind focused on an exit from the enormities of what is being discussed in these pages; the lies about AIDS and AIDS 'medicines'; the lies about AIDS in Africa and the Third World; and the lies about the supposed 'hopelessness' of the African situation.

And then...an exit appears. A huge sigh of relief...*"OF COURSE! If thousands upon thousands of people in countries the world over were being routinely exposed to callous pharmaceutical experiments, and if hundreds of thousands were dying as a direct result of these highly toxic chemicals, or as an indirect result of basic human needs purposely not being met.... if anything as monstrous as this were going on in our world, then surely..... IT WOULD BE IN THE PAPERS! "*

Unfortunately that exit does not provide the necessary means of escape. Before a packed New York Press Club, John Swinton, the former chief of staff at The *New York Times* approached the podium to address his colleagues. Known as 'The Dean of His Profession', the legendary newspaperman proceeded to deliver a monumentally important statement on the notion of an independent press.

"There is no such thing, at this date in the world's history, in America, as an independent press. You know it and I know it. There is not one of you who dares to write your honest opinions, and if you did, you know beforehand that it would never appear in print. I am paid weekly for keeping my honest opinion out of the paper I am connected with. Others of you are paid similar salaries for similar things, and any of you who would be so foolish as to write honest opinions would be out on the street looking for another job. If I allowed my honest opinion to appear in one issue of my paper, before twenty-four hours my occupation would be gone. You know it and I know it, and what folly is this - toasting an independent press? We are the tools and vassals of rich men behind the scenes. We are the

jumping jacks, they pull the strings and we dance. Our talents, our possibilities and our lives are all the property of other men. We are intellectual prostitutes." [353]

The recent multi-billion-dollar merger between Time Inc. and AOL makes this conglomerate now the most powerful information disseminator in the world. Independently fostering enormous influence before the merger, the two groups combined will now exert even more influence in the global arena of film, TV, Internet, advertising and public information services. In her recent article on the AOL/Time merger entitled "Dangerous Liaisons", Wendy Grossman, writing for *Intellectual Capital*, stated:

"What disturbs me about these scenarios is the concentration of media into too few, extremely powerful hands. The danger is not so much that all media will express the same opinions; people are quite capable of reading an opinion and disagreeing with it. The danger is that certain kinds of stories simply will not get covered - and despite the Internet's capacity for lengthy, detailed exposes of all types, most people derive their sense of what today's important issues are from the major media." [354]

Health writer Martin Walker has this to say on the influential medium of television news:

"Like almost everything else on television, news programmes leave us feeling bereft of control over our own lives. They report with certainty what has happened through the eyes and mouths of the most powerful groups in society. Except for some inevitable exceptions, the news is rarely news, but a presentation of the virtual consensus decreed by the most powerful. The news is brought to us like a meal in a restaurant; we question the way it is served only when we find the content distasteful.... We the public, in all our diversity, have struck a contract with our governors: realising that life is short, we refrain from criticising or disturbing consensus as long as it does not disturb us, and that we are left alone to be

---

[353] Campaign Against Fraudulent Medical Research, 'Vaccinations,' Winter newsletter, 1995. www.pnc.com

[354] **Grossman, Wendy** "Dangerous Liaisons", *Intellectual Capital,* 20th January 2000

ourselves."[355]

On the subject of our news being organised for us by powerful groups, Richard M Cohen, senior producer of CBS Political News, stated:

> *"We are going to impose our agenda on the coverage, by dealing with the issues and subjects that we choose to deal with."* [356]

And Richard Salent, former president of CBS, had this to say:

> *"Our job is to give not what they want, but what we decide."* [357]

So who are the rich men, the decision-makers behind the scenes at Time Warner/AOL?

'Time-Warner Inc' is a corporate member of the Council on Foreign Relations or CFR. Time's president Richard D Parsons and its editor-in-chief Norman Pearlstine are longstanding CFR members. Formed in 1921, CFR membership requires wealth, influence and a desire to shape international policy. In his biography of CFR member Henry Kissinger, Walter Isaacson describes this élitist group as:

> *"...a private organisation that serves as a discussion club for close to three thousand well-connected aficionados of foreign affairs. Beneath chandeliers and stately portraits in its Park Avenue mansion, members attend lectures, dinners and round-table seminars featuring top officials and visiting world leaders."* [358]

Wining and dining at these CFR round-table discussions are the people at the top of every influential organisation on our planet, including the media. We must realise that when it comes to the stories that matter, our 'news' is invariably given to us in accordance with the directives of Swinton's 'rich men behind the scenes'.

---

[355] **Walker, Martin** "Totalitarian Science and Media Politics," *Continuum*, Vol 5, No 5, January 1999

[356] Campaign Against Fraudulent Medical Research, ibid.

[357] CAMFR, Ibid.

[358] **Isaacson, Walter** *Kissinger, A Biography*, Simon & Schuster, 1992

In keeping with NSSM 200, a CFR policy objective is substantial world-wide depopulation.[359] This policy, which naturally has received no public airtime whatsoever, is largely funded by the Rockefeller Foundation and the Merck Fund, both financially linked to Merck Pharmaceuticals, the world's largest vaccine manufacturer.[360] *Parenting Magazine*, a subsidiary of Time Inc., contained a feature on vaccines and vaccination in its March 1999 issue, which included glowing passages such as *"...saving countless children from death and permanent disability..."* The article did not however include the French government's recent moratorium on childhood hepatitis B vaccinations as a result of links to neurological disorders including multiple sclerosis; neither did it include the current civil actions facing Merck and other manufacturers with regard to tainted oral polio vaccines, now being linked to certain forms of human cancer.[361]

What solace then is gained from this latest Norman Pearlstine announcement, reassuring the planet of TIME/TIME WARNER/TIME Inc./AOL/CNN/TNT/TURNER Inc. global commitment to maintaining editorial values?

"...We should be honest in our judgments and truthful in our reporting. We've had a lot of practice applying this principle over the past 10 years.... A respect for journalistic independence has been part of our company's values for so long that it's encoded in our DNA... As we cover the corporate complexities that swirl around us, let us assure you that we - as individual journalists and critics with pride in what we do - will continue to be loyal to and represent the interests of our most important constituency, our readers. [362]

The above statement is of course devoid of anything meaningful. In reality, Time Inc. and its massive network of media subsidiaries print

---

[359] Horowitz, Leonard. *Emerging Viruses...* ibid.
[360] Merck is over 400 years old, achieving $10.96 billion per year in sales today. It has numerous links with IG Farben and was instrumental in producing chemicals and pharmaceuticals in Germany during the power of the Third Reich. (Leading Edge Research Org. www.trufax.org)
[361] **Horowitz, Leonard** *Parenting with Deadly Timely Propaganda*, Atlantean Press. Summer 1999
[362] *Time*, 24th January 2000

and screen only what Time Inc. and its subsidiaries want us to know. Billionaire media mogul Ted Turner of CNN, TNT and other cable networks fame, and now vice-chairman at Time Warner recently stated:

> *"We are the ones who determine what people's attitudes are. It's in our hands."* [363]

And here is a glimpse into the mind and philosophy of Turner, the man who dictates so much of the globe's media content; the man who describes his management style as *"lead, follow or get out of the way."* [364]

CNN'S TURNER CALLS FOR ONE CHILD PER FAMILY, June Preston. Reuters. 11th September 1998 - ATLANTA: *"Ted Turner called for a world-wide one-baby-per-family policy and said of his five children, "If I was doing it over again I wouldn't have done it, but I can't shoot them now that they're here." Turner said he considers it his personal responsibility to worry about overpopulation. "I've got to worry about the totality of the planet…. They think we can just let Africa and Central and South America and parts of Asia stew in their own juices. I don't agree," he said. "A lot of people will stay in India and Bangladesh and Africa and El Salvador and starve. But a lot of them won't. They're going to come where the prosperity is, and they know where the prosperity is, baby! We should work to try to convince everybody that they should have one child like China has. People who abhor the China one-child policy are dumb-dumbs."*

And Turner's worry about overpopulation and care for the planet is further reflected in this generous donation to UNFPA:

TED TURNER'S UN FOUNDATION GIVES UNFPA $4.3 MILLION TO ADOLESCENT SEXUAL HEALTH - *Executive Director Dr Nafis Sadik today welcomed the announcement by the United Nations Foundation, directed by Ted Turner: "The Foundation's funding of our programs demonstrates an extraordinary commitment.*

---

[363] Taken from a speech given to broadcasters and presenters. www.holysmoke.org/turner
[364] www.cyber-nation.com "Quotes to Inspire", January 2000

We appreciate the speed and determination with which the United Nations Foundation has acted...." [365]

On Turner's desire to reduce the planet's population to no more than 350 million, the following question was posed by one member of the population, less favourably disposed to Turner's viewpoint: *"How will this be achieved? Will Turner and wife lead the way?"* [366]

It is inarguable that population control is being forcefully implemented by the most powerful influences on the planet. And there are a number of reasons why western powers would want to 'thin out' Africa in particular, reasons succinctly expressed in African publication *The Baobab Press.*

"The West has a great deal at stake in Africa - both because the continent is a source of minerals critical to military-industrial uses, and because of its strategic location. The emergence of populous, powerful African nations, capable of developing their own trade systems and able effectively to bargain for fair trade, would threaten the economic interests of Western powers. Thus the presence of strong, nationalist leadership in any African nation - even a relatively small one - would give rise to heightened aspirations on the part of others on the continent. The ultimate result, of course, would be a monumental increase in Third-World liberation movements that would place grave limits on US imperialism and perhaps even cause the permanent decline of the Western hegemony." [367]

And the following text details Africa's incredible wealth of natural resources:

"In terms of resources, Africa has 90% of the world's cobalt, 80% of the world's chrome, 50% of the world's gold, the same in platinum and the majority of the world's industrial diamonds: the bulk of the world's gems, including diamonds, sapphires, topaz, malachite, opal, rubies, tanzanite, substantial amounts of manganese, iron ore, copper, vanadium, bauxite,

[365] *Independent Daily News*, 28th September, 1998

[366] **Muelhenbury, Bill** www.thewinds.org

[367] *Baobab Press*, Vol 2, No 6, 1992

lead and zinc. The biggest beneficiary of all this mineral wealth is the West and its industries. And the West is the main manager of this wealth."[368]

And a study written after the 1974 world population conference in Bucharest (not declassified until 1990) is considered the primary theoretical document on US demographic intervention overseas. It advises that population control is in the political and economic interests of the United States because large populations in developing countries could jeopardise American foreign investments, provoke rebellions, and threaten access to important raw minerals and other resources. It recommends that several strategically important countries be targeted for massive efforts to reduce birth-rates. [369]

Western agitators who have probably had the most influence in shaping not only Africa's population control policies, but also the gross inequality of Western/African business opportunities are the Rockefellers.

In all of world history, it would be difficult to link as much mischief to any one name as can be traced to the Rockefeller family over the past century. [370]

So begins one account of the Rockefellers, one of so many detailing a dynasty of absolute power sliding rapidly towards absolute corruption. It was John Davison Rockefeller who built the family fortune with the Standard Oil Company he founded in 1870 at the age of 31. By the mid 1880s, John D Rockefeller had become a millionaire many times over. He had also become probably the most hated man in America, if not the world. Several state attorneys tried in vain to have him jailed for his corrupt business dealings. The Rockefeller fortune was amassed by extortion tactics, by implementing totally ruthless business practices to eliminate competition and employing some of the most oppressive labour practices imaginable.[371] Rockefeller labourers worked scandalously long hours under extraordinarily risky conditions, receiving only substandard family housing and food and no

---

[368] **Mazrui, Aia** *The Africans*, BBC publications, 1986
[369] www.africa2000.com
[370] *Baobab Press,* Vol 4, No 13, 1994
[371] **Kutz, Myer** *Rockefeller Power*, Pinnacle Books, 1974

expendable wages. Rockefeller, a staunch 'survival of the fittest' evolutionist, said of his business practices:

"This is not an evil tendency in business. It is merely the workings out of a law of nature and a law of God." [372]

The Rockefellers knew well the science of creating a need and then filling it to massive profit. New substances began to be licensed as 'drugs' and approved by the Rockefeller-sponsored American Medical Association and Food & Drug Administration with doctors and specialists trained in their dispensation and use through Rockefeller-financed institutions. Author G Edward Griffin reports:

"Abraham Flexner, author of the famous Flexner Report of 1910, led the crusade for upgrading the medical schools of America, all the while he was in the employ of Andrew Carnegie and John D Rockefeller who had set up gigantic tax-exempt foundations for that purpose. The end result was that all medical schools became heavily oriented towards drugs and drug research, for it was through the increased sale of drugs that the donors realized a profit on their donations.

A brief backward glance at the total landscape will help us appreciate more fully the present extent of [pharmaceutical] cartel influence, not only in the FDA (United States Food & Drug Administration) but at all levels of the federal government. The list of men who are or were in key positions within the Rockefeller group reads like a 'Who's Who' in government." [373]

Rockefeller money almost single-handedly transformed medicine from the old-fashioned barber's shop practices into the modern, well-organised allopathic[374] industry we recognise today. JD's organisational abilities were legendary in the projects to which he turned his hand and impressive fortune. Ironically JD's father William had peddled quack remedies off the back of his wagon in the mid-1800s, the family firm making outrageous profits palming off bottled petroleum called 'Nujol' as a supposed cure for cancer and later

---

[372] **Ghent, William** *Our Benevolent Feudalism*, MacMillan Press, 1902
[373] **Griffin, G Edward** *World Without Cancer*, American Media, 1996
[374] **allopathy** – orthodox medical practice, treatment of diseases by drugs.

constipation.[375] But William's son JD was to have altogether more grandiose designs. Largely through JD's efforts, doctors underwent the metamorphosis from poorly paid wagon-quacks to sophisticated, well-educated and highly paid luminaries, trained in the new centres funded and built by Rockefeller and billionaire Andrew Carnegie. Foundations were formed; chemical research financed. The 20th century began with obvious medical promise of great deeds to come.

In 1913, the Rockefeller Foundation was launched, describing its goal as the advancement of *"...the civilization of the peoples of the United States and its territories and possessions and of foreign lands..."* In 1928 the Drug Trust was formed by an alliance of the Rockefeller Empire and the German chemical company, IG Farbenindustrie or IG Farben. Drug profits from that time onwards rose exponentially and by 1948, drugs had become a $10 billion a year industry.[376]

IG Farben's unsavoury past is highlighted by the fact that during the Second World War it built and operated a massive rubber and chemical plant at Auschwitz using slave labour. Approximately 300,000 concentration camp workers passed through the IG Farben facility at Auschwitz, and at least 25,000 of them were worked to death. Farben eventually built its own corporate concentration camp at the site to eliminate the need to march prisoners several miles to and from the Buna plant every day, as had been the practice. Known as Monowitz, it had a sign over the gate which read 'Arbeit Macht Frei' or 'work makes one free'. Starvation was a permanent guest at Auschwitz. After three months, the workers were either dead or so unfit for work that they were marked for release to the gas chambers at Birkenau.

Others were brutally killed in IG Farben's drug testing programs.[377] Degesch, a subsidiary of Farben, was responsible for the manufacture of the notorious death camp gas Zyklon B.[378] Twelve of IG Farben's

---

[375] Kutz, Myer, ibid.

[376] Ghent, William, *Our Benevolent Feudalism*, ibid.

[377] **Braithwaite, John** *Corporate Crime in the Pharmaceutical Industry,* Routledge, 1984

[378] **Blumen, Jonathan** *The Auschwitz Alphabet,* [www.spectacle.org in memory of Primo Levi].

top executives were sentenced to terms of imprisonment for slavery and mistreatment offences at the Nuremberg war crime trials.[379]

Rockefeller influence and money accrued from partnerships such as these were to become the foundation stone for virtually every medical college in the US from 1945 onwards. Morris Bealle writes:

"The Rockefeller Foundation 1948 Annual Report itemizes the gifts it has made to colleges and public agencies in the past 44 years, and they total somewhat over half a billion dollars. These colleges, of course, teach their students all the drug lore the Rockefeller pharmaceutical houses want to be taught. Otherwise there would be no more gifts, just as there are no gifts to any of the 30-odd drugless colleges in the United States."[380]

By the early 1950s, the Rockefeller multi-billion dollar financial empire extended over much of the world, and had been a major funder of such influential associations as the Council on Foreign Relations, the Center for Strategic and International Studies and the Overseas Development Council. In 1952, John D Rockefeller III, Nelson's older brother, established the New York-based Population Council and a pattern of influence soon emerged. Two years after the Population Council was inaugurated, the China Family Planning Association was formed.

By the mid 1960s, such 'planned parenthood' societies had been set up in almost every developing country, leading later to organisations such as the International Planned Parenthood Federation, now a powerful voice in the US for all methods of birth control.[381] In 1968, a Presidential Committee on Population and Family Planning was organised. Under the leadership of John D Rockefeller III, the panel recommended that foreign population programs be

---

[379] Borkin, Joseph, ibid.

[380] Bealle, Morris, ibid.

[381] Not unsurprisingly, in a slick marketing move by UNFPA and IPPF, Geri Halliwell of Spice Girls fame has recently been inaugurated into the fold as the 'acceptable face' of population control. Ignorant or otherwise of the end result of her PR, Ginger Spice is now helping to promote UNFPA's sex education, abortion and sterilisation programs across the globe (www.altavista.com image search on UNFPA).

expanded *"...as rapidly as funds can be properly allocated by the US."*[382]

It was Rockefeller money that aided the meteoric rise of Henry Kissinger, the man responsible not only for NSSM 200, but also for the 1970 Department of Defense Appropriations request: HB 15090. In 1969, Kissinger demanded a report on US biological weapons capabilities. This in turn prompted a DOD request to Congress for ten million dollars to update the US bio-weapons arsenal. This huge sum of money was apparently to be used for the express purpose of developing artificial viruses with the capacity to attack the human immune system. The precise terminology of 'HB 15090 pt. 5' memorandum was that the funds be used to develop *"...an agent refractory to the immunological and therapeutic processes upon which we depend to maintain our relative freedom from infectious disease."*[383]

The money was granted, and contracts were awarded to major defence contractors across the US, particularly Litton Bionetics, a subsidiary of Litton Systems and Litton Industries, one of the most frequently contracted biological warfare companies in the US at that time.[384] Litton Bionetics was Robert Gallo's employer throughout his virus research years in Maryland. Alongside research into viruses that might catastrophically disrupt the human immune system, there is ample evidence that Gallo was one of a number of virologists, including Peter Duesberg, working specifically on cancer viruses. Duesberg's work in particular was to study *"...the mechanism by which tumour viruses might bring about malignant changes in humans."*[385]

Rockefeller money continues to be a major force in public and private 'security' operations in the US, and despite government assurance to the contrary, Western biological weapons research continues to this day, and on a huge scale. Millions of Rockefeller dollars are also spent each year for research and policy studies related to US political and economic interests abroad. In recent years,

---

[382] "The Pharmaceutical Drugs Racket," www.trufax.org 2000

[383] DOD Appropriations for 1970. US government Printing Office, Washington DC

[384] Special Virus Cancer Program. Progress report 8 and 9, Viral Oncology, US Govt. Printing Office, p 233, 1971

[385] Special Virus Cancer Program, ibid.

Rockefeller grants have significantly funded African enterprises, including thousands of dollars for population 'education' in Benin, Nigeria, Tanzania and the Sahel. A UN directory of population activities lists still more operations, the same type attributed to the Population Council.[386]

If confirmation was needed that JD Rockefeller was the founding father of 20th century population control policy, that confirmation is surely represented in this single sentence, delivered by Rockefeller himself to a group of Sunday school children, his country's flowering youth:

"The 'American Beauty' Rose can be produced only by sacrificing the buds that grow up around it." [387]

It was the general malevolence of Rockefeller influence that prompted one critic to comment:

"Those who fornicated with the devil and deceived all the kings and the wealthiest men of all the nations are the Rockefellers." [388]

In her paper "AIDS in Africa?" Dr Eleni Papadopulos-Eleopulos includes the following observation:

"The uppermost question in the minds of intelligent Africans and Europeans is this: Why do the world's media appear to have conspired with some scientists to become so gratuitously extravagant with the truth?" [389]

The answer very simply is population control. Today, at the start of the new millennium, under the finest crystal chandeliers, population control is just one of a number of élitist ideologies being planned for world-wide implementation. To safeguard the power and influence of western political supremacy, officials from the World Bank, IMF, Trilateral Commission, CFR, WHO, USAID, UNAIDS, UNICEF[390],

---

[386] US National Archives, the Library of Congress, published resources of the United Nations Population Fund and the US Agency for International Development.

[387] Kutz, Myer. Ibid. *"Rockefeller power is real, far-reaching and much of it hidden from view. A provocative probe into the origins, extent and misuse of Rockefeller power."*

[388] *Bio Warfare, Who or What is the Threat?* www.thewinds.org

[389] **Papadopulos-Eleopulos, Eleni** *AIDS in Africa?* Rethinking AIDS, 2000

[390] *"Public records reveal United Nation's Children's Fund works closely with WHO, UNDP,*

CNN, Time Inc., Rothschilds, Bilderberg Group,[391] Rockefeller/Ford/Gates Foundation, and related media consortia are meeting to decide on their exact approach to 'solving' certain presentation problems pertaining to the 'Third World and Sub-Saharan AIDS' campaign.

As per the Dewar protocols, the entire operation will be well planned and centrally co-ordinated, so as to be consistent and sustained. Officials will be thoroughly familiar with their audience, and able to gauge its probable reaction to the campaign. They will have prepared a great deal of false information which will appear absolutely logical, seeming neither out of harmony with current events nor in any way suspicious. They will fully utilise the wide variety of media resources at their disposal to disseminate this false information. They will pay particular attention to the timing which is critical, people generally noticing marked events, but not gradual change. And they will endeavour to keep this whole operation and its purpose concealed from the enemy. Consequently, the following items from CNN, Time, SKY, Reuters etc., regarding the latest developments in the African AIDS 'crisis', tell us only what 'the rich men behind the scenes' want us to know.

IN AFRICA, AIDS IS NOW A SECURITY PROBLEM, TIME, JANUARY 2000 – *"The UN Security Council turns its attention to the*

UNFPA and other organisations promoting population control programs world-wide, including China, Angola, Philippines, Vietnam, Guinea Bissau, Nigeria and Tanzania. UNICEF director James Grant called for the US government to give more money to UNFPA '...as a means of giving an important boost to family planning.'" CRI Information pack, *Behind the Mask of UNICEF.* www.pop.org Special Publications

[391] The Bilderberg meetings were founded by HRH Prince Bernhard of the Netherlands, a former SS officer and employee of IG Farben. The group was named after the Bilderberg Hotel in Oosterbeck, Holland, where the first meeting took place in 1954. Comprising international financiers, politicians, media and other key global leaders, and by invitation only, the Bilderberg meetings are conducted in the strictest secrecy, at varying world venues, the agendas unpublicised, and the group's existence almost entirely unreported. All attempts by Credence to gain further information on the May 1998 Bilderberg meeting held at the Turnberry Hotel, Scotland, were met with *"No comment."* 1998 Turnberry attendees included Conrad Black, chairman UK *Telegraph Newspapers,* Anatole Kaletsky, associate editor UK *Times,* Christopher Hogg, chairman *Reuters,* Jim Hoagland, associate editor *Washington Post,* David Rockefeller, chairman of *Chase Manhattan Bank,* Henry Kissinger, *Kissinger Associates,* James Wolfensohn, president *World Bank,* Jan Leschly, CEO *SmithKline Beecham Pharmaceuticals.* For an insight into Bilderberg influence over the current British, European and US governments, visit www.watch.pair.com/ discernment.html and related links.

need for funding, education and medicine in African nations devastated by the AIDS epidemic. The debate over the distribution of AIDS drugs will be particularly heated; it's complicated in Africa by the fact that most people are unable to find or pay for the necessary drugs, such as AZT and protease inhibitors. "At this point, pharmaceutical companies are doing everything they can to keep the drugs to themselves," says Dowell... Fierce public sentiment could clear the way for more accessible AIDS therapy in the countries where the need is so great... "Many people feel this is such a monumental problem it surpasses market issues," says Dowell. Stay tuned to see if the UN can convince the drug companies to buy into that distinctly non-capitalist sentiment."

And this from Turner's CNN:

US STEPS UP GLOBAL FIGHT AGAINST AIDS. CNN, 10TH JANUARY 2000 – *"US military to be used in anti-AIDS effort. "The administration is seeking another $50 million for research, purchase and distribution of life-saving vaccines in developing nations," said Gore. The administration's budget request for next year would contain specific funding for the US military to work with the armed forces of other nations to combat AIDS. Gore urged other nations to consider the AIDS epidemic a true threat to peace in Africa and make it a priority on the world's security agenda."*

In complete accord with Colonel Dewar's essentials for the covert approach, public opinion has been expertly influenced in the required direction. We will 'stay tuned' to the heroic entreaties of the UN and will no doubt identify positively with the *"fierce public sentiment."* [392] This combination will then gradually 'convince' the pharmaceutical industries to do the humanitarian thing and let Africa have AZT and its derivatives at below market cost. We will then applaud the generosity of the pharmaceutical industries who will be seen to be bowing to the

---

[392] Carthage, TN NEWS 16th June 1999 **AIDS ACTIVISTS DISRUPT GORE'S PRESIDENTIAL CANDIDACY ANNOUNCEMENT**. *15 protesters blew air horns and chanted "Gore is killing Africans. AIDS drugs now!" calling attention to the pivotal role the Vice President has played in preventing HIV positive South Africans from obtaining the drugs they need to survive. "Al Gore's devout loyalty to the drug industry is literally costing millions of lives," said Emily Winkelstein from AIDS Drugs for Africa, the grass-roots activist group that organized today's event.*

pressure. And now, according to Ted Turner, this whole 'humanitarian aid' operation will be 'reassuringly' overseen by WHO and the full might of the US military.

With NSSM 200 a live agenda, and HB 15090 immune crashing programs being worked on to this day, along with the enormous amounts of money now being invested in gene and vaccine research, the implications for Africa are potentially catastrophic. Who will be able to tell what is being injected into the bloodstream of the African people? How long will it be before we hear CNN telling us *"...despite the best efforts of the US army vaccination program, we are witnessing unprecedented numbers succumbing to the deadly HIV"*. What statutory agencies will be in place to assure us that these widespread deaths are not the by-product of indiscriminate vaccine research? Will the global viewer be able to differentiate between slow death by pharmaceuticals and those suffering from perfectly treatable malnutrition? Who will carry out the post-mortems? Will there even be any post-mortems?

Concerns over drug efficacy and the HIV=AIDS hypothesis has led to recent requests by President Thabo Mbeki of South Africa to include AIDS dissident scientists in the Durban 2000 conference. This request has upset the AIDS establishment, some members even threatening to boycott the event.[393]

Meanwhile, in a cynical move to counter growing world attention to Mbeki's concerns over western policy towards AIDS, the US media announced on 30th April 2000 that President Clinton has formally determined that AIDS is now a national security threat.[394] In an unprecedented move, Task Force meetings involving various government-affiliated health agencies have already taken place in the National Security Agency situation room. Those opposing the consensus view on AIDS – the AIDS dissidents, have been deemed a threat to US national security. The US National Security Agency, acting on a 'report' from the National Intelligence Council, has moved to put the control of AIDS 'health' under military intelligence command (CIA/NSA). As a result we can expect in the very near future that CIA

[393] *Newsweek*, "Flirting with Strange Ideas", 17th April 2000
[394] *Washington Post*, 29th April 2000

action against dissidents will intensify and become a priority, as dissidents by direct implication are a now threat to US national security.

CIA assets in mainstream media will begin a negative propaganda campaign against all sources of true information about AIDS and HIV and a character assassination of Mbeki, through the controlling power's many media sources, is sure to begin. Such a campaign in fact may have already started. In its regular 'winners and losers' column, *Time* magazine has described Thabo Mbeki as a loser - *"ignoring the weight of science by insisting HIV may not cause AIDS."* The winning column opposite features World Bank chief James Wolfensohn, who glowingly *"promises unlimited money to fight AIDS in developing countries."* [395]

The World Bank's web-page commitment is to strive towards 'the eradication of poverty'. [396] The facts indicate that what we are witnessing is an ongoing eradication of population.

James Wolfensohn

> WILLARD: *"Part of me was afraid of what I would find and what I would do when I got to Kurtz. I knew the risks, or imagined I knew. But the thing I felt the most, much stronger than fear, was the desire to confront him… Everything I saw told me that Kurtz has gone insane."*

Who then is Kurtz?

In her book *Positively False*, Joan Shenton recounts the battle she had to get acceptable media and TV coverage for her work on exposing the fraudulence of the AIDS industry. After the screening of *The AIDS Catch*, an exposé on AIDS, the production team soon found itself having to sit before the Broadcasting Complaints Commission for 'misleading' the viewers on a number of accounts, not least the

---

[395] *Time* Magazine, 1st May, 2000. On the same page as the 'Mbeki loser' column, World Trade Organization chief Michael Moore is quoted as saying, *"Blaming the World Bank for poverty is a bit like blaming the Red Cross for starting World Wars 1 and 2."*
[396] www.worldbank.org

hazards of AZT. Despite Joan Shenton's team having in its hands the Wellcome AZT trial results - trials funded and supervised entirely by Wellcome - the Shenton team were judged to have been unfair to Wellcome on three of four counts, the predominant count being the misrepresentation of established views.[397]

Joan Shenton's team was pressing in on the 'restricted area'. It had ventured into Kurtz's territory.

Jeremy Paxman, the bulldog interviewer of the BBC, has written several books. One book in particular demonstrates Paxman's understanding of the 'restricted' areas. Entitled *A Higher Form of Killing*, this book was co-written by Robert Harris and contains a detailed account of the history of biological warfare. It is regarded by many as the definitive 'behind the scenes' guide to the many covert operations carried out by various governments world-wide, and includes details of what is probably the first US biowarfare operation, namely the US government's winter distribution of deliberately infected smallpox blankets across various Indian reservations.[398] Paxman's undoubted intellectual ability, and his track record of tough questioning (winning him 'Interviewer of the Year') made him the ideal candidate in the public's eyes to grill the richest man on the planet, Microsoft multi-billionaire William Gates III.

At the time of writing, Gates does not walk the corridors of 'perceived' power. He walks the corridors of CFR, World Bank, IMF, Rockefeller, Ford, Chase, Time, Turner's CNN and Bilderberg - *real* power. Gates roams freely within the 'restricted' areas. These areas are not unfamiliar to Paxman. So it was with much anticipation that cognisant viewers waited for the much-billed 'Paxman-Gates' showdown.[399]

---

[397] Shenton, Joan. ibid.

[398] Paxman, Jeremy & Robert Harris *A Higher Form of Killing*, Hill and Wang, 1982. Documenting numerous accounts of bio-warfare operations. *"This definitive bio-warfare study stands as a testimony of man's inhumanity to man. Required reading for everyone interested in protecting our planet from this biologic 'higher form of killing.'* **Cantwell, Alan**, *Queer Blood*, Aries Rising Press, 1994. ISBN: 091721126X

[399] BBC2 8:00pm Sunday, 17th October 1999

196

The viewers were treated to nothing further than a pleasant discussion on electrical hobbies, early life, family memories and other non-event questions. Not even the superficially important questions such as software market-share wheeling and dealing were approached with any vigour. Exactly the same thing happened when earlier in the year, Paxman's 'Start the Week' was guested by none other than Henry Kissinger. Admittedly his time on air was short, but yet again we were treated to a meandering discussion about inconsequential matters. Ironically a receiver of several peace awards, Kissinger is a man who also roams freely in the 'restricted' areas, the man who co-ordinated not only NSSM 200, but also HB 15090 and numerous other directives. [400]

Little of this would have been outside the realm of Paxman's understanding. Whilst Paxman is to be congratulated for documenting high level corruption in the biowarfare arms race, Credence Publications attempted to contact Mr Paxman several times, specifically to discuss the possibility of him having been directed by 'rich men behind the scenes', with regard to the Gates and Kissinger interviews. To date there has been no reply from Mr Paxman on these matters. [401]

---

[400] Paxman, Jeremy, ibid. See also **Preston, W** *The Real Treason*, Covert Action Information Bulletin #25 1986. William Preston, Professor of History at John Jay College, New York, and Ellen Ray were chief administrators for the Fund for Open Information and Accountability Inc., and were frequent contributors to the Covert Action Information Bulletin. Kissinger played an important recruitment role in Project 63 – to secure the employment in the US of certain German and Austrian WW2 scientists, specialising in rocketry and biological warfare. By altering, hiding and/or destroying evidence of human atrocities, US officials were able to subvert judicial proceedings and bring some 900 Nazi specialists out of Nazi Germany, (via the 'Rat Line'), men including V1 & V2 rocket scientist Wernher von Braun, Traubb, Klaus Barbie, Josef Mengele, Blome and Schreiber. Chief among the many inhumane experiments carried out at Auschwitz were direct injections into the eyes for eye colour experimentation, removal of limbs, with and without anaesthetic, Mengele's infamous 'twins' experiments and the mass murder in the extermination camps. Stangl, chief of the notorious Treblinka camp, escaped down the 'Rat Line', and later worked in Latin America for Volkswagen, as did Adolf Eichmann for Mercedes Benz. Walter Rauff, the designer of the gas ovens at Auschwitz, later worked for a Latin American subsidiary of IG Farben. **Farago, L** *Aftermath*, New York: Avon, 1975

[401] After asking Mr Paxman repeatedly if he could please reply to our simple question, Credence Publications eventually received an email on 18th February 2000 containing a single word - "No."

Mr Paxman had ample opportunity to confront Kurtz. But a long way up-river, did Jeremy Paxman abandon his audience and climb out of the boat?

Anatole Kaletsky, associate editor of Times Newspapers, is a frequenter of the inner circle of power and has himself attended Bilderberg meetings. Credence wrote to him, asking him why his newspaper never reports on these meetings. After all, in these meetings are gathered the most influential and perhaps even the most newsworthy people on the planet. Kaletsky replied:

> *"There are lots of meetings going on all over the world all the time between all kinds of people. Most of them are of no interest whatsoever to our readers. In any case, what people say to each other in private meetings is up to them."* [402]

A similar reply was received from the corporate relations department at *Telegraph* Newspapers:

> *"In reply to your query regarding our chairman Conrad Black being a member of the Bilderberg group: The meetings are held in complete privacy with no accompanying staff or media present. The sessions are entirely expressions of opinion and have no executive consequences. It would be totally inappropriate for the Telegraph titles to report on these confidential meetings, and would contradict the purpose of the Bilderberg Group, which is to encourage international relations and problem resolution in a completely 'safe' environment away from public scrutiny and the media. It would also violate the undertaking of those who attend to maintain discretion, thus to encourage the frankness and spontaneity of the discussion."* [403]

The information contained in *World Without AIDS* highlights the absolute bankruptcy of the above statements and especially those two lines *"of no interest whatsoever to our readers"* and *"of no executive consequence."* Of course the content of these meetings is of interest to the reader, and of course decisions made at these meetings have immediate and direct executive consequence. Rather it is the utterly unsavoury nature of the Bilderberg agenda which demands discretion

---

[402] Credence correspondence, 31st January 2000
[403] Credence correspondence, 8th February 2000

and *"a completely safe environment away from public scrutiny".* The replies from both Kaletsky and Telegraph Newspapers serve only to reveal the double-standards that prevail in the editorial departments of our revered British newspapers. Their replies also mirror Swinton's definition of the 'fawning, intellectual prostitute, owned and in the pockets of the rich men behind the scenes'.

And now the central question remains: With the truth about AIDS now 'out of the bag', will our newspaper editors demonstrate the necessary will to break the mould? Using the vast media resources at their disposal, will these 'shapers of public attitude' now help firmly to establish the truth about AIDS and HIV in the public domain? Will they stand for truth and honest debate? We hope so.

* * * * *

Who then is Kurtz?

Kurtz is western apathy. Kurtz is corporate vested interest and 'rich men behind the scenes'. Kurtz is compromise. Kurtz is *"...you have kids all over the place."* Kurtz is turning a blind eye or *"hiding under a pile of blankets and hoping it all goes away."* Kurtz can masquerade as an angel of light.[404] Kurtz's reign will continue wherever and whenever even the genuinely motivated aid agency work includes his lies.[405]

WILLARD: I felt I knew one or two things about Kurtz that weren't in the dossier.

And Durban 2000?

WILLARD: This was the end of the river alright…. hundreds of miles up a river that snaked through the war like a main circuit cable and plugged straight into Kurtz. At first, I thought they handed me the wrong dossier. I couldn't believe they wanted this man dead. Third generation West Point, top of his class, Korea, Airborne… About a

---

[404] 2 Corinthians 11:14 New International Bible.

[405] This calls for a major reassessment of genuine aid agency work and the supporting corporate literature, particularly those well-intentioned and people-focused NGOs and church programs.

thousand decorations. He was being groomed for one of the top slots of the corporation. General, Chief of Staff, anything...

The gathering so respectable...

And what of the following agencies, the respectable WHO, UN, USAID, UNFPA, UNDP, IMF, World Bank, Rothschild/Rockefeller/Ford Foundation, Bilderberg, Time Inc., Turner, CNN and other colluding associates?

CONRAD: *We glided past, secretly appalled, as sane men before an enthusiastic outbreak in a madhouse... No, they were not inhuman. Well, you know, that was the worst of it - this suspicion of their not being inhuman. It would come slowly to one. They howled and leaped, and spun; but what thrilled you was just the thought of their wild humanity - like yours - the thought of your remote kinship with this wild and passionate uproar.*

And Kurtz?

"His covering had fallen off, and his body emerged from it, pitiful and appalling. I could see the cage of his ribs all astir, the bones of his arms waving...an animated image of death carved out of old ivory... I saw him open his mouth wide – it gave him a weirdly voracious aspect, as though he had wanted to swallow all the air, all the earth and all the men before him.[406] His was an impenetrable darkness."[407]

* * * * *

---

[406] Isaiah 14:13-16
[407] Conrad, Joseph, ibid.

Through a complex series of interlocking companies and devious corporate name changes, the Rockefellers were able to use men like **Walter Teagle**, president of Rockefeller Standard Oil, to hold stock in drug giant IG Farben to mask their involvement with the German drug corporation. Teagle would later tell a Securities and Exchange Commission investigation that he had no idea who actually owned a block of 500,000 shares in IG Chemie, a subsidiary of Farben, that had been issued in his name.

John D Rockefeller Sr., hated for his ruthless business practices, spared no effort to improve his public image. At public gatherings, he would often give away shiny dimes to young children on the advice of his public relations advisors.

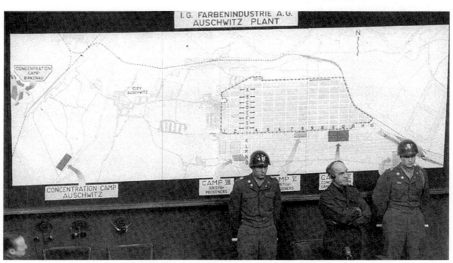

SS Lieutenant General **Oswald Pohl**, later hanged for war crimes, explains to the Nuremberg tribunal how IG Farben had operated Buchenwald and Auschwitz concentration camps. Although Farben had developed poison gas that had been used on untold numbers in the camps, its leaders largely escaped the tribunal's judgment due to their long-held policy of remaining 'behind the scenes'. Author G Edward Griffin writes: *"The fact that the Nazi war machine had received tremendous help from its cartel partners in the US is one of the most uncomfortable facts that surfaced during the investigation at the end of the war. It constituted direct collaboration during those same years Nazi troops were killing American soldiers on the field of battle. (World Without Cancer, ibid. p.207)*

DEPARTMENT OF DEFENSE APPROPRIATIONS FOR 1970

HEARINGS
BEFORE A

SUBCOMMITTEE OF THE COMMITTEE ON APPROPRIATIONS HOUSE OF REPRESENTATIVES
NINETY-FIRST CONGRESS

FIRST SESSION

SUBCOMMITTEE ON DEPARTMENT OF DEFENSE APPROPRIATIONS

GEORGE H. MAHON, Texas, *Chairman*

ROBERT L. F. SIKES, Florida
JAMIE L. WHITTEN, Mississippi
GEORGE W. ANDREWS, Alabama
DANIEL J. FLOOD, Pennsylvania
JOHN M. SLACK, West Virginia
JOSEPH P. ADDABBO, New York
FRANK E. EVANS, Colorado [1]

GLENARD P. LIPSCOMB, California
WILLIAM E. MINSHALL, Ohio
JOHN J. RHODES, Arizona
GLENN R. DAVIS, Wisconsin

R. L. MICHAELS, RALPH PRESTON, JOHN GARRITY, PETER MURPHY, ROBERT NICHOLAS,
AND ROBERT FOSTER, *Staff Assistants*

[1] Temporarily assigned.

PART 6
Budget and Financial Management
Budget for Secretarial Activities
Chemical and Biological Warfare
Defense Installations and Procurement
Defense Intelligence Agency
Safeguard Ballistic Missile Defense System
Testimony of Adm. Hyman G. Rickover
Testimony of Members of Congress and Other
Individuals and Organizations

Printed for the use of the Committee on Appropriations

The infamous **HB 15090** has sparked many rumours that this
was the document that unleashed AIDS. In spite of the
provocative wording though, known immuno-suppressant drugs
pre-dated this committee meeting by some years.

agents that we have ever considered. So, we have to believe they are probably working in the same areas.

SYNTHETIC BIOLOGICAL AGENTS

There are two things about the biological agent field I would like to mention. One is the possibility of technological surprise. Molecular biology is a field that is advancing very rapidly, and eminent biologists believe that within a period of 5 to 10 years it would be possible to produce a synthetic biological agent, an agent that does not naturally exist and for which no natural immunity could have been acquired.

Mr. SIKES. Are we doing any work in that field?

Dr. MACARTHUR. We are not.

Mr. SIKES. Why not? Lack of money or lack of interest?

Dr. MACARTHUR. Certainly not lack of interest.

Mr. SIKES. Would you provide for our records information on what would be required, what the advantages of such a program would be, the time and the cost involved?

Dr. MACARTHUR. We will be very happy to.

(The information follows:)

The dramatic progress being made in the field of molecular biology led us to investigate the relevance of this field of science to biological warfare. A small group of experts considered this matter and provided the following observations:

1. All biological agents up to the present time are representatives of naturally occurring disease, and are thus known by scientists throughout the world. They are easily available to qualified scientists for research, either for offensive or defensive purposes.

2. Within the next 5 to 10 years, it would probably be possible to make a new infective microorganism which could differ in certain important aspects from any known disease-causing organisms. Most important of these is that it might be refractory to the immunological and therapeutic processes upon which we depend to maintain our relative freedom from infectious disease.

3. A research program to explore the feasibility of this could be completed in approximately 5 years at a total cost of $10 million.

4. It would be very difficult to establish such a program. Molecular biology is a relatively new science. There are not many highly competent scientists in the field, almost all are in university laboratories, and they are generally adequately supported from sources other than DOD. However, it was considered possible to initiate an adequate program through the National Academy of Sciences-National Research Council (NAS-NRC).

The matter was discussed with the NAS-NRC, and tentative plans were made to initiate the program. However, decreasing funds in CB, growing criticism of the CB program, and our reluctance to involve the NAS-NRC in such a controversial endeavor have led us to postpone it for the past 2 years.

It is a highly controversial issue, and there are many who believe such research should not be undertaken lest it lead to yet another method of massive killing of large populations. On the other hand, without the sure scientific knowledge that such a weapon is possible, and an understanding of the ways it could be done, there is little that can be done to devise defensive measures. Should an enemy develop it there is little doubt that this is an important area of potential military technological inferiority in which there is no adequate research program.

CROSS-COUNTRY SHIPMENT OF LETHAL AGENTS

Mr. SIKES. Now, let's talk about shipments. There has been a great deal of discussion—most of it hostile—about the proposal to ship certain stocks of nerve gas across country for transporting to a deep

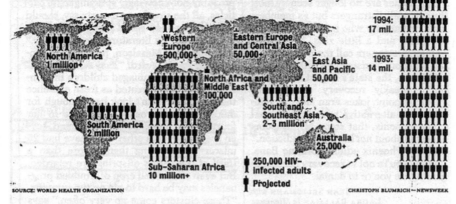

The Demographics of Death

Since the mid-1970s, HIV has infected more than 17 million people, most of them in Africa. With the epidemic now exploding in Asia, experts say the number of infections worldwide will exceed 40 million by the year 2000.

Western Europe 500,000+

North America 1 million+

Eastern Europe and Central Asia 50,000+

East Asia and Pacific 50,000

1994: 17 mil.

1993: 14 mil.

North Africa and Middle East 100,000

South America 2 million

South and Southeast Asia 2–3 million

Australia 25,000+

Sub-Saharan Africa 10 million+

250,000 HIV-infected adults

Projected

SOURCE: WORLD HEALTH ORGANIZATION

CHRISTOPH BLUMRICH—NEWSWEEK

Promoting the HIV Product – Articles and write-ups such as this *Newsweek* feature serve to reinforce in the public's mind the concept of an unstoppable global AIDS plague. This in turn compels populations and their governments to allow huge resources (and even extra funds raised through tax increases) to be allocated to global UN agencies in order to combat this supposed threat to world health.

CNN media giant **Ted Turner** is an outspoken advocate of population control, having donated millions of dollars towards élitist aims.

Henry Kissinger – Architect of peace or a man espousing a more sinister agenda?

It's been a rather harrowing journey to Kurtz's compound. There's a Bible verse that says, *"My people die through lack of knowledge."*[408] If ever there was a syndrome that had the capacity to wreak so high a death toll through lack of knowledge, that accolade must go AIDS. But to HIV must go the ultimate prize – the trophy given for the most complete and convincing global fraud ever to have been perpetrated on trusting humankind - the killer virus that never was.

But with knowledge comes power; power to reverse mindsets, circumstances and situations. We remind the reader that both Conrad and Willard witnessed the demise of the mighty Kurtz.

Lies are the ally of Kurtz.

But truth his conquering enemy.

---

[408] Hosea 4:6, New International Bible

Part 3

ENDING AIDS

SOME CONQUERORS

*"The greatest darkness cannot extinguish the radiating
light of even the smallest candle."* (anon)

And now for some good news! Let us remind ourselves that lies
are conquered by truth. What better way can there be to introduce the
beginning of the end of AIDS than by reading the tremendous
testimonies of those individuals who are alive and well in spite of their
diagnosis. These are the stories of people who have come out or are
coming out from under the curse of the myth of HIV.

**Details for the following testimonies are on file with Credence
Publications and associated organisations. Please contact us on
steve@worldwithoutaids.freeserve.co.uk if you have a genuine
enquiry, and if you too have a testimony you would like to share.**

"I had my positive diagnosis in 1987. In setting up the Long Term
Survivors Network, I have been challenged on using the term 'survivor',
the argument being that if the HIV test is not an indication of future ill-
health then we haven't survived, as we had nothing to survive. I would
dispute that, for we have survived an assault on the very basic human
spirit; ostracism from society, poisoning of the mind by fear, attempts to
control our sexual and reproductive needs as well as pressure to take
toxic and experimental drugs. No mean feat! The point is, it's a
possibility we may not be survivors of HIV, but we are survivors in life.
We should not forget that alongside the questions around HIV and the
dilemmas and decisions we make, we are dealing with other things that
life throws at any of us." **Claire W**.

"When I tested positive in 1988, I was told I had only three years to
live. Twelve years later, I'm doing just fine. I have never taken any
AIDS drugs, even though they were suggested and even pushed. In
1996, I got married – five years after I was supposed to be dead. I'm
very much alive and healthy and wish people would listen to me and
other people like me for a change. Ignorance is the real epidemic."
Michele M.

"I've known over 200 people who died of so-called AIDS. Every one of them had sufficient drug abuse or medical terrorism to account for their immune suppression. When I was told in 1988 that I was HIV positive and had about two years to live, it came as a complete shock to me because I did not have a history of what was considered high-risk behaviour. By 1992, I had learned enough to convince me that AIDS was the greatest medical error of all time. As I write this, it has been eleven years since I first got tested. I've never developed any AIDS-defining illnesses. In fact I've never had a cold in nineteen years. I ride a bike, I take no medications and no treatments – just good food and ten minutes a day exercise for the immune system. I thank God I was smart enough to 'just say no' to the doctors, so it didn't cost me my health. If anything, as a result of what I've learned, I'm healthier today than I have ever been." **Ed L.**

"I tested positive in 1989 and have been living in wellness without the meds [medications] for ten years - something that still shocks people, even though I've always been just fine. After watching my friends get sick and die on AIDS drug therapies, I decided that HIV drugs are poison and you can't poison yourself back to health. I learned to do nothing for HIV. Instead, I focus on being healthy." **Kim F.**

"In 1989, my husband Philip and I were tested HIV positive. We couldn't believe that two people like us, nice people from nice families, were having to deal first-hand with AIDS. The doctor provided Philip with experimental drugs six months to a year before they were available to the public. At least ten times the doctor told me that Philip would not pull through whatever infection he was going through. Ten times I went through the fear, heartache and panic that I was losing my husband.

Six years after being told he had just months to live, Philip died in my arms. When I was told it was my turn to take the drugs, I realised I had to make the most important decision of my life. In desperation, I called Christine Maggiore. I asked Christine to give me just the scientific information and nothing else. No stories, no emotional hype, only the facts. I had to go to her office several times to read because I became so distraught that I couldn't continue for more than fifteen minutes.

Everything I was reading described and explained what I had been through with my husband. My worst fears were being confirmed - the drugs had made my husband suffer tremendously and had eventually killed him. I started attending 'Alive and Well' events... ultimately deciding that AIDS drugs were not for me. I decided to trust my own life. Believing in health is the first step to creating a healthy life. Holding onto the possibility of health is everything." **Cynthia R.**

"I tested positive in 1990 and nine years later I am healthy and medication-free. When I was first told I was positive, I went through the standard terror with my life flashing before my eyes. I followed my doctor's orders for treatment with AZT. After a year of feeling sick, I listened to my inner voice and quit AZT. Except for a brief foray into ddI, I've been off meds ever since. I have three recommendations for anyone who tests positive - education, education and education about all aspects and points of view on HIV and AIDS." **Erik D.**

"What I find hardest is living with the stigma of HIV. I'm young, healthy, intelligent and very well educated on HIV and AIDS. Yet I am isolated by the fear and ignorance surrounding a condition I don't even believe in. Being a leader rather than a follower can be lonely and difficult. Maintaining a stance against the majority of the human population is a trying task. I don't have the time to educate everyone, even if they were interested. When I do tell others about what I know, they are so convinced that HIV=AIDS=Death, that they think I am doomed and that my optimism is merely fear or hope or both.

I do have hope. I hope that people will look deeper and listen more. That they will demand to be treated as precious beings more important than politics, money and abstract theory. It takes people like us to be the first and the most determined. Life goes on. Choose to be part of it." **Dean W.**

"I was required by law to take an HIV test in June 1995. The test is mandatory in Colorado for pregnant women, and I was expecting my second child. I was shocked when the result came back positive, because I'd been married and monogamous for nine years.

I started taking AZT in my fifth month. After ten months on AZT, I was sick all the time. I had constant diarrhoea, nausea, fever, night sweats and was totally exhausted. I was crawling to the bathroom and vomiting for hours. My doctor told me the HIV was making me ill, and that the virus had mutated into a form that was resistant to AZT.

Further drugs turned my skin yellow with jaundice. Since it was clear that the drugs weren't keeping me from getting AIDS and were actually destroying my liver, I let my prescription run out. I figured I'd rather die from AIDS than liver failure.

Almost immediately after I stopped taking my medicines, within a matter of days I started to feel much better.... My daughter is considered a success by medical standards because she tests negative(!), but I don't care about HIV anymore. I am concerned about the effects of the AZT she was poisoned with while I was pregnant. Rachel has an enlarged cranium, seizures and a strange deformity near the base of her spine. At age three she still does not speak. I went to this conference on HIV and pregnancy at The Children's Hospital here in Denver. A lot of mothers there had taken AZT during pregnancy and had their kids with them. Every single one of those kids had enlarged craniums. Their heads looked exactly like Rachel's. They're all AZT babies. I'm working now to repeal Colorado's mandatory [HIV] testing law." **Kris C.**

"In those days, the late eighties, the media pressure was unbearable. I had used heroin for more than two years between 1979 and 1982, so I knew I was at risk. I still remember the dreadful feelings I had, seeing and hearing the TV press campaigns. They pictured tombs, blood and zombie faces, with frightening headlines like "AIDS KILLS... DON'T DIE OF IGNORANCE."

In February 1988, I finally summed up the courage to go and be tested for the AIDS virus. I waited nervously in the infectious diseases clinic. I can still remember the doctors' sad faces as they told me I was HIV positive and that I shouldn't think to get pregnant until more research on the issue brought better news. The world fell in on me. Having successfully fought drug use six years previously, the future looked hopeless. According to the impression I had been given, I had at best another five years....

I had met my husband in 1992 and, after we got married in 1994, we started to think about having a child. The doctors tried hard to discourage me from the idea of conceiving. I was disturbed by their conviction that it would be advisable to take AZT during pregnancy, to have a caesarean section and to refrain from breast-feeding. I took AZT for one month only before stopping.

I gave birth to a wonderful, bouncy baby girl. My daughter had her first HIV test when still in hospital, and then when she was three and six months old. The tests were all positive. I resisted the intense pressure to administer AZT to her. The last test was done when she was one year old, which was negative. I have decided not to go for any more ritual blood tests. What's the point if I am convinced there is a gross error at the very base of HIV theory? Meanwhile, I hope to remain as healthy as I am, enjoying my life together with Michael and our daughter." **Monica G.**

To Robin Keene, SCHNS,
Communicable Disease Supervisor,
Manatee County Health Department
3rd June 1999

Dear Ms Keene,

Please accept my resignation from employment with the Health Department. After months of struggle and extensive research, I regret I can no longer fulfil the Public Health mandate requirements of my position in good conscience.

Upon careful investigation, it is woefully apparent that a grand schism has existed in AIDS since Robert Gallo's politically charged announcement to the world that HIV is the probable cause of AIDS. Unfortunately, only one side of the scientific data has been made readily available to the general public. This side is far more powerful, backed by the financial storehouses of federal government agencies like the CDC and the NIH, who fund most public information campaigns and research programs. This dominant science is promoted and even manipulated by pharmaceutical giants who have an obvious profit motive. Aided by a willing media, the Public Health Service has all but silenced contrary scientific opinions and thus denied the people their fundamental right to informed consent.

I hereby withdraw my participation in what may one day be seen as the greatest violation of the principle of informed consent in the history of Public Health.

Most sincerely,
Mark Pierpoint
HIV/AIDS Prevention Program Co-Ordinator.

"As a child of the sixties' sexual revolution I participated in the craziness like everyone else. Sex was freely available, and was 'de rigeur' for all sexual persuasions. When the 'great epidemic' arrived from the US in the early eighties we were all told to be terrified, and that many would die.

Well many did, and nearly all of my gay friends of that time are now gone. All of them accepted the HIV=AIDS paradigm as promoted by the American AIDS industry. Fortunately, I was sceptical enough not to believe in this lethal virus. When I finally tested 'positive' after already two negatives, I resolutely kept away from all conventional AIDS doctoring. I observed that my immune system remained intact and I had no health problems at all that I couldn't cope with myself.

I took a job as an 'HIV Educator' with our major government organisation in New South Wales, Australia, generously funded also by drug companies. On my own initiative I discovered the *Reappraising AIDS* team in the US and *Continuum* in the UK, confirming that my intuition was right. Upon informing my 'AIDS education' employer of my suspicions I was quickly relieved of my post.

Seventeen years later in the year 2000, in the wake of hundreds of deaths of my friends, I enjoy exceedingly good health, and I remain AIDS drug- and AIDS doctor-free. But I am eternally frustrated by the continued ignorant and misleading reports in all the media about the ongoing expansion and fear of this 'World Epidemic'. May this book help to educate." - **Paul B.**

"When I first came across this book, suggesting that AIDS was not the threat that it was supposed to be, I was very sceptical. I had heard nothing but the most serious of warnings and dreadful stories of people suffering from AIDS. However, when I started reading *World Without AIDS*, I was shocked that I had been so taken in, and for so long, by so many misleading "facts". What used to be a confusing issue for me, has now become rather too clear. It is vitally important that everyone should hear about the contents of this book, so the truth can be exposed. I will not hesitate to give a copy to anyone who is considering taking an HIV test, or who is suffering from "AIDS". As everyone's Dad used to say; "Don't believe everything you read in the papers." **Simon H.**

"To my shame I have absorbed and relayed facts and figures about the 'AIDS pandemic', and not asked fundamental questions such as, 'does the Human Immunodeficiency Virus exist?' and 'where have they got the African nations' fatality rates from?' I assumed they came from test results. *World Without AIDS* has stirred me to find out the truth for myself and has given me a sharper focus as I work amongst British teenagers in sexual health education. As a response I recognise my need for increased compassion, integrity, righteousness and strength to confront these huge financial and power strongholds. Thank you for your research and provocation." **Rachel M.**

"When I was tested positive, my doctor told me I was exceptionally healthy, that I was fortunate to have detected the condition early, but that there was nothing I could do to prevent devastating disease and eventual death from AIDS. He warned me against wasting money on vitamins and other foolish attempts to save my immune system, advising me that I simply wait to become sick and then take AZT....

Life came to a grinding halt. I bought a wedding ring to ward off potential suitors. A year or so into my diagnosis, I found a caring doctor who urged me to take another test. Further testing produced a positive followed by a negative and another positive. In my search for more information, I became more and more convinced that AIDS research had jumped on a bandwagon that was headed in the wrong direction. In the seven years since receiving my death sentence, I have gone from frightened victim to AIDS activist to HIV dissident to spokesperson for new views about HIV and AIDS. Although my HIV status has been decidedly positive for the last five years, I enjoy abundant good health and live without pharmaceutical treatments or fear of AIDS. My book *'What if Everything You Thought You Knew About AIDS was Wrong?'* is now in its fourth print, with editions in Spanish, Portuguese and Italian, and even a bootleg version in French. In 1996 I met a wonderful man I plan to marry as soon as I take a day off. Robin and I have a beautiful healthy little boy aged two, our miraculous little Charles Dexter. Between them, they fill my days with so much love, joy and laundry! **Christine Maggiore**

Open Letter to the World Health Organization No.14

From: Dr Michael Mulugheta
PO Box 4221
Asmara, Eritrea,
Africa
Tel/Fax 291-1-641-323

After having worked as a tropical doctor in Malawi, I returned to the Netherlands at the end of 1988. I worked in Malawi for 3 years in a mission hospital where I was the only doctor. My duties included, among other things, surgical and gynaecological operations, especially caesarean sections.

AIDS was at that time about 4 years old and the issue was 'hot'. Six months after my return, I developed a urinary tract infection and decided to take antibiotics. To avoid what we call the 'ping-pong' phenomenon, I gave the same regimen also to my wife. Seven days after the start of therapy, I developed partial deafness. Over the next several months, both of us subsequently (but only temporarily) developed an array of illnesses with an astounding similarity to those attributed to HIV. Because of my worries of the possible infection with HIV, I suggested an ELISA test for myself. I turned 'strongly' positive on ELISA. An Amsterdam specialist, Dr Meenhorst, ordered a confirmatory Western Blot test. He told me I had antibodies against HIV. I started asking him questions.

Not satisfied, I went to the Tropical Institute in Antwerp, Belgium. The head of that institute was Professor Peter Piot, the current director of the World Health Organization's (WHO) Global Program on AIDS (GPA). He prescribed AZT and other drugs for me to take immediately. Had I followed his advice, I would have long been in my grave by now. His personal prescriptions are still in my possession.

My next stop was the University of Hamburg, Germany. Professor H G Thiele did the same as the others before. He falsified on the instructions from Netherlands and Germany. I don't want to dwell on my experiences in more than 10 countries - there is a book on this matter being prepared.

For trying to disprove AIDS scientifically, my doctors declared me insane and threw me out of my job. When I insisted to seek the truth through disseminating their conspiracy to the rest of the world, they even resorted to physical harassment. I crossed Europe many times, covering 40,000 kilometres, wrote to more than 40 universities, research centres, medical journals, and in so doing spent over $40,000. I appealed to the European Commission for Human Rights in Strasbourg, France, but they gave me no heed. I staged a hunger strike at the International Court of Justice in The Hague, Netherlands, but they gave me a deaf ear also.

I appealed to the Ministers of Justice of five European countries where the conspiring doctors live, but there was no response from any one of them. I sent copies of documentation to many medical journals, such as *Nature, Lancet, New England Journal of Medicine, Journal of the American Medical Association, Scandinavian Journal of Medicine*, etc., and got no positive response. The *Lancet* editors wrote to tell me that I *"write a very good tale"*. Finally, I filed an action against the conspiring Dutch doctors at the National Commission of Complaints on Medical Malpractice, but they didn't want to listen to my complaints. Worst of all, they kept me in suspense for two years, and finally discarded my complaints as "unfounded" without listening to my arguments or reviewing the documentation.

On 22 February 1991, having tried all possible options, I paid a visit to the WHO offices in Geneva, Switzerland to air my complaints. For trying to present my documentation and arguments to the WHO, Professor Peter Piot advised a Dr Dorothy Blake of the GPA to have Swiss police take me away to jail. I then knew there was no justice in Europe, especially when the offenders are white and high in social status, and the victim is a black man.

When all attempts to uncover the truth failed, and my very existence and those of my family was in danger, I fled the country (Netherlands) where I had lived for around 15 years as a political refugee and went to Eritrea. Now that I live in the relative safety of a country I can call my own, I am writing again to unravel the scandalous acts of these European doctors.

Ladies and gentlemen, if my wife and I have never employed the condom or any other mechanisms of the so-called "protection" and yet are alive and thriving after more than 10 years, where is the HIV? We are still robust and energetic and fit to compile this report.

* * * * *

"I am taken aback by the determination of many people in our country to sacrifice all intellectual integrity to act as salespersons of the product of one pharmaceutical company [AZT manufacturer, Glaxo Wellcome]. *I am also amazed at how many people, who claim to be scientists, are determined that scientific discourse and inquiry should cease, because 'most of the world' is of one mind. The debate we need is not with me, who is not a scientist, or my office, but with the scientists who present 'scientific' arguments contrary to the 'scientific' view expressed by 'most of the world'. Undoubtedly, such 'consensus' and 'available evidence'* [for HIV=AIDS] *also existed on the use of Thalidomide. Faced with the findings indicated in this letter, I am afraid that my own conscience would not allow that I respond only to the 'consensus'."* **Thabo Mbeki**, President of South Africa, taken from an open letter to the *Johannesburg Star* 25th March 2000. (As *World Without AIDS* goes to print, President Mbeki is calling for a government debate on the toxicity of AZT and the ramifications for the people of South Africa.)

"In 1985, I decided to take the test. I tested positive. Since I had heard and read that the virus could be dormant for a long time, I opted to eat well, exercise, take high quality vitamins and limit 'risky sex'. However, my gut feeling was that something wasn't adding up with AIDS, and I almost immediately chose not to accept the virus as detrimental to my health. To this day I have never been hospitalised, and have not taken any of the drugs that are supposed to control or eradicate HIV." **C.J.**

"My friends started to die in 1982. Ann was the first to go. We used to 'shoot up' together. My room-mate Diane tested positive and moved in with her lover, Julie. I moved into a squat. I was shooting dope or coke every hour and I weighed about 90 pounds. My friends were all dying around me and I knew if I didn't take charge of my life, I'd join them.

I kicked coke, ate well and renovated my self-esteem. Diane's condition worsened. She ate her AZT and gave up the ghost. Had I followed my doctor's advice to take AZT, I wouldn't be writing this - I'd be dead. I know now that my low T-cell count was because of my depression, and my depression was as a result of my diagnosis.

I now no longer believe the prophecy of doom. I consider myself cured, and I haven't had to spend a dime. I'm as healthy as a horse, have lots of energy and look ten years younger than I am. But don't be envious. I've been through hell and back. I'll continue to fight for a reappraisal of the HIV hypothesis as long as I live. I only wish that Ann, Diane and Julie were still here to fight with me." **Frank G.**

"I attribute my wellness to refusing doctor's orders, listening to my body and practising a pretty good diet. Love and support from the family helps too." **J.P.**

"In May 1998, I found out I was pregnant with my first child. I received a frantic phone call from my doctor informing me I had been tested HIV positive. I had no idea I had even been tested. My husband also tested positive. Nothing seemed to add up - we have been together many years, we are completely monogamous and exceptionally healthy.

I was told to take AZT for the remainder of the pregnancy, and my husband was told to take the cocktails. These should have been the darkest days of my life, but as serendipity would have it, there was a copy of *What if Everything You Thought You Knew About AIDS Was Wrong?* sitting on our bookshelf. I read it, contacted Christine Maggiore and HEAL and with their help, began an immediate plan of action that included leaving my doctor of seven years in order to elude the HIV police.

The result is a healthy, happy, breast-fed baby girl. Our family leads a totally normal life, normal except for the fear that we could have our daughter taken away from us because of the choices we'd made regarding our health. The only sense we have discovered is in the data that shows that most of the ideas we all have about AIDS are wrong." **Stacey A.**

"I've been positive for sixteen years. In 1996, I came down with pneumonia, one of the hallmark AIDS diseases, and I began taking the cocktails. I felt my body was falling apart, not from the HIV, but from the drugs. I was always very aware of my body, and I could feel I was putting poison into it. I finally went to my doctors and told them I didn't want to take the drugs anymore. They called me a fool. They were very dramatic and told me it was suicide to stop. So instead of stopping I went onto a new combination of drugs. My speech was slurred and I kept losing my equilibrium. When I fell down a flight of stairs, that was the last straw. I stopped taking them. Two years after quitting the treatment, I feel better than ever." **Steven G.**

"I have taken responsibility for my own life and have not allowed someone in a white coat to do it for me. Had I chosen the path they offered me, I know I would be dead. I'm a survivor because someone had the guts to tell me the truth about the HIV=AIDS=Death lie. It's bad science in the hands of bad government." **Scott Z.**

Dear Phillip

Having just read your publications regarding Cancer and AIDS sufferers, I felt compelled to write to you in order to corroborate the authenticity and accuracy of your writings.

I read through the articles with the greatest of sadness, as my own family has been touched with the tragedy of losing a loved one, perhaps unnecessarily, to a disease that has become a fashion statement for the various governments to be associated with. In my opinion, AIDS is a disease that brings millions of pounds of profit to the drug companies, all the while contributing to the suffering and ultimate death of its victims. Let me tell you why I believe this.

I had a young brother who was gay. He was a trained district nurse, fully conversant with the dangers associated with his lifestyle. He lived quietly with his long term partner for many years, but became diagnosed as 'HIV positive' after being accidentally jabbed with a needle whilst treating a patient.

Like most medically trained people, he trusted his peers when they advised him to take AZT in order to preserve his immune system. My brother was demonstrating no symptoms of AIDS when he commenced AZT. Little did he realise that AZT would ultimately cause the onset of the very diseases he was trying to avoid; opportunistic diseases that would kill him at just 44.

These AZT tablets were inordinately difficult for my brother to swallow and, in the first instance, produced ulcers all down his oesophagus, making it impossible for him to eat. An ordinary mouth ulcer is painful enough, but when you consider an open wound over two inches across in your throat, the pain must have been unbearable. Eventually, after several bouts of increasingly severe pneumonia, during which he was continuously hooked up to an antibiotic machine, he began to waste away, his weight falling from seventeen stone (238lbs) to five stone (70lbs).

His muscle tissue ceased working and became flabby, until he couldn't walk at all, eventually succumbing to terrible pains that racked his body. He was then prescribed amitriptyline as an antidepressant, which did no good whatsoever, all the time taking these awful AZT tablets. Merciful release only came with the morphine, addling his once-alert brain, until he could fight no more. Finally his heart just stopped and my brother died.

Other patients in St. Mary's Hospital where my brother was admitted refused to take AZT AND LIVED ON INDEFINITELY, in spite of the HIV diagnosis they were given. It is my opinion that AZT killed my brother, not 'AIDS'. Please accept my best wishes for your excellent book, which I feel sure will save many lives that would otherwise be lost. **Frank R**

"I feel I perpetuated AIDS. I stood in front of Harvard Medical Center and demanded the release of ddI and ddC. I wonder how many people I harmed with my AIDS activism. And I'm really trying to figure out what my life has been devoted to. I feel we need to get to the bottom of this and put an end to the madness." - **Michael B.**

William's Senseless Act: "In 1990, I was diagnosed HIV positive after a short bout of pneumonia. I come from a wealthy Los Angeles family and the news devastated my parents. We all decided to keep quiet about what was the matter with me because my father was a successful and high-profile professional who strongly disapproved of my gay lifestyle. He was expecting a directorship of the entertainment company for which he worked and I don't think he needed the hassle.

I was advised by the clinic's doctors immediately to start anti-viral treatment with AZT in order to halt the spread of the HIV. My pneumonia had cleared up prior to taking the meds but I began to get a constant buzzing and ringing in my head, night sweats, assorted fungal infections and appalling body odor.

Right around Christmas of 1990, I was getting extremely sick. A friend gave me a private paper written by British researcher Phillip Day on the fraudulence of the HIV=AIDS connection and the dangers associated with AZT. At first I dismissed it. There was a lot of hype going around in those days about AIDS being a government germ warfare project, etc. etc. But I was curious. I did some more hunting and talked with other gays in the West Hollywood community. Two of them were quite up-front. They told me those who were taking the drugs (either clinical or recreational) were dying, while those who cleaned up their lifestyles, ate nutritiously and slept well were remaining symptomless.

I managed to track down Phillip, who was living in Los Angeles at that time. We met and talked. He took me through the information and answered all my questions, but told me the ultimate decision to quit my medication was down to me, not my doctors. I think mentally that had

218

to be one of the most difficult decisions I have had to make in my life. It was harder because I was considering going against the advice of some of the most brilliant minds in medicine on the West Coast.

Long story short, I decided to stop the meds and I actually flushed them down the toilet. When I later told my doctor what I had done with the drugs I'd bought, he got angry and said it was a 'senseless act'. Anyway, senseless or not, I can trace my recovery from that special day, and that was ten years ago, nine more years than that doctor gave me. I gained my weight back, my various problems checked themselves out and today I am older and wiser - angry and still confused about why this happened to me and why this insanity is allowed to continue. But the upside to this whole story? I am now in the very best condition of my life." – **William S.**

No doubt, there are many more such testimonies and the number will only increase as the truth about AIDS and HIV spreads exponentially into the populations. If you have a story to tell, then please write to us at Credence Publications in confidence, and if it is your wish, your testimony may well find its way onto our page of conquerors.

FREQUENTLY ASKED QUESTIONS

Q: What exactly is AIDS?

A: AIDS is an acronym for Acquired Immune Deficiency Syndrome and is an umbrella term to describe a range of existing diseases, known to mankind, that afflict the patient as a result of immune suppression or immune system damage. That this immune damage is caused as a result of infection by a virus known as the Human Immunodeficiency Virus (HIV) has not only never been proven, the alleged virus has never even been isolated, its genetic material mapped and its proteins identified – the usual protocol for establishing the existence of a new viral micro-organism. Interestingly, Stefan Lanka states that the term AIDS is actually misleading. *"AIDS is an energy deficiency problem. The term 'AIDS' is absolutely misleading because it has nothing to do with immune defect or immune deficiency. 'AEDS' or Acquired <u>Energy</u> Deficiency Syndrome has a rational basis and can be treated."*[409] This would seem to make sense, the deficiencies arising as a result of outside destructive toxins and/or lack of input of the necessary energy resources, and not as a result of initial immune system defects or a virus known as HIV.

Q: Why exactly can HIV NOT be the cause of AIDS?

A: Firstly, as mentioned, *HIV has never been isolated, its supposed presence has only been inferred*. Secondly, for HIV to be the sole cause of AIDS (a hypothesis that is taught and accepted as fact by the medical establishment and thus by most of the public), HIV would have to occur in every case of AIDS. It doesn't (see section entitled *Cooking up HIV*). Thirdly, if HIV is the infective agent, it should proliferate and be easily detectable in patients suffering from AIDS in the final stages of their life (ie, when the opportunistic diseases are at their most rampant). But HIV cannot be traced in these patients, only inferred by a bewildering series of dubious markers. Fourthly, AIDS does not satisfy Koch's Postulates as an infectious syndrome, it does not satisfy Farr's Law as an infectious syndrome – these are two of medicine's most basic benchmarks for identifying viral pathogens and infectious disease. Fifthly, AIDS does not behave like an infectious

---

[409] *Zenger*, December 1998

220

disease AT ALL. It hasn't spread equally into both sexes, it is still almost exclusively restricted to its original risk groups.[410] As is widely known, viral epidemics spread exponentially into the population, producing indiscriminate infection in men, women and children. AIDS hasn't done this, and the expected AIDS holocaust has of course failed to materialise.

Q: So is there actually such a thing as AIDS?

A: Yes, albeit an incorrect definition. In the early 1980s, certain victims began being identified with immune system damage. They went on to die from opportunistic infections that took advantage of their damaged immune system. The problems began when this 'new' syndrome was declared viral in nature, when there was no evidence to support this theory.

Q: So what causes AIDS?

A: All the evidence points to AIDS being a syndrome of immune deficiency brought on by long-term exposure to recreational and pharmaceutical toxins and other immuno-suppressive behaviour. This being the case, It is no coincidence that AIDS appeared when it did. The late 1960s saw the start of the new global drug culture and the beginning of the gay liberation movement. Part of this new hedonistic lifestyle necessitated a chronic consumption of hard and soft recreational drugs, antibiotics, nitrite inhalants, promiscuous sex (risking STD infections and parasites), very little sleep, poor diet and constant alcohol abuse. This is the first time in history that this type of lifestyle has become prevalent and given the tacit endorsement of governments anxious to attract the powerful gay vote.[411]

---

[410] Cases where AIDS apparently affects heterosexuals can almost always be attributed to an HIV positive diagnosis, after which the patient is prescribed AIDS drugs prior to exhibiting any symptoms at all. In many cases, these drugs themselves bring on the very symptoms of 'AIDS'. In the US, AIDS tests can be mandatory for couples getting married. An inadvertent positive test result can result in a perfectly healthy individual being prescribed AZT or similar.

[411] During the 1993 Gay March on Washington, attended by 300,000 homosexuals, lesbians, transvestites and transsexuals, participants lobbied for a change in the 1964 Civil Rights Act, championed by Martin Luther King Jr three decades before for the protection of black people. For the first time in American history, a gay and lesbian inaugural ball was held to celebrate a president's entry into the White House. During the ball, President Clinton, via video, thanked the gay and lesbian community for their support of, and financial contributions to his successful campaign, declaring to them, *"I have a vision and you're part of it."* (*Gay Rights, Special Rights*, a video documentary, Jeremiah Films, PO Box

Sexual revellers and intravenous drug users over a period of time appear to have damaged their immune systems either reversibly or irreversibly with these lifestyles. It is interesting to note that deaths were occurring in the 1960s that looked remarkably like AIDS – wasting brought on by malnutrition, malabsorption of food, chronic diarrhoea, pneumonias, etc. These deaths were always as a result of chronic long-term drug abuse or other immuno-suppressant behaviour and were understood clearly by the medical establishment at the time to be so caused. It is worth remembering that prior to Robert Gallo's 'AIDS as virus' announcement, the immune deficiency cases cropping up in San Francisco, Los Angeles and other gay metropolitan areas in the early 1980s were widely accepted to be caused by an excessive and drug-fuelled lifestyle – not a virus, sexually transmitted or otherwise.

Today the leading cause of AIDS in the western world is believed by many to be the AIDS drugs themselves. Shocking though this might be to contemplate, AIDS is by no means the first syndrome where this has happened (see section entitled *Entrenched Scientific Error*). Recreational drugs and excessive lifestyles though still play a large part as, like pharmaceutical drugs, they are toxic by nature (foreign to the biological experience of the human organism) and so, by default, increase the toxic load on the subject. And then of course you can 'have AIDS' just by being presumptively diagnosed, being identified by medical science as belonging to a 'high risk group' or by having a low T-cell count. In this way, patients are often diagnosed as 'having AIDS' long before they have exhibited any immune deficiency diseases and are then prescribed the drugs which later fulfil the AIDS death sentence prophecy.

The plain fact is, you do not need HIV to explain the phenomenon of AIDS. The drug and excessive lifestyle model fits all the criteria of AIDS to the letter.

Q: Isn't putting out the message that AIDS is NOT spread sexually sending a dangerous message to those who have previously been practising 'safe sex'?

A: A good question, and one that is often used to counter any dissident views on HIV. We come back however to the central point: No evidence has ever been produced to demonstrate that AIDS is

1710, Hemet, CA 92546 USA ISBN 1878993445)

spread sexually, either through an HIV or any other medium. This has nothing to do with the issue of an individual routinely practising safe sex to protect themselves from other sexually transmitted infections. If AIDS were transmitted sexually, we would definitely see a proliferation of infection spreading equally into both sexes and the rate of transmission increasing exponentially. As already reviewed, the predicted AIDS holocaust never materialised. Not only that, but AIDS has remained almost exclusively within its declared risk groups for almost twenty years. This is absolutely not typical of an infectious, viral syndrome. Also, if you are going to declare AS FACT that AIDS is being spread sexually, and that one virus is causing 29 disparate AIDS-defining diseases (no small undertaking), then you actually have to come up with this virus. Also you have to demonstrate that this causal agent (virus or bacterium) can be identified in all cases of AIDS. A dedicated and unique viral agent has never been proven to exist that can directly or otherwise cause over two dozen of these supposed HIV=AIDS indicator diseases.

So, are we advocating a dangerous message here? Are we implicitly condoning liberal sexual practices as a result of the information we describe in this book? Absolutely not. We are recommending an end to toxic and extreme lifestyles that, over the long term, are creating cumulative toxicity within the body that is causing immune damage. The social issues of homosexuality, as society sees them, are not under discussion here and are not the focus of this book.

Q: You mentioned that over 100,000 papers have been written on HIV. How can so many people all be wrong about AIDS?

A: The first reaction of many members of the public when they hear a challenge to the HIV=AIDS hypothesis is usually one of disbelief. *"Everyone believes that HIV causes AIDS!"* First of all, not everyone believes HIV=AIDS. Many well-qualified doctors and biochemists hold dissident positions on the HIV=AIDS issue. Secondly, even if everyone did believe HIV=AIDS, would that still make it FACT? Majority opinion is often meaningless in an argument. All too frequently the majority can be wrong, as Galileo would have told you from his jail cell.

Public misconceptions arise when the medical opposition to a disease becomes centrally managed and a central hypothesis is

223

accepted, for a wide variety of reasons, to guide the subsequent research. This state of affairs, although appearing at first to be a streamlined and efficient way forward, has one disastrous side-effect. It shuts out dissident views challenging the central hypothesis - a challenge which in the past has often performed the role of a check and balance system, exposing fraud, mismanagement and entrenched error.

Most people involved with AIDS have no access firsthand to the research, and so they go along with whatever scientific papers have already been published on the subject. They assume the experts know what they are talking about. It is also worth noting that peer pressure and fear of losing their grants or jobs have compelled many medical researchers and doctors to ignore science's fundamental laws in order to accommodate the establishment's view of AIDS.

Q: What about those babies who are born with AIDS?
A: Firstly, you must ask yourself, "How are these babies being diagnosed with AIDS?" The answer is, if their mothers have been diagnosed with 'AIDS', the babies are given an AIDS test which may turn up positive. Medical science interprets this positive result to mean that the baby is carrying the HIV virus given to it by its mother. In reality, a positive ELISA is doing nothing more than highlighting the presence of antibodies in the baby's blood. HIV has never been isolated and no antibody is specific to any one disease, so the test is not recognising HIV either directly or through antibody identification.

Now, the baby may be carrying a high toxic load if its mother has been, for example, taking crack and fast-tracking in the lead-up to birth. So if we are right and the baby is suffering toxicity problems inherited from its toxic mother, then we should see these babies getting better once they are physically free from the mother after birth. And this is indeed what we see happening. Babies diagnosed as HIV positive have been found to sero-revert and give an HIV negative result within eighteen months in 87% of cases without therapeutic intervention[412]. The tragedy is, these little ones are still treated with AZT and subsequently killed.[413]

---

[412] **Peckham et al**. *Infant Seroconversion Profile*, London 1990. Also New York University Medical Center Pediatric Department, 1990

[413] *Los Angeles Times*, 30th March 1995, reports the child sero-conversion phenomenon. Then adds: *"In the past year, physicians have begun routinely prescribing the anti-HIV drug AZT to HIV-positive women who are pregnant. Studies show that the drug reduces*

The phenomenon of babies sero-reverting just isn't supposed to happen in the AIDS world because HIV is portrayed as a relentless killer from which there is no escape. The facts state otherwise and, in the case of AIDS pediatrics, most definitely there are charges of negligent homicide to answer, and perhaps even murder.

Q: Why has the medical establishment fixated so strongly on HIV to the exclusion of other potential causes for AIDS?

A: Because HIV is a huge money earner and exposing toxic syndromes isn't. That's a harsh statement but a simple one. But this question bears closer examination. Drug companies formulate drug 'solutions' to diseases. These drugs are patented by the drug companies and sold for huge profit. Pharmaceutical drugs are huge business. And when their drugs run out of appeal in the West, either because they are out of fashion or have been shown over time to be ineffective, manufacturers often palm these leftovers off to Third World governments desperate for supposedly respectable western medication. (These 'palmed off' medications are often interpreted by onlookers in the West as 'benevolent Third World aid'.)

So, when you have a disease as widely promoted by the media as AIDS, which has been officially classified as viral in cause, the demand created for drug treatments becomes very pronounced. With AIDS, you take a fearsome sounding disease, link it to two of mankind's most potent taboos – sex and death – then put out stories that this is the new bubonic plague that is going to devastate humanity. Then finish off by telling the public that you own the patent to the only drug treatments available to combat the coming plague and see what happens. Firstly the share price of your drug company is going to sky-rocket. Secondly, you will be perceived as an authority on the disease because you have a potential answer for it. Thirdly, your company is going to have large sums of grant and research money thrown to it by government to encourage you to develop your drugs faster (for the benefit of humanity).

Alongside these endeavours, the media also plays its part, shaping public opinion to raise even more money and 'awareness' to give further credibility and speed to your work. At all costs, HIV must be

---

transmission of the virus to the infants by two-thirds." (p.A22) This, and other studies to do with AZT are funded by the manufacturers of the drug itself, Glaxo-Wellcome. When Credence researchers pressed to be given a copy of this research to investigate, no reply was forthcoming. The attitude was, *"It's just recognised…"*

seen to exist because HIV is the *vicious* viral enemy your expensive drugs are being designed to combat. Without HIV, there are no profitable drugs and all funding will cease.

This more than adequately explains the highly charged rhetoric and unreasonable defence of HIV in the face of all the evidence to the contrary. Telling people the simple truth such as "Don't do drugs!" does not make Mercedes payments. Telling people to clean up their toxic lifestyles and adopt proper nutrition will not please your shareholders. They will not earn out of this advice.

The handling of AIDS from the very beginning was steered in the direction of vested interests and the medical establishment, who originally misdiagnosed AIDS as viral in nature, has painted itself into a corner with all the publicity it has willingly propagated. No doubt there are individuals within the establishment who are now desperately seeking some kind of exit from AIDS establishment dogma before the truth emerges, as truth invariably does. What is holding back a public pronouncement that the medical establishment was so wrong about AIDS and HIV is the realisation that this admission would have catastrophic consequences for certain sections of the medical industry. Who would ever trust medicine again?

Q: Can all AIDS patients be saved by proper nutritional and detoxification procedures?

A. No. In certain cases, excessive drug-taking and immuno-suppressant behaviour have damaged the immune system beyond repair and the patient will eventually die of AIDS-related diseases. However, if drug abuse is viewed like alcohol and tobacco abuse, the model becomes clear. You are not likely to get irreversible lung cancer smoking a couple of cigarettes behind the bicycle sheds. Smoke enough of them over years though and you will. With drug abuse, there is no hard and fast point beyond which immune system damage becomes irreversible, only that eventually it will if the abuse continues. Ceasing highly toxic lifestyles and highly toxic 'medicines' can often bring immediate benefit, Peter Duesberg reporting that *"one doctor took eleven of his worsening AIDS patients off AZT. The immune systems of ten immediately rebounded, and several continued improving."* [414]

---

[414] Duesberg, Peter H, *Inventing*... ibid.

Immediate cessation of toxic lifestyle and drug abuse (be it recreational or pharmaceutical) is essential. There are no guarantees that a patient will respond to nutritional therapies, but the place to start is by ending the abuse and lifestyle, and then setting forth a responsible program for proper rehabilitation.

Q: What other treatments are beneficial for those who have AIDS?

A: There are things to do, and then there are things NOT to do. Treatment for those manifesting AIDS-related diseases largely depends on the nature of the opportunistic infections afflicting them. Patients should closely examine the treatments offered to them in the light of increasing an already toxic situation. For instance, those manifesting any of the major epithelial cancers would do well to understand that toxic chemotherapy and harmful radiation treatments have no proven track record of extending life and can actually kill the patient before the cancer does. Vitamin B17 Metabolic Therapy, on the other hand, is a simple nutritional protocol, outlawed by the medical establishment, that has been used to great effect in treating all forms of cancer in the countries where it is available.[415] Immune deficiency diseases are of course a serious matter and qualified health advice should always be sought. But the patient should exercise strict discernment in accepting or rejecting the types of treatments offered to them by traditional medicine in the light of a diagnosis of 'AIDS'.

Symptomless individuals living with an HIV positive diagnosis should get educated on the issues raised in this book. They might wish to consider moving into a detoxification and full nutrition regimen. Neways International is one such supplier of high quality and effective treatments. And there may well be other natural treatments that have some measure of efficacy. The important point to remember is to stop the toxic build-up by ending the toxic lifestyle. This is where recovery has to start.

Q: What do you say to rumours that AIDS was a covert US government project designed to wage war on the undesirable elements of society?

A: Most who have kept an ear open to the conspiracy theories surrounding AIDS will have heard them all: that AIDS came from the

---

[415] Day, Phillip, *Cancer: Why We're Still Dying to Know the Truth*, ibid.

green monkey in Africa, that it was a biological warfare agent developed at Fort Detrick, Maryland. That it originated out of the Porton Down research facility in the UK.

The facts surrounding AIDS and HIV necessarily impose a number of restrictions that help us to determine what AIDS is and what it is not. Firstly, AIDS is clearly not viral, so any theories expounding some doomsday virus incubated in the beakers of mad scientists working in secret underground New World Order institutions hold little credibility. Conspiring globalists are unlikely to unleash an unstoppable virus into the world when they themselves would be at risk from it. We know very little about how to control even flu and cold viruses, so how likely is it that some scientists (even mad ones) would release such an agent for some specific agenda?

In his book, *Emerging Viruses, AIDS and Ebola,*[416] Leonard Horowitz includes references to HIV as perhaps accidentally making its way into the populace as a result of biowarfare tinkering at various labs across the world. At no time does Horowitz spend time researching whether HIV actually exists. His work to uncover governmental corruption notwithstanding, his theories on 'HIV as germ warfare' are yet another example of an incorrect course being followed with the maximum of precision.

Did HIV originate in Africa? The question is meaningless. First *find* HIV.

Did AIDS originate in Africa? No. AIDS, or immune deficiency, manifests itself wherever there is chronic, long-term self-abuse and/or malnutrition.

Is there evidence that the authorities know about AIDS as a collection of illnesses brought on by fast-track, toxic lifestyle and/or malnutrition and are deliberately not considering it? Yes.

Is there evidence that the authorities know how to save AIDS patients through removing toxicity and/or adding the necessary nutrition and basic medicines, but are not promoting this agenda? Yes.

Do the authorities know that AIDS drugs kill adults and babies? Yes.

---

[416] **Horowitz, Leonard** *Emerging Viruses, AIDS and Ebola*, Tetrahedron Publishing, 1998

Are there population control programs currently underway which are benefiting from a continued misunderstanding of the true facts about AIDS? To the very great shame of humankind - yes.

Q: A large number of influential Christians in America have been responsible for hyping AIDS as the wrath of God on wicked homosexuals and drug users. Where do you stand on this issue?

A: There is no question that certain powerful Christian platforms leapt on the AIDS bandwagon to promote their own agendas with regard to opposing gay rights and highlighting 'God's judgement on homosexuals'. One example is a famous annual Christian conference held in the Mid-West, organised by several large Christian groups, in which the 'AIDS on a doorknob' idea was given some airing and dark sentiments preached that God was exacting punishment on evildoers through the agency of AIDS.

There are also organisations who have used AIDS as a springboard for their own bigotries. God is not wreaking havoc on homosexuals with AIDS. If AIDS were divine and exclusive judgment on homosexuals and drug-abusers, then why are only a small proportion of these demographic groups actually affected by the syndrome? Bigotry and AIDS have always gone hand-in-hand. Jesus Christ always taught people righteousness by His loving, non-judgmental actions as well as His words. Yes, the Bible does indeed promote morality and condemns certain behaviour. But just as clearly, the Bible speaks about there being only one Judge...and it isn't us. Our stance at Credence is that all people are equally loved by Jesus Christ and equally in need of our loving Father's forgiveness and personal mercy.

Q: Where does this information on AIDS leave the AIDS charities and celebrity charity concerts?

A: It was Vance Packard, the author of numerous works on subliminal advertising, who, in his book *Hidden Persuaders*, made the observation that in order to gain the moral/political/philosophical high ground in a given debate, your chances of gaining that ground are improved considerably by pre-empting the opening vocabulary. The work of 'God Bless the Child'[417] is a classic example. Funded by Abbott Laboratories, Bristol-Myers Squibb, Pharmacia & Upjohn and other

---

[417] www.iapac.org The International Association of Physicians in AIDS Care.

financially interested parties, 'God Bless the Child' is currently distributing conventional AIDS medications to children in Romania, South Africa and Cambodia. To argue against this 'compassionate' and 'Godly' form of doctoring is to be seen as divisive and going against the flow of human kindness.

In reality those beautiful children are being given known toxic medications. The emotive photography means nothing. In cynically using the word 'God' in their campaign, the think tanks behind organisations such as these adequately fulfil the description of those who 'masquerade as angels of light'.

There are also a great number of genuinely caring and compassionate conventional 'AIDS care' organisations who literally have no idea what effect their pharmaceutical ministrations are having on those in their care. The following text was used to support the photograph of Ida, reproduced in Part One (see photo section). Credence contacted Ida's care agency to request the possibility of being supplied with further details. The care, love and concern the carers had for Ida were self-evident and beyond question. Their moving tribute to Ida reads as follows:

"After a year of gradual decline, Ida Janel left her physical body on 2nd January 1997 at 12:02am. We lost our sweet Ida to a myriad of systemic failures, toxic shock, respiratory failure and heart failure all brought on by that vicious virus, HIV." [418]

Was it a vicious virus which finally caused Ida to leave her physical body? Or was it not the case that Ida died of toxic shock through AIDS medications, albeit innocently dripped into her little body, every bedside action being carried out with the best of intention? A copy of *World Without AIDS* has been sent to Ida's carers.

In a different vein, Joan Shenton writes about the compassionate celebrity.

"We've all seen them, the compassionate celebrities who, with sad expression, don the mantle of corporate grief for AIDS victims and sufferers and feel they are doing good. Granted they are doing this with the best of intentions, but far from good, they are actually doing damage, using their celebrity status to

---

[418] www.thebody.com/loel poor

raise funds for AIDS research that is totally misdirected and orchestrated by a profit-oriented and commercially blinkered pharmaceutical industry." [419]

As well as with the maximum of *precision*, one can just as easily follow an incorrect course with the maximum of *compassion*. An extensive rewrite of all compassionate but wildly incorrect literature is now needed in order to bring truth to bear on the subject of global AIDS. We hope these organisations face up to their responsibilities in this matter, and do just that.

---

[419] *Continuum*, Vol 4, No 6, July 1997

OK. SO WHAT CAN YOU DO?

King Canute was told by a fawning courtier that even the waves of the sea would obey him. Upon arriving at the water's edge however, Canute came face to face with the uncompromising forces of nature and ended up with wet feet (history does not record what happened to his courtier). The tide of AIDS however is not of nature, it is of man. And with the concerted effort of man, this tide can indeed be turned back. So what can you do?

Listed on the following pages are a wide variety of useful names, addresses and telephone numbers of organisations who, in one way or another, are worthy of inclusion. They are divided into self-explanatory sections.

ADDING YOUR VOICE TO THE DEBATE

World Without AIDS is ideal for giving people the facts they need on this subject. Why not do further research with some of the sources contained in this book? Let everybody know about this book and have a chance to end their fear of AIDS. We believe also that every time you tune in to a public service provider such as CNN or the BBC reporting on HIV and you hear those expressions "HIV, the virus that causes AIDS" or "Africa devastated by AIDS", that station should receive your emails, faxes and telephone calls by the thousand. As enlightened viewers and listeners, you can make a difference. Tell them *"This debate is fundamentally dishonest. We're not taking it any more!"* Nothing is more powerful. People take notice of strident voices – especially yours!

Write to your local politician, your local doctor, to the health authorities, to national government bodies, to local and national newspapers. In so doing, for the first time in your life perhaps, you run the risk of becoming... a dissident! The Collins dictionary defines a dissident as *'a person who disagrees with a government or powerful organisation.'* This current section will give you all the names, addresses and phone numbers to lodge your legitimate dissident view. Dare to be counted a dissident.

If you have seen or read something on AIDS that you would like to raise with the appropriate bodies, here are a few simple guidelines.

Strike while the iron is hot. If writing, be polite and concise. Always be prepared to give your name and address, the date, time and title of the program concerned, and state precisely what you liked or what caused you offence. If phoning, consider first what you want to say and stay calm. If you are not satisfied with the answer you are given, write to the program producer. Part of the inscription above the door at BBC Broadcasting House, Portland Place in London reads as follows, *"..that everything offensive to decency and hostile to peace will be expelled, and that the nation will incline its ear to those things which are lovely, pure and of good report and thus pursue the path of wisdom and virtue."* Let's hold them to it.

Listed below are the major UK and US media consortiums and regulatory bodies. Go for it!

Independent Television Commission
(regulates all commercially funded television)
33 Foley St
London
W1P 7LB
Tel: 020 7255 3000
Fax: 020 7306 7800
e-mail: publicaffairs@itc.org.uk

The Broadcasting Standards Commission
(considers complaints about standards and fairness)
7 The Sanctuary
London
SW1P 3JS
Tel: 020 7233 0544
Fax: 020 7233 0397
e-mail: bsc@bsc.org.uk

Radio Authority
regulates radio programming
Holbrook House
14 Great Queen St
Holborn
London
WC2B 5DG
Tel: 020 7430 2724
Fax: 020 7405 7062
e-mail:
info@radioauthority.org.uk

UK TV and RADIO STATIONS

BBC Television Centre
Tel: 0208743 8000
Fax: 0208576 7450
e-mail: Vlc@bbc.co.uk

BBC Radio 1-5
Tel: 020 7580 4468
Fax: 020 7705 3030
e-mail: Vlc@bbc.co.uk

Carlton Television
Tel: 020 7240 4000
Fax: 020 7240 4171
e-mail:
dutyoffice@carltontv.co.uk

GMTV Ltd
Tel: 020 7827 7000
Fax: 020 7827 7001
e-mail: talk2us@gmtv.co.uk

Independent Television News Ltd (ITN)
Tel: 020 7833 3000
Fax: 020 7430 4228
e-mail:
viewer.liaison@itn.co.uk

Channel 4
Tel: 020 7396 4444
Fax: 020 7306 8347
e-mail: viewer-enqs@channel4.co.uk

British Sky Broadcasting Ltd
Tel: 020 7705 3000
Fax: 020 7705 3030
e-mail: feedback@sky.co.uk

US TV NEWS STATIONS

NBC
Dateline NBC -
dateline@nbc.com
Meet the Press - mtp@nbc.com
NBC Nightly News -
nightly@nbc.com

Today Show - today@nbc.com
(718) 656 1350

CBS
www.cbsnews.cbs.com,
Feedback section
(212) 975 4321

ABC
www.abcnews.go.com
(212) 456 7777

CNN
www.cnn.com - Feedback
section
(212) 714 7800

OTHER GROUPS

UK All-Party Parliamentary Group on AIDS
Houses of Parliament
Westminster
London SW1
Tel: 020 7219 6916

World Health Organization
Avenue Appia 20
1211 Geneva 27
Switzerland
Tel: +41 22 791 2111
Fax: +41 22 791 3111
e-mail: Dr Gro Harlem Brundtland
Director General info@who.ch

UNAIDS
As above (WHO)

UNFPA
220 East 42nd Street
New York
NY 10017
USA
Tel: (212) 297 5279
e-mail: Dr Nafis Sadik
ryanw@unfpa.org

World Bank
1818 H Street, NW,
Washington DC, 20435
USA
Tel: (202) 477 1234
How to report fraud
www.worldbank.org
e-mail re African campaign
rtoye@worldbank.org
e-mail Dr Peter Piot
unaids@unaids.org

PEOPLE HELPING PEOPLE
TO RETURN TO HEALTH

> **Please note: The following information is provided for educational purposes only. No claims are made or implied in providing this information. Readers must use their discretion, and a qualified medical practitioner should always be consulted in the matter of treatment decisions for any disease.**

AIDS, as a syndrome of toxic load, can be viewed as one more example of a wider poisoning underway. Each year our cities, towns, neighbourhoods and homes become ever more industrialised and toxic. In addressing the parallel rise in cancer incidence (another toxic syndrome) with a nation's increasing industrialisation, Dr Alexander Berglas had this to say in 1957:

> *"Civilization is, in terms of cancer, a juggernaut that cannot be stopped... It is the nature and essence of industrial civilization to be toxic in every sense... We are faced with the grim prospect that the advance of cancer and of civilization parallel each other."*[420]

Samuel Epstein MD, the world-renowned authority on the causes and prevention of cancer, was named the 1998 winner of the Right Livelihood Award (also known as the "Alternative Nobel Prize"). Toxins expert Dr Epstein has devoted the greater part of his life to studying and fighting society's toxicity and the commensurate rise of cancer. He is Professor of Occupational and Environmental Medicine at the School of Public Health, University of Illinois Medical Center at Chicago, and the chairman of the Cancer Prevention Coalition.

Epstein has authored over 280 scientific articles and seven books, including *Hazardous Wastes in America*, *The Politics of Cancer*, and has co-authored *The Safe Shopper's Bible* and the *Breast Cancer Prevention Program*. Invited to speak at a recent health convention, Dr Epstein had the following interesting insight to share with his audience as a result of his considerable research:

---

[420] **Berglas, Alexander** preface to *Cancer: Nature, Cause and Cure*, Paris, 1957

"You and I have become virtually powerless in our ability to influence governmental decisions. This power now rests in the hands of major political, multi-billion dollar corporations that have taken this power from us."

Today society faces a double-edged sword. Industry and chemical manufacturers are flooding the public domain with chemicals which find their way into our food, into the pharmaceutical substances we consume on a daily basis and into the household and personal care products we believe are safe for us and our families to use. On the other hand, a surprising attack is underway by both industry and government on the public's right to care for its own health through the consumption of vitamins, minerals and other benevolent food factors – a public that has increasingly come to distrust the conventional drug wisdom promoted by government and the medical establishment.

Such a health revolution has come about largely because the public perceives that drug-based medications and chemical treatments are not the magic bullets it has been led to believe. And it is this surge of interest *away* from drug-based establishment medicine and *towards* natural and nutritional alternatives acceptable to the body that has fuelled probably the greatest health revolution the world has ever seen. Epstein, like many other professionals, is familiar with the stranglehold over public information exercised by government and the corporate world. And he welcomes the advent of informed choice for the health conscious individual.

Maximising the Body's Ability to Combat Danger

Our bodies combat industrialised society's toxic onslaught in a variety of ingenious ways. But our body's ability to maintain health in the face of such toxic invasion depends upon it working in optimum condition. The problem is, almost everyone today suffers from some kind of nutritional deficiency for reasons we will examine in a minute – a deficiency which hugely compromises our body's ability to combat ill-health. Those suffering from AIDS-related symptoms are usually in a far more serious mineral deficiency situation.

There has been a lot of controversy over whether nutritional (food) supplements are really necessary when we are told we can 'get all the nutrients we need from the four food groups.' Nutritional supplements are simply food factors that may not be present in our regular foods in the amounts we need. Quite literally, we are what we eat. So correct nutrition is about as important as it gets since every cell that makes up who we are must be manufactured by our body from the nutrients it receives from the foods we consume.

The problem is, our farm soils and food chain no longer contain adequate minerals for us to maintain sound health with food alone, a fact which makes a mockery of the four-food-group mantra. This was the central premise of US Senate Document #264[421] which warned the American people in 1936 that even foods considered healthy were lacking vital minerals and therefore slowly starving the populations of their vital nutritional requirements. It was a pressing issue back then. Today this situation has immeasurably worsened.

The reason this continues to happen is economic. The crops farmers produce draw the minerals out of the soil and hold them in a suspended 'colloidal' form which we later eat. Farmers are paid for tons and bushels per acre and have no economic incentive to replenish the soil with minerals, save those in the form of fertiliser (NPK) that directly affect the bounty of their harvest. Thus the mineral deficiency problem becomes worse year by year, and so do the afflictions that come upon humanity as a result.

Therefore mineral and food supplementation is not some quaint health fad pushed by your local vitamin shop. It can literally make the difference between life and death. To this end, Credence recommends that AIDS sufferers and other readers interested in personal health recovery focus on researching the body's nutritional needs. Credence has many testimonies on file from individuals who argue that their recovery is the direct result of concentrating primarily on providing their bodies with the optimum nutrition they need to maintain health.

The watchwords for a longer-lasting and healthier life just make common sense: stop the poisoning and give the body the vital nutrients it needs to repair itself and thereafter maintain optimum performance. You do it for your car. Do it for yourself and your family too!

---

[421] See section entitled *Why Are the Nations Dying?*

During the course of researching this and other projects, Credence researchers have come into contact with many companies who offer nutritional products to the public. However one company kept appearing before us with their excellence as we researched the various nutritional options open to sufferers of cancer and AIDS. So Credence decided to pay this particular company a visit at its US headquarters to find out more about its operation.

NEWAYS INTERNATIONAL, SALEM, UTAH, USA

Neways International was founded by Tom Mower, a biochemist who previously worked in the chemical industry. Mower has had considerable experience in handling toxic chemicals and understands all too well their effects upon humans and the environment. What Mower discovered during his industry years urgently impressed upon him the vital need to provide the public with safe and effective alternatives to many of the products society was currently using – products that over time were damaging and even ending valuable lives.[422]

Mower subsequently put his plan into action and, from humble beginnings, **Neways** has today achieved impressive success in over forty countries, providing the public with a range of over two hundred products that are as unique as they are startlingly effective. Dr Epstein himself is enthusiastic about the groundbreaking work **Neways** has done and awarded the company the "Seal of Safety" from the Cancer Prevention Coalition: *"Neways has pioneered and succeeded in providing consumers with cosmetics and toiletries free of cancer-causing and harmful ingredients and contaminants."* Epstein states. *"I warmly congratulate them on their accomplishments."*

It is in the realm of health supplements and nutritional support too that Credence believes **Neways** is in a league of its own. From powerful antioxidant formulas through to complete vitamin and mineral support, anti-parasite programs and immune system enhancers, what makes these products unusually effective is the special way in which they are formulated and cleaned. To find out more about **Neways** and

---

[422] Day, Phillip *Cancer: Why We're Still Dying to Know the Truth*, ibid.

the products they make, you can make use of the contact details below:

> US/Canada: 1(888) 575 7812
> International: +44 1622 832386
> US Fax: (425) 969 2940
> UK Fax: (0870) 137 7441
> www.neways.com

HEAL is a non-profit, community based education network with independent chapters throughout the United States and around the world. Originally founded in 1982 as an AIDS support group under the direction of president Dr Michael Ellner and science advisor Dr Frank Buianoukas, **HEAL** New York became the inspiration for an international movement challenging the validity of the HIV=AIDS hypothesis and the efficacy of HIV-based treatment protocols.

For more than a decade, **HEAL** has been the leading source for comprehensive information on effective, non-toxic approaches to recovery from AIDS defining illnesses and has served as a consistent voice calling for honesty in AIDS issues.

HEAL
Tel: +1 (1) 212 873 0780
Fax: +1 (1) 212 873 0891
E-mail: healintl@aol.com

ALIVE & WELL AIDS ALTERNATIVES
ALIVE & WELL questions the HIV=AIDS=Death paradigm based on a growing body of scientific, medical, and epidemiological data. This organisation also promotes awareness of life-affirming facts to HIV positive diagnosed persons and concerned citizens worldwide. In addition to sponsoring scientific and medical studies, **ALIVE & WELL** offers a yearly calendar of free community events, produces books,

videos, and other materials that present alternative views of AIDS, and shares resources with **ALIVE & WELL** affiliates and other organisations around the world that support informed choices for people affected by HIV and AIDS.

ALIVE & WELL
Christine Maggiore, Director
11684 Ventura Boulevard
Studio City
CA 91604 USA
Toll-Free: +1(1) 877 92-ALIVE
Fax: +1(1) 818 780-7093
Email: christine@aliveandwell.org

THE NATIONAL VACCINE INFORMATION CENTER (NVIC)
Founded in 1982 by parents of vaccine-injured children, the **NVIC** is a non-profit, educational organisation dedicated to preventing vaccine injuries and deaths through public education and defending the right of all citizens to informed consent to vaccination. **NVIC** takes the position that scientific evidence to date is not sufficient to prove HIV causes AIDS and that if any HIV vaccine is made available to the public in the future, no citizen should be required to use it without their voluntary, informed consent. **NVIC** maintains that the ethical principle of informed consent, which is applied to all other medical procedures carrying a risk of injury or death, must be applied to all vaccinations, including any future AIDS vaccine.

THE NATIONAL VACCINE INFORMATION CENTER
512 West Maple Avenue, Suite 206
Vienna
VA 22180 USA
Tel: +1 (1) 703 938-0342
Fax: +1 (1) 703 938-5768

REAPPRAISING AIDS
This is the monthly publication of the Group for the Scientific Reappraisal of the HIV/AIDS Hypothesis. Every issue offers very readable and highly informative insights into the facts behind the current AIDS news. An excellent guide to understanding the realities of

the latest claims, number games and hype from the AIDS establishment. Annual subscriptions are available for a $25 donation and are tax-deductible. Please send your cheque or money order to:

THE GROUP
7514 Girard Avenue #1-331
La Jolla
CA 92037
USA
Tel: +1 (1)810 772 9926
Fax: +1 (1) 619 272-1621

CONTINUUM
A full-size magazine published bi-monthly in England. Covers AIDS news and events from around the globe and features extensive articles on standard AIDS-think, on the dangers of pharmaceutical drug treatments and on alternative approaches to examining AIDS and HIV. An intelligent publication produced by a non-profit group of international dissidents (some of whom have been labelled 'HIV positive'). Annual subscriptions are $40. Call if overseas to obtain correct details on postage.

CONTINUUM
Unit 4a Hollybush Place
London E2 9QX
Tel: +44 (0)20 7613 3909
e-mail: continu@dircon.co.uk

ORGANISATIONS WORTHY OF SUPPORT

PARTAGE TANZANIE
Box 1404
Bukoba
Kagera
Tanzania
Africa

PARTAGE (French for 'share') supports some four thousand people in and around the Kagera area. The Krynen's outreach program brings

242

them into direct contact with families, widows, orphans and destitute children. Donations to this valuable work can be made direct to the organisation's above address.

WATERAID
FREEPOST (SW1644)
Prince Consort House
27-29 Albert Embankment
LONDON SE1 7YY
Tel: +44(0)20 7793 4526

2 billion people around the world (a third of the world's population) do not have access to basic sanitation. Over 1 billion do not have a safe supply of water close to their homes. Every six seconds, one person dies from a water-contamination illness.

WATERAID'S vision is of a world where everyone has access to safe water and effective sanitation. To date, **WATERAID**-funded projects have enabled over 5 million people to gain access to safe water. Tax-deductible donations are gratefully accepted at the above address or credit card line.

➤ £10 ($16) will provide a lasting supply of safe water for someone living in the developing world.
➤ £25 ($40) will train a local person to maintain handpumps in India.
➤ £100 will enable two families in Ghana to build their own latrines.

TRUE FREEDOM TRUST
PO Box 13
Prenton
WIRRAL CH43 6YB
UK
Tel: +44 (0)151 653 0773
Fax: +44 (0)151 653 7036
e-mail:martin@tftrust.u-net.com

EXODUS NORTH AMERICA
PO Box 77652
SEATTLE
WA 98177
USA
Tel: (206) 784 7799
www.exodus.base.org

TRUE FREEDOM TRUST and **EXODUS** are two organisations dedicated to giving men and women the necessary emotional and practical support who find themselves struggling with social addictions and fast-track lifestyle problems.

It is said that history is written by the victors. It is our fervent hope that this book, along with your dissident voice and helpful actions, will contribute to the rewriting of the true history of HIV and AIDS.

IF YOU WOULD LIKE FURTHER INFORMATION OR WISH TO OBTAIN MORE COPIES OF THIS BOOK, PLEASE USE THE CONTACT INFORMATION BELOW:

International: +44 1622 832386
Fax: +44 870 137 7441
www.credence.org
e-mail: sales@credence.org

Appendices

ENTRENCHED SCIENTIFIC ERROR

it can happen... and it does

(Virus-Hunting Disasters)

For those of us who cannot come to terms with the possibility that the medical establishment could have been wrong about AIDS for so long, a quick trawl through medical history serves as a salutary wake-up call. History is replete with flashes of medical inspiration which have proven to be nothing more than *an incorrect course followed with the maximum of precision*. This is the classic definition of entrenched scientific error. The chief flaw comes when a new public health emergency is centrally organised with little room for wider debate or correction.

The first president of the United States, George Washington, was bled to death in 1797 by some of the most well-educated medical practitioners of his day. No doubt, had you been at the august president's deathbed raising a fuss as they incised his wrists, these learned professionals would have angrily turned on you: *"We know what we're doing. We're DOCTORS!"* It must be noted that the men who killed George Washington were extremely intelligent. They were among the most experienced practitioners of their day – they were highly educated. And they were wrong.

King Charles II of England's doctors were also wrong. When His Majesty fell into a swoon in 1685 (possibly suffering a stroke), he was attended by fourteen of the nation's most well-educated and skilled physicians. His treatment is recorded thus:

> *"...the king was bled to the extent of a pint from a vein in his right arm. Next his shoulder was cut into and the incised area was supped to suck out an additional eight ounces of blood. An emetic and a purgative were administered followed by a second purgative followed by an enema containing antimony, sacred bitters, rock salt, mallow leaves, violets, beetroot, camomile*

245

flowers, fennel seed, linseed, cinnamon, cardamom seed, saphron, cochineal and aloes. The king's scalp was shaved and a blister raised. A sneezing powder of hellebore was administered. A plaster of Burgundy pitch and pigeon dung was applied to the feet. Medicaments included melon seeds, manna, slippery elm, black cherry water, lime flowers, lily of the valley, peony, lavender and dissolved pearls. As he grew worse, forty drops of extract of human skull were administered followed by a rallying dose of Raleigh's antidote. Finally bezoar stone was given." [423]

Curiously His Majesty's strength seemed to wane after all these heroic interventions and as the end of his life seemed imminent, his doctors tried a last ditch attempt by forcing more Raleigh's mixture, pearl julep and ammonia down the dying king's throat. Further treatment was rendered more difficult by the king's death." [424]

Hopefully posterity will not judge us too harshly with the barbaric treatments dispensed by the orthodoxy to AIDS patients today – treatments which have as much in common with sound medicinal practice today as pigeon dung had for King Charles II's welfare then.

Included below is a brief study of a number of other very costly and very incorrect medical courses.

Scurvy

Scurvy had traditionally been a fatal scourge to seafarers. Between 1497 and 1499, veteran Portuguese explorer Vasco da Gama lost over a hundred men to the disease on one voyage alone. And according to naval records, between 1600 and 1800 over one million British sailors died of scurvy. Yet for hundreds of years the cure for this gum-rotting, organ-destroying disease was well known to peoples credited by the West with limited medical intelligence.

---

[423] **Buckman, Dr Robert & Karl Sabbagh** *Magic or Medicine?* Pan Books, 1993 Dr Buckman explains that a bezoar was held by legend to be the crystallized tears of a deer which had been bitten by a snake. In fact most bezoars used in therapy were gallstones found in the stomachs of goats. See also **Silverman, W A** *Controlled Clinical Trials*, "The Optimistic Bias Favouring Medical Attention", Elsevier Science, New York, 1991

[424] Noted by H W Haggard and quoted in **Silverman, W A** *Human Experimentation*, Oxford Medical Publications, Oxford, 1985

In the winter of 1534/5, French explorer Jacques Cartier found himself stranded when his ship became trapped in the ice in a tributary of the St Lawrence River in Canada. Soon his crew began dying of scurvy. Out of one hundred and ten men, twenty-five had already perished of the disease and many others were so sick they were not expected to recover.

Believing that the condition was caused either by bad vapours lurking in the hold of his ship or some malignant cause to do with the 'sea airs' (a common belief at that time), Cartier was astonished when help came from an unexpected direction. Some friendly local Indians showed Cartier how to boil pine needles and bark from the white pine, later found to be rich in Vitamin C.[425] His sailors swiftly recovered after drinking the prepared beverage. Upon his return, Cartier enthusiastically reported this miraculous cure to medical authorities. But Cartier's observations were dismissed as "witchdoctors' curses of ignorant savages" and the authorities did nothing about the information they were given, except to log it into their records.

On a lengthy voyage to Brazil, Sir Richard Hawkins, the famous British Elizabethan admiral, faced scurvy among his crew and discovered that eating oranges and lemons cured the condition very quickly. However, despite reporting this phenomenon to the British Admiralty and to any physicians who would listen, this valuable information was again ignored by the medical establishment.

Deaths from scurvy became so numerous that by the eighteenth century more British sailors were dying from ascorbic acid deficiency than were being killed in combat. In 1740, British admiral George A Anson set sail to circumnavigate the globe in his flagship *Centurion*. Originally starting with six ships and almost 2,000 men, *Centurion* was the only ship that eventually returned. Anson reported that scurvy alone had killed over 1,000 of his men.

---

[425] Interestingly, the main ingredients in the pine needles and bark offered to Cartier's sailors by the Indians are contained in a number of beneficial antioxidant products available today. Details on these and other health products are included in the section entitled *People Helping People*.

The great embarrassment this event caused in British Admiralty circles prompted naval surgeon John Lind to seek a cure for the dreaded disease. On 20th May 1747, Lind began an experiment which dramatically demonstrated that fresh greens and plenty of fruits eaten by scurvy sufferers produced stunning recoveries. Later experiments clearly showed that those who ate a balanced diet, fortified with these vegetable and fruit elements, did not contract scurvy.

Yet what was the reaction of the establishment? Once again, the British Admiralty and numerous other physicians, who were attempting to solve the same problem (and at the same time earn both grants and fame), barely acknowledged Lind's findings. It took 48 more years and thousands more scurvy deaths before his diet advice finally became official Navy quartermaster policy. Ironically, after implementing this simple measure, the British, who became known as 'limeys' because of their new nutrition procedure, soon gained strategic ascendancy on the world's seas. After 1800, British sailors never contracted scurvy. The naval might of Britain's enemies however continued to be decimated by it. Author Edward Griffin surmises that the founding of the British Empire in large measure *"was the direct result of overcoming scientific prejudice against vitamin therapy."*[426]

One would have thought that scurvy ended there. But that was not the case. As the obsession with virus and microbe hunting began to grip developing medicine during the late nineteenth century, it was easier to blame a bacterium than to isolate the elusive vitamin. Scientists became distracted. Suddenly a simple nutritional deficiency no longer seemed the plausible and complete answer to scurvy. It had to be something more complicated, more scientific. Whilst there were indeed some blessings which arose from increased scientific knowledge, there were also the attendant pitfalls. The new milk-pasteurisation techniques for instance unwittingly destroyed the milk's ascorbic acid content, leading to hundreds of fresh scurvy cases among children each year.

Professor C P Stewart of Edinburgh University remarks:

"One factor which undoubtedly held up the development of

---

[426] Griffin, G Edward, *World Without* Cancer, ibid. p.54

the concept of deficiency diseases was the discovery of bacteria in the nineteenth century and the consequent preoccupation of scientists and doctors with positive infective agents in disease. So strong was the impetus provided by bacteriology that many diseases which we now know to be due to nutritional or endocrine deficiencies were, as late as 1910, thought to be 'toxemias'." [427]

By the 1930s, purified Vitamin C had been successfully isolated and scurvy was officially declared vanquished. For the correct cure to reach this status in Europe, all it had taken to conquer scurvy was 400 years of following an incorrect course, many, many thousands of deaths, and finally the realisation that the answer did indeed lie in a simple diet of fruit.

Beriberi

Though more well known as a disease of the Orient, beriberi put in a fearsome appearance after the French Revolution. Professor Peter Duesberg explains:

"Though it has primarily plagued Asia throughout history, beriberi appeared with a vengeance in the West after the French Revolution, when the French population rejected the dark bread of peasantry in favour of the royal milled white bread, from which the thiamin [Vitamin B1] had been unknowingly removed. Bread processing soon swept throughout Europe and the United States, and beriberi followed closely." [428]

A Japanese doctor and later Surgeon General to their navy, Dr Kanehiro Takaki, was appalled at the attrition beriberi was wreaking among his sailors. He began by experimenting with their diets and soon found that he could cure and prevent the disease completely. He reported his results to his superiors, and the military acted without delay, changing the official diet of the Japanese Navy. The Japanese beriberi epidemic was eradicated in 1885.

---

[427] **Stewart, CP** and D Guthrie, *Lind's Treatise on Scurvy,* Edinburgh University Press, 1953 pp. 408-409

[428] Duesberg, Peter H, *Inventing...* ibid. See also **Williams, R R** *Towards the Conquest of Beriberi,* Harvard University Press, 1961

Takaki enthusiastically spread the word, even having his findings written up in the British medical journal *Lancet*. However, instead of the British medical establishment acknowledging beriberi as a chronic metabolic deficiency disease brought on by the missing food factor thiamin, Takaki's research and results were ignored. Once again, it was the height of the bacteria-hunting craze, and Robert Koch had only just isolated the bacillus for tuberculosis, bringing the promise of ending the rampage of other global killers through the lens of microbiology. Even in Takaki's own country, the virus hunters began sniping at him, insisting that the beriberi outbreak had merely been cured by improving the sailors' sanitary conditions and stamping out 'a beriberi micro-organism'.

Christian Eijkman, a Dutch army physician, also observed beriberi among Dutch soldiers in Java in the late 1800s. He noticed that the soldiers were getting sick while the natives were spared the illness. Nevertheless, his microbe hunting background led him to believe that there was an infectious cause to the disease. Yet while investigating microbes as the cause of beriberi, Eijkman's experiments consistently failed to meet Koch's Postulates. He could not produce any guilty agent common to all his patients. Frustrated, he tried to transmit the disease to chickens using the blood from beriberi victims. At first nothing happened. Then the chickens began to get sick from a syndrome quite similar to beriberi. Further experimentation revealed that the birds were succumbing to sickness because they were eating polished (de-husked) rice. Eijkman realised that the Dutch all ate polished rice, while the local population did not.

Eijkman's findings though were not met with the approbation he expected. His colleagues, busy hunting down protozoa, bacteria, viruses and fungi for beriberi, were openly contemptuous of his nutrition theory. Between 1890 and 1911, while thousands died across the world from the disease, the medical research establishment remained largely fixated with the notion of an infectious beriberi.

Bacteriologist Robert Koch himself got to grips with his own failure to provide the causative microbial agent and graciously published his negative results, prompting a search for the answer in new arenas. Sadly, this did not stop the more enthusiastic virus hunters from recommending that patients with beriberi suffer the necessary treatments for the 'deadly microbe'. Those treatments included quinine, arsenic, strychnine and an awesomely agonising death.

Vitamin B1 (thiamin) was finally isolated in 1911 and again in 1926. Today the vitamin is always added back into bread after the refining process and as a result beriberi has all but disappeared. Robert Williams, one of the scientists who pioneered the isolation of Vitamin B1, later commented on the tragic blindness that had caused so many needless deaths.

> *"Because of* [the work of Pasteur and Koch] *and other dramatic successes bacteriology had advanced, within twenty years after its birth, to become the chief cornerstone of medical education. All young physicians were so imbued with the idea of infection as the cause of disease that it presently came to be accepted as almost axiomatic that disease could have no other cause. This preoccupation of physicians with infection as a cause of disease was doubtless responsible for many digressions from attention to food as the causal factor of beriberi. "*[429]

Pellagra
(Trouble in the South)

Pellagra was a fatal disease that affected the poor. Noted originally in the eighteenth century as a European condition that appeared to be linked to corn diets among the impoverished, pellagra's symptoms were as exotic as they were fatal. Named 'pellagra' (the Italian for 'rough skin'), sufferers of this disease were affected by dermatitis, inflammations of the mucous membranes, chronic diarrhoea and mental problems, including depression, irritability, anxiety, confusion, migraine headaches, delusions and hallucinations.

Most European doctors working in the eighteenth and early nineteenth century had correctly noted two things about pellagra. Firstly, that it only occurred within groups that were poor. Secondly, that it was linked in some way to corn diets, which had become popular among the poor as a cheap and convenient staple diet. Some

---

[429] Williams, R R, ibid.

theorised that a fungus growing on corn produced a poison that caused pellagra. Others surmised that corn was not nutritious enough, and that pellagra was some kind of nutritional deficiency disease.

Many doctors being trained around the end of the 1800s were specialising in the new medical science - microbiology. And so inevitably, new disease syndromes were analysed as microbiological illnesses. For instance, Titius, a prominent German bacteriologist, pronounced pellagra infectious, even though he had never been to the afflicted areas and had a cursory knowledge of the condition. Other doctors began treating pellagra as infectious, and so the remedies of the day employed against infection were used to appalling effect - quinine, arsenic and strychnine.

The Italian researcher Ceni claimed that a fungus growing on mouldy corn was responsible for releasing poison into the patient, thus causing the disease. Ceni's work inspired others to come up with their own proprietary bacteria, which then created a new problem: the sheer volume of papers being written on these new 'infectious agents' for pellagra were consuming prodigious amounts of time to study and refute, thus preventing any possibility that closed minds could be opened to other potential causal factors. The European microbe-hunting bonanza continued, and a cure for pellagra remained as remote as ever.

And then in 1902, an isolated first case was noticed in Georgia, USA. Then in 1906, a rash of pellagra cases occurred in Alabama in a hospital for the insane. Eighty-eight patients contracted the condition and most subsequently died. Soon cases were appearing everywhere, even in some major metropolitan areas of the United States.

Convinced that they were facing a grave new public health threat, the Public Health Service of the US government swung into action. It set up a pellagra institute in South Carolina and appointed Claude Lavinder to head up the research. Lavinder was convinced that pellagra was microbe-driven, but became frustrated when his experiments failed to produce a spread of the disease in animals. In 1909, a national conference on pellagra was convened, again in South Carolina. Once again, pellagra's links with corn diets and poverty were reiterated. The prevailing mood of the conference was that pellagra was either airborne or infectious in nature. The following year, John D Long replaced Lavinder as head of the PHS's pellagra lab. Long's theories on pellagra were influenced by the well-known British doctor, Louis Sambon, who also believed pellagra to be infectious.

With no evidence to back his claim, Sambon declared to the press in 1910 that pellagra, like malaria, was transmitted by insects. Now flies were apparently picking up the deadly pellagra 'microbe' from horses, who then transferred it to blackbirds, who then flew to other areas, where more insects became infected and then spread the pellagra 'microbe' to humans. Sambon had of course failed to consider the significance that, unlike malaria, pellagra was not spreading outside its declared risk groups like other insect-driven diseases.

But Sambon was considered a genius and he did have the advantage of the full weight of the medical establishment behind him. In 1912, the Department of Agriculture even sent a special team to South Carolina to study the role of insects in the transmission of pellagra. Newspapers began fanning the flames of fear, and soon those who had been diagnosed with the disease found themselves social and community outcasts. Researcher E W Etheridge gives us a picture of what it was like living under the shadow of pellagra in the early 1900s - a picture all too reminiscent of the hype and public fear that would later surround AIDS:

"So great was the horror of the disease that a diagnosis of pellagra was synonymous with a sentence of social ostracism. A severe case of eczema was enough to start a stampede in a community, and 'pellagrins' sometimes covered their hands with gloves and salve, hoping to conceal their condition.

Many hospitals refused admission to pellagra patients. One in Atlanta did so on the grounds that it was an incurable disease. At another hospital in the same city, student nurses went on strike when they were required to attend to pellagrins. Physicians and nurses at Johns Hopkins Hospital in Baltimore were forbidden even to discuss the pellagra cases that might be there. Fear of the disease spread to schools and hotels too….

Tennessee began to isolate all its pellagra patients. The state board of health declared pellagra to be a transmissable disease and required physicians to report all cases.... Exhibits on pellagra were prepared for the public, creating fear of the disease along with interest in it... There was pressure for a quarantine in Kentucky, and pellagra patients at the Western Kentucky Asylum of the Insane were isolated...

Isolation did not prevent the spread of pellagra, but only heightened the panic over it." [430]

The turn in the disease came in 1914. Two important things happened that year. Britain declared war on Germany, and the United States Public Health Service appointed the unknown Dr Joseph Goldberger as head of its pellagra team. By this time, a quarter of a million people had perished from the pellagra epidemic in the United States.

Goldberger arrived in the South and, although a bacteriologist by profession, immediately began noticing obvious indications that pellagra was not infectious. He saw that even when pellagrins were kept in close confinement, their doctors and nurses did not contract the condition. He also noticed the different diets shared by the two groups. The poor ate the staple diet of corn, while the more affluent doctors, nurses and other hospital staff ate meat and vegetables. Dr Goldberger then set about following the *correct course with the maximum of precision*. He changed the diets of the pellagrins and was able to rid the disease entirely from hospitals, prisons, asylums and orphanages, demonstrating that the occurrence of pellagra was related to a deficiency of fresh green material in the diet. Goldberger approached this problem by the use of brewer's yeast, which would completely prevent and cure pellagra. Further studies years later would show that the factor in brewer's yeast that was most active in the curative effect was niacin, Vitamin B3.

What happened next amazed even the stoic Goldberger. The *New York Times* published the story of Goldberger's success with pellagra, explaining his hypothesis concerning poor diet and nutritional

---

[430] **Etheridge, E W** *The Butterfly Caste: A Social History of Pellagra in the South*, Greenwood Publishing Co, 1972. p.11

deficiency. As a result, Goldberger began to draw intense criticism, most notably from the medical establishment and their bacteria hunters. They accused Goldberger of propagating a dangerous and reckless philosophy in the light of so lethal a disease. A doctor at one medical conference drew considerable applause when he described the newspaper publicity on Goldberger's work as 'pernicious', expecting people to believe that such a lethal epidemic was solely the result of poor diet.[431]

Goldberger continued to receive major criticism from his peers, culminating in the most vicious attacks in 1916. Finally becoming exasperated, Goldberger, his wife and 14 workers decided to perform a series of rather extreme experiments for the benefit of the log-jammed medical establishment. They injected themselves with samples of blood, mucus, faeces other bodily fluids from the pellagrins. None of them contracted pellagra. The medical establishment was less than impressed and the attacks continued. As a result, Goldberger's dietary recommendations to end pellagra were completely ignored for the next twenty years, resulting in hundreds of thousands of further needless deaths. Many pellagrins who developed the mental anguishes associated with the condition were pronounced insane and shut away in asylums. Here they were subjected to electric shock treatment, powerful sedative drugs and prefrontal lobotomies in the hopes of rendering them controllable.

Goldberger continued trying to break the establishment's intransigence on pellagra up until his death in 1929. His work was continued by his faithful colleague Dr W Henry Sebrell. Cases of pellagra were still being reported up to the onset of World War 2 in 1939, even in spite of the fact that Vitamin B3 (niacin) had been isolated as the missing pellagra factor in the mid-1930s.

Soon after the end of World War II, it was finally admitted by the European and American medical establishments that pellagra had, all along, been a chronic metabolic deficiency disease brought on by an absence of green material in the common diet.

---

[431] Etheridge, E W, ibid.

Neurosyphilis
(Playing Medical Mind Games)

Neurosyphilis was supposedly identified along with syphilis, a genuinely infectious venereal disease, in the first few decades of the 20th century. Apparently, neurosyphilis was the result of the syphilis bacterium invading the central nervous system and the brain (sometimes years after the original infection), thus causing dementia and insanity. Today syphilis is still identified with insanity, and yet neurosyphilis and its accompanying dementias were subsequently found to be caused, not by the syphilis microbe at all, but by the toxic mercury and arsenic treatments used before 1950 in an attempt to stem the disease. It was only following the introduction of penicillin to treat syphilis in the 1950s that the mercury and arsenic treatments disappeared, and with it, neurosyphilis. It later became apparent that doctors had been confusing the long-term poisonous effects of their mercury and arsenic treatments with the syphilis itself.

Other false virus and microbe trails resulting in needless deaths and millions of wasted dollars include the hunt for non-existent microbes for Legionnaire's Disease (later found to be pneumonia), Pernicious Anemia (later found to be a Vitamin B12 Cyanocobalamin and B9 Folic Acid deficiency) and the most serious of them all, cancer (pancreatic enzyme and Vitamin B17 deficiencies, exacerbated by damaging environmental factors).[432]

SMON (Subacute Myelo-Optico-Neuropathy)
(Trouble In The Orient)

But the virus mis-diagnosis disaster that most clearly prefigures AIDS is surely the SMON fiasco of the 1960 - 1970s. In 1959, patients in Japan began falling ill from a combination of intestinal problems, internal bleeding, diarrhoea and a mysterious nerve disorder which paralysed limbs. As Japanese doctors began to notice the rising statistics, they recognised the spectre of a new syndrome. Almost

---

[432] **Day, Phillip** *Cancer: Why We're Still Dying to Know the Truth*, Credence Publications, 1999 A comprehensive coverage of the medical establishment's chronic mishandling of the cancer crisis, the deadly toxicity of existing treatments that are not working, and the cover-up over the marked anti-cancer properties of Vitamin B17 (amygdalin/laetrile) in its place within the treatment known as B17 Metabolic Therapy.

immediately, it was assumed the syndrome was infectious – even its sudden appearance was enough to convince many that a new virus was on the loose. Infection clusters broke out around villages and towns. One family member would succumb, followed by another within several weeks. Hospital staff too were not immune from the new epidemic – even doctors and medical workers became sick from the illness.

Yet there was striking evidence that SMON did not display symptoms indicative of an infectious disease. It was not spreading exponentially into the population, nor was it infecting both sexes equally – the classic infection pattern. The new syndrome favoured middle-aged women, was less common among men and was virtually non-existent among children, who are usually the first to succumb to any volatile infection. Neither did those suffering from SMON demonstrate any tell-tale signs of rash or fever, indicating that their body was fighting off an infectious micro-organism. These factors alone should have started the alarm bells ringing. Sadly they did not.

By 1964, with the Olympics looming, the SMON syndrome remained very much at large. The media had whipped Japan into national hysteria. Japanese politicians, formerly delighted with the idea of hosting the world's tourists at the long-awaited Olympic Games, ended up dreading the famous event, imagining in their worst fears an uncontrollable plague devastating the Games. Grant money was speedily allocated, an SMON commission convened, and Japanese virus hunters got to work in search of the guilty microbe.

After three years, no virus had been isolated and SMON was still killing the Japanese public. During the fruitless investigation however, one research team discovered that about half the SMON patients had been previously prescribed a diarrhoea-fighting drug known as Entero-vioform. The other half had received a compound marketed under the name Emaform. Both drugs were routinely prescribed for problems of the digestive tract, the early symptom of SMON, and for the first time, suspicion arose that maybe the two drugs had something to do with the disease. But after studying the evidence, the SMON commission remained intent on a viral explanation for the disease, and summarily dismissed the medication-linked theories, citing the improbability that two different drugs could cause the same illness.

By 1969, the Japanese government had become thoroughly unnerved by the medical establishment's continued failure to come up with any explanation or cure for SMON. A new SMON Research Commission was convened, an entity which was to become the largest and most well-funded medical commission ever devoted to a single disease in Japan. Dr Reisaku Kono, Japan's leading virologist, was chosen to chair the commission, sending a strong message to medical institutions world-wide that the centralised SMON research program was to remain dominated by the virus establishment. Yet by 1970, after twelve hard years of virus-centred research into SMON, researchers were still yielding the same dismal results. No virus behind SMON, and no relief in sight for the victims. To make matters worse, the death toll from the disease continued to rise, two thousand Japanese victims alone being claimed by SMON in 1969.

But one pharmacologist was on to something. Dr H Beppu had also noticed the Entero-vioform-Emaform connection with SMON victims. Beppu realised that both compounds were different brand names for the same substance, the Ciba-Geigy drug, clioquinol. Beppu conducted experiments where he fed the green clioquinol to mice, expecting to see the nerve damage disorders typical of SMON manifest in his rodents. The mice merely died, exposing the drug's extreme toxicity. Clioquinol had been marketed for years on the assumption that it was not absorbed by the body, but remained in the intestinal tract to kill germs. But SMON's victims produced a green coating on their tongues and produced green urine, symptoms that quite remarkably went unnoticed until nation-wide data on the disease was gathered. These green discharges were later isolated and tested to reveal an altered form of clioquinol in the patient's body. For the very first time, even the élite within the medical establishment were compelled to consider the unthinkable: that SMON was being caused by clioquinol consumption, not by a virus.

Doctors at the hard end of the crisis became horrified as the truth leaked out. They had been prescribing Entero-vioform and Emaform to patients with intestinal complaints for years and had been in the habit of innocently but arbitrarily increasing the doses of clioquinol as more diarrhoea and abdominal cramps manifested in the sufferer. Once

Beppu had established the SMON-clioquinol connection, other seemingly irrelevant information began to make sense. For instance, SMON's tendency to make its presence felt in hospitals, family groupings, medical workers and in summertime all reflected the pattern of Japan's chronic clioquinol consumption. Cases of SMON were also found to have risen and fallen with the sales of clioquinol. That Japan suffered more cruelly from the syndrome than other countries in which clioquinol was available has been put down to Japan's well-known, traditional over-consumption of pharmaceutical drugs in general.

On 8th September 1970, the Japanese government banned sales of clioquinol. That same month SMON cases dropped to below twenty. The following year saw only 36 cases. Three more were reported in 1972, and one in 1973. At last, this tragedy had run its course, and SMON could now be entered into the medical history books, archived under 'widespread needless death'.

Ironically, the fight over whether SMON had been the result of clioquinol or a mystery virus was to prevail for many more years in spite of the clear evidence, the virus hunting establishment refusing to consider that they had been wrong. Or was it that it was refusing to consider that SMON was actually that most despicable of syndromes, a classic iatrogenic illness – a disease brought on by the very medication prescribed by doctors to treat it? The concept of iatrogenic diseases is rarely considered because it understandably horrifies many doctors who in almost all cases have the care and well-being of their patient at heart.

For this reason, very few doctors outside Japan are aware of SMON, let alone the cause of the disaster that claimed so many lives. A bad mistake is rarely discussed by the guilty and so the lessons of SMON went unheeded. Today, the virus still dominates medical research and, as we have discovered, this fact alone led to the myopic research mindset which paved the way for the widespread, needless deaths in AIDS.

MODERNUS TOXICUS
(Trouble in the 21st Century)

WHY ARE THE NATIONS DYING?

Degenerative diseases are taking hold of industrialised nations like never before. The following excerpted US Senate document warned us of the reason for the health hazards to come.

Senate Document No. 264, 1936
74th Congress, 2nd Session

Do you know that most of us today are suffering from certain dangerous diet deficiencies which cannot be remedied until depleted soils from which our food comes are brought into proper mineral balance?

The alarming fact is that foods (fruits, vegetables and grains), now being raised on millions of acres of land that no longer contain enough of certain minerals, are starving us - no matter how much of them we eat. No man of today can eat enough fruits and vegetables to supply his system with the minerals he requires for perfect health because his stomach isn't big enough to hold them.

The truth is, our foods vary enormously in value, and some of them aren't worth eating as food... Our physical well-being is more directly dependent upon the minerals we take into our systems than upon calories or vitamins or upon the precise proportions of starch, protein or carbohydrates we consume.

This talk about minerals is novel and quite startling. In fact, a realization of the importance of minerals in food is so new that the text-books on nutritional dietetics contain very little about it. Nevertheless, it is something that concerns all of us, and the further we delve into it the more startling it becomes.

You'd think, wouldn't you, that a carrot is a carrot - that one is about as good as another as far as nourishment is concerned? But it isn't; one

260

carrot may look and taste like another and yet be lacking in the particular mineral element which our system requires and which carrots are supposed to contain.

Laboratory tests prove that the fruits, the vegetables, the grains, the eggs, and even the milk and the meats of today are not what they were a few generations ago (which doubtless explains why our forefathers thrived on a selection of foods that would starve us!)

No man today can eat enough fruits and vegetables to supply his stomach with the mineral salts he requires for perfect health, because his stomach isn't big enough to hold them! No longer does a balanced and fully nourishing diet consist merely of so many calories or certain vitamins or fixed proportion of starches, proteins and carbohydrates. We know that our diets must contain in addition something like a score of mineral salts.

It is bad news to learn from our leading authorities that 99% of the American people are deficient in these minerals [this was in 1936!], **and that a marked deficiency in any one of the more important minerals actually results in disease. Any upset of the balance, any considerable lack or one or another element, however microscopic the body requirement may be, and we sicken, suffer, shorten our lives.**

We know that vitamins are complex chemical substances which are indispensable to nutrition, and that each of them is of importance for normal function of some special structure in the body. Disorder and disease result from any vitamin deficiency. **It is not commonly realized, however, that vitamins control the body's appropriation of minerals, and in the absence of minerals they have no function to perform. Lacking vitamins, the system can make some use of minerals, but lacking minerals, vitamins are useless. Certainly our physical well-being is more directly dependent upon the minerals we take into our systems than upon calories of vitamins or upon the precise proportions of starch, protein of carbohydrates we consume.**

This discovery is one of the latest and most important contributions of science to the problem of human health."

* * * * *

Today our world faces an unprecedented crisis in healthcare. Toxin diseases that were all but unknown before the Industrial Revolution are now prolific. Cancer, multiple sclerosis, AIDS, ME, Alzheimers, diabetes, Parkinsons, coronary heart disease are all illnesses familiar to us, striking down family and friends with such grim reality that few expect these days to die of 'natural causes'. The average apple sold off the supermarket shelf has been saturated with chlorpyrifos, captan, iprodione, vinclozolin and then sealed in wax for longer shelf life. These pesticides, when tested, have variously caused birth defects, cancer, impaired immune response, fungal growth, genetic damage and disruption to the endocrine system. The average vitamin-depleted white bread roll can be tested positive for pesticides such as chlorpyrifos-methyl, endosulfasulphate, chlorothalonil, dothiocarb-amtes, iprodione, procymidone and vinclozolin. [433]

But are we just the innocent bystanders? The fast-trackers party, snorting coke and poppers, smoking cigarettes and dope. We fill our tooth cavities with mercury amalgam, a slow-release neurotoxic metal.[434] We lace our drinking water with fluoride and chlorine, both deadly poisons. The very food we eat has become corrupted by organophosphates, permeated with pesticides, stripped of minerals and now is increasingly being genetically modified.

So, for those 'diagnosed with AIDS', 'HIV' or for those suffering the now myriad health disorders associated with slow, long-term poisoning, let the battle-cry be: "Let's clean up our lives!" Seek the help you need to deal with the drugs and the lifestyle problems. Forget political correctness. Take a critical look at your lifestyle. Being

---

[433] *The New Zealand Total Diet Survey*, 1990/1

[434] Some Mexico cancer clinics, such as the Oasis Hospital, commence a patient's laetrile cancer therapy by first removing all mercury amalgam fillings and replacing them with non-toxic substitutes.

sensible about your lifestyle doesn't mean you have to take the fun of life. Just be smart.

And live.

ACRONYMS

AIDS   Acquired Immune Deficiency Syndrome
APHIS   Animal, Plant Health Inspection Services
CAFMR Campaign Against Fraudulent Medical Research
CDC   Centers for Disease Control (US)
CIA   Central Intelligence Agency (US)
DFID   Department For International Development (UK)
DOD   Department of Defense (US)
EIS   Epidemic Intelligence Service (US)
FBI   Federal Bureau of Investigation (US)
HIPCs Heavily Indebted Poor Countries
HIV   Human Immunodeficiency Virus
HL23V Human Leukaemia 23 Virus
HTLV1 Human T-cell Leukemia Virus
ICPD   International Conference on Population and Development (Cairo, 1994)
ICPD+5 Five years on from the International Conference on Population and Development
IL2   Interleukin 2
IMF   International Monetary Fund (UN)
JAMA   Journal of the American Medical Association
KS   Karposi's Sarcoma
LAV   Lymphadenopathy-associated Virus
NCI   National Cancer Institute (US)
NIH   National Institutes of Health (US)
OPA   Office of Population Affairs (US)
PCP   Pneumocystis Carinii Pneumonia
PCR   Polymerase Chain Reaction
SMON Subacute Myelo-Optico-Neuropathy
T-Cell Immune system lymphocyte cells
UCLA University of California Los Angeles
UN   United Nations (global)
WHE   Whole Human Embryo
WHO   World Health Organization (UN)

BIBLIOGRAPHY

WRITTEN REFERENCES

Africanus, Leo *A Geographical Historie of Africa*, 1600_____128

*AIDS and Africa*_____139

AIDS: A Second Opinion, a video documentary, Gary Null & Associates, PO Box 918, Planetarium Station, New York, NY 10024 USA _____56

Albany Business Journal _____26

Baobab Press _____185, 186

Barron's _____85

Berglas, Alexander preface to *Cancer: Nature, Cause and Cure*, Paris, 1957 ___236

*Bio/Technology Journal*_____72

Braithwaite, John *Corporate Crime in the Pharmaceutical Industry*, Routledge, 1984 _____188

Brand, Dr Paul *The Forever Feast*, Monarch Publications 1994 _____113

British Medical Journal _____87

Brown, George *Life Events and Illness*, Guildford Press, 1999_____80

Brown, Michael *Africa's Choices*, Penguin, 1995 _____127, 142

Buckman, Dr Robert & Karl Sabbagh *Magic or Medicine?* Pan Books, 1993 __246

Callen, Michael *Surviving AIDS*, Harper and Row, London: 1990 _____117

Cantwell, Alan, *Queer Blood*, Aries Rising Press, 1994 _____196

Chapman, Howard *Too Many Stars in the Sky*, Image National Conference manual, 1994 _____158

Chicago Tribune _____34

Cohen, S S *New England Journal of Medicine*, 317 (1987) _____81

Cooper, William *Behold a Pale Horse*, Lite Technology Publishing, 1991__ 157, 158

Daily Express _____29

Daily Mail _____130

Day, Phillip *Cancer: Why We're Still Dying to Know the Truth*, Credence Publications, 1999 _____35, 227, 256

Dayton Daily News _____92, 170

de Wind, John "Aiding Migration, The Impact of International Development Assistance on Haiti," Columbia University Research Program 1987 _____26

Dewar, Michael *The Art of Deception in Warfare*, David and Charles, 1989 ____162

Douglas-Hulme, Ethel *Pasteur Exposed. The False Foundation of Medicine*, Ennisfield Press, 1989 _____168

Duesberg, Peter H "AIDS Epidemiology: Inconsistencies with Human Immunodeficiency Virus and with Infectious Disease," *Proc. Natl. Acad. Sci., USA* 88 (1991) _____112

265

Rosenberg, Steven *The Transformed Cell,* Putnam, New York: 1992 _____ 43
Sacremento Bee _____ 130
Said, Edward *Orientalism. A historical Perspective of Cultural Imperialism in the West*, Vintage Books, 1979 _____ 130
Satinover, J *Homosexuality and the Politics of Truth*, Baker Books, 1996_____ 117
Science Magazine _____ 87
Scientific American _____ 117
Seligman, et al. "Concorde: MRC/ANRS Randomized Double-Blind Control Trial." _____ 88
Shilts, Randy *And the Band Played On,* St Martin's Press, New York: 1987_____
_____ 19, 114, 120
Silverman, W A *Controlled Clinical Trials*, "The Optimistic Bias Favouring Medical Attention", Elsevier Science, New York, 1991 _____ 246
Silverman, W A *Human Experimentation*, Oxford Medical Publications, Oxford, 1985 _____ 246
Sonnabend, J A Report on MultiCenter Study of AZT to FDA, 1987 _____ 89
Spin _____ 139, 140
Stewart, CP and D Guthrie, *Lind's Treatise on Scurvy,* Edinburgh University Press, 1953 _____ 249
Sunday Telegraph _____ 29
The New Zealand Total Diet Survey, 1990/1 _____ 262
Thompson, Kenneth *Moral Panics*, Routledge Press, 1997 _____ 29
Time _____27, 160, 172, 181, 182, 183, 192, 196, 200
Von Hoffman, N *Citizen Cohn. The Life and Times of Roy Cohn*, New York, Doubleday Press, 1988 _____ 118
Wall Street Journal _____ 72
Whitehead, Neil, *My Genes Made Me Do It. A Scientific Look at Sexual Orientation*, Huntingdon House Publishers, 1999 _____ 117
Williams, R R *Towards the Conquest of Beriberi*, Harvard University Press, 1961 249
Willner, Dr Robert *Deadly Deception*, Peltec Publishing Co, Boca Raton, FL __ 160
Wood, John *Thomas Robert Malthus. A Critical Assessment*, Croon Helm, 1986 158
Zenger _____ 66, 80, 108, 109, 121

INDEX

269

Burton, Philip, 27
Bush, George H, 157

C

Cable News Network (CNN), 150, 183, 184, 192, 193, 194, 196, 200, 232, 234
Callen, Michael, 115, 117, 119
Cambodia, 160
Camden, 99, 100
Cancer, 18, 20, 35, 36, 37, 38, 42, 43, 44, 45, 46, 64, 81, 87, 89, 104, 109, 112, 183, 187, 190, 226, 256, 262
Candidiasis, 19, 56
Carbolic acid, 169
Carnegie, Andrew, 187
Cartier, Jacques, 247
Carty, Todd, 29
CBS, 182, 234
CCR5, 175
CDC, 19, 20, 21, 22, 23, 24, 25, 26, 31, 37, 47, 53, 57, 58, 59, 75, 77, 84, 111, 112, 131, 178, 209
Ceni, 252
Center for Strategic and International Studies, 189
Charles II, King, 245
Chemotherapy, 18, 81, 83, 227
Child Protection Services (US), 101
China, 154, 184, 189
Chirac, Jacques, 49
Chirimuuta, Richard, 127, 133
Chiro-Science, 173
CIA (Central Intelligence Agency), 157
Ciba-Geigy, 258
Clioquinol, 258, 259
Clumeck, Nathan, 130
Cocaine, 107, 108, 110, 111, 118
Cohen, Richard, 81, 110, 182
Columbia, 157, 160
Compound S, 85
Concorde study, 87, 88
Conference on Retroviruses and Opportunistic Infections (1996), 90
Connor, Steve, 64, 65, 66
Conrad, Joseph, 129, 130, 145, 198, 200, 201

Continuum (UK), 37, 55, 62, 65, 66, 67, 71, 74, 92, 95, 96, 106, 137, 149, 171, 182, 231
Contraception, 153
Council on Foreign Relations (CFR), 182, 183, 196
Credence Publications, 5, 11, 35, 44, 64, 75, 76, 80, 92, 102, 120, 150, 153, 175, 197, 198, 205, 219, 225, 229, 256
Crixivan, 90, 91
Curran, James, 19, 47
Cyanocobalamin. *See* Vitamin B12

D

d4T, 80, 98
da Gama, Vasco, 246
Daily Telegraph (UK), 29, 72, 88, 198, 199
ddC, 80, 90, 218
ddI, 80, 90, 177
Degesch, 188
Department for International Development (DFID), 166, 167, 168
Department of Agriculture (US), 25, 253
Department of Defense (DOD) (US), 177, 190
Department of Health & Human Services (US), 160
Depression, 82, 108, 215, 251
Dewar, Michael, 162, 192, 193
Diarrhoea, 24, 43, 56, 80, 82, 83, 94, 97, 136, 148, 150, 165, 207, 222, 251, 256, 257, 258
Dominican Republic, 25
Drug Enforcement Agency (DEA), 107
Duesberg, Peter, 18, 21, 22, 24, 27, 54, 57, 58, 59, 60, 61, 62, 63, 71, 84, 85, 86, 107, 108, 109, 110, 111, 112, 190, 226, 249
Duke University, 85
Durban 2000, 178, 199
Durex, 133

E

East Enders, 29
Egypt, 157

Eijkman, Christian, 250
EIS, 21, 22, 23, 24, 31, 37
El Salvador, 160, 165, 184
ELISA, 69, 70, 74, 76, 97, 99, 100, 131, 146, 212, 224
Ellison, Bryan, 22, 23, 24, 37
Emaform, 257, 258
Emerson, Valerie, 98
Emery, Frank, 128, 129
Emphysema, 109
Enfield, 96, 97
Entero-vioform, 257, 258
Epidemic Intelligence Service (EIS), 19, 21
Esparza, José, 176
Essex, Max, 131
Etheridge, E W, 20, 253, 254, 255
Ethiopia, 157
Ethyl-glycol, 169
Eugenics, 156
Europe, 63, 104, 112, 127, 213, 214, 249
Evening Standard (UK), 100

F

Family planning, 153, 154, 161, 162, 167
Family Planning Association, 189
Farber, Celia, 106, 139, 140
Farr, William, 58, 220
Farr's Law, 58, 220
Fatigue, 80, 117, 148
Ferguson, Thomas, 160
Fiala, Christian, 138, 171
Fischl, Margaret, 87
Flexner, Abraham, 187
Folic Acid. See Vitamin B9
Food, 17, 36, 82, 83, 90, 134, 135, 137, 138, 142, 148, 151, 157, 158, 166, 178, 186, 206, 238, 250, 251, 260, 262
Food & Drug Administration (FDA), 72, 73, 75, 84, 85, 88, 89, 90, 91, 170, 177, 187
Ford Foundation, 178, 200
Ford, President Gerald, 22
Formaldehyde, 169
Fort Detrick, 228
Frankfurt, 49

French Revolution, 249
Friedman-Kein, Dr, 20, 104, 112
Fruit, 248, 249

G

Gabon, 131
Gallo, Robert, 31, 33, 34, 35, 38, 39, 40, 41, 42, 43, 44, 45, 46, 47, 48, 49, 50, 52, 53, 55, 57, 58, 60, 62, 63, 66, 67, 68, 71, 75, 84, 85, 93, 110, 114, 131, 169, 190, 209, 222
Gates, Bill & Melinda, 171, 172, 173, 196, 197
Genomics, 173
George VI, King, 156
George, Susan, 158
Germany, 54, 121, 127, 183, 197, 213, 254
Geshekter, Charles, 136, 142, 146, 151, 168, 176
Ghana, 161, 162, 163, 243
Glickman, Dan, 25, 26
God, 42, 86, 117, 175, 187, 206, 229
Goldberger, Joseph, 254, 255
Gore, Albert, 193
Gottlieb, Michael, 18, 19, 20, 21, 24, 26, 37, 45
Gould, Donald, 62
Griffin, Beverly E, 55
Griffin, G Edward, 55, 187, 248
Groopman, Jerome, 88
Grossman, Wendy, 181
Guardian (UK), 29, 99, 175

H

Haemophilia, 71
Haemophiliacs, 21, 71
Haight Ashbury, 28
Haiti, 24, 25, 26
Hallucinations, 251
Hamer, Dean, 116
Hanks, Tom, 29
Harding, Jeremy, 133, 134, 135, 136
Haringey, 96, 97
Harrison, Paul, 142

Harrison, Peter, 142
Harrison, Rosalind, 127, 131, 132, 143
Haverkos, Harry, 24, 108, 112
Hawkins, Richard, 247
HB 15090, 190, 194, 197
Heavily Indebted Poor Countries (HIPCs), 165, 166
Henry, Patrick, 79, 100
Heroin, 21, 107, 108, 110, 111, 208
Heyward, William, 176
Himmler, Heinrich, 156
Hippocrates, 102
Hippocratic Oath, 102
HIV-free AIDS, 59
Hodgkinson, Neville, 54, 55, 64, 88, 137
Hoffman La-Roche, 47, 75, 90, 95
Homoeopathy, 92
Homosexuals, 21
Horowitz, Leonard, 183, 228
Hoxha, Sjedullah, 151
Hudson, Rock, 29
Human chorionic gonadotrophin (hCG), 164, 165
Human Genome Sciences, 175
Human Immunodeficiency Virus (HIV), 3, 9, 10, 12, 27, 28, 29, 30, 31, 33, 34, 44, 45, 46, 47, 48, 51, 52, 53, 54, 55, 56, 57, 58, 59, 60, 61, 62, 63, 64, 65, 66, 67, 68, 69, 70, 71, 72, 73, 74, 75, 76, 78, 79, 80, 82, 83, 84, 87, 88, 89, 91, 92, 93, 95, 96, 97, 98, 99, 100, 102, 106, 108, 110, 111, 112, 114, 115, 121, 125, 126, 131, 133, 134, 136, 137, 138, 140, 141, 143, 144, 146, 149, 150, 153, 158, 168, 172, 175, 176, 177, 178, 193, 194, 201, 205, 206, 207, 208, 209, 210, 211, 212, 214, 215, 216, 218, 219, 220, 221, 222, 223, 224, 225, 226, 227, 228, 230, 232, 240, 241, 242, 244, 262
Human Life International, 163
Hume, David, 128
Hurricane Mitch, 166
Huxley, Julian, 156

I

I G Farbenindustrie (IG Farben), 188
Incubators, 151

Independent, The, 65
India, 30, 99, 157, 184, 243
Indonesia, 157
Insects, 253
Inter-American Development Bank, 152
International Monetary Fund (IMF), 134, 141
International Planned Parenthood Federation, 189
Intestinal tract, 258
Intra-uterine devices (IUDs), 153
Irritability, 251
Isaacson, Walter, 182

J

Jackson Memorial Hospital, 24
Jaffe, Harold, 57, 108, 110
Japan, 256, 257, 258, 259
Japanese Navy, 249
Jesus Christ, 229
Jillani, Lisa, 170
Johns Hopkins University (JHU), 21, 161, 253
Johnson, Christine, 56, 70, 71
Jubilee Campaign, 165
Justice Department (US), 107

K

Kagera, Tanzania, 139, 242
Kaletsky, Anatole, 198, 199
Karposi's Sarcoma, 19, 20, 56
Kasun, Jacqueline, 158, 159, 165, 166, 178
Kay, Cathy, 105
Kissinger, Henry, 156, 157, 166, 182, 190, 197
Koblenz, 54
Koch, Robert, 56, 57, 58, 220, 250, 251
Koch's Postulates, 56, 58, 220, 250
Kono, Reisaku, 258
Krafeld, Karl, 62, 63
Krynen, Philippe, 136, 137, 138, 139, 142, 148, 150, 171, 178
Kumah, Opiah Mensah, 161, 162

Non-Governmental Organizations (NGO), 146, 199
NSSM 200, 156, 157, 158, 166, 183, 190, 194, 197
Nujol, 187
Null, Gary, 56, 76, 80, 107, 108, 109, 117, 118
Nussbaum, Bruce, 85, 86

O

Observer Online, 101
Office of Research Integrity, 48, 60, 116
Olympic Games, 257
OPA (Office of Population Affairs), 160
Organophosphates, 262
Oriel College, Oxford, 116
Orphan, 138, 150
Osmanov, Saladin, 176
Overseas Development Council, 189

P

Packard, Vance, 229
Pakistan, 157
Pancreas, 90, 177
Papadopulos-Eleopulos, Eleni, 67, 191
Paralysis, 22, 23, 170
Parasites, 24, 70, 72, 135, 221
Parsons, Richard, 182
Partage, 136, 150, 242
Paxman, Jeremy, 196, 197, 198
Pearlstine, Norman, 182, 183
Pellagra, 251, 254
People Advocating Vaccine Education (PAVE), 170
People Magazine, 98
Pertussus, 169
Pesticides, 262
Pharmacia & Upjohn, 92, 229
Philadelphia, 23, 29, 91
Philippines, 157, 163, 164
Pinching, Tony, 88
Pine needles, 247
Piot, Peter, 125, 213, 214, 235
Placebo, 86, 87
Pliny the Elder, 127

Pneumocystis carinii, 18, 19, 37, 56
Pneumonia, 18, 19, 23, 24, 37, 56, 71, 216, 218, 256
Polished rice, 250
Poppers, 20, 107, 262
Population control, 151, 153, 154, 155, 157, 158, 159, 160, 161, 162, 163, 165, 166, 167, 168, 178, 185, 186, 191, 229
Population Council, 165, 189, 191
Port-au-Prince, 26
Porter Adventist Hospital (Denver), 94
Porton Down, 228
Positive Treatment News, 98
Press Complaints Commission, 65
Pristina Hospital, 151
Project AIDS International, 59, 84, 89, 100, 178
Promiscuity, 106, 117, 128, 131, 133, 151, 152
Prostitutes, 136
Protease inhibitors, 31, 90, 91, 92, 93, 94, 98, 177, 193
Public Health Service (US), 35, 209, 252, 254

Q

Quinine, 251, 252

R

Rape, 28, 151, 152
Rath, Richard, 147
Reagan, Ronald, 43, 49
Recreational drugs, 222
Red Cross, 139
Regush, Nicholas, 120
Retrovirology, 60, 61
Revelle, Roger, 142
Rhone Poulenc Rorer Inc., 173
Ritonavir, 91, 94, 98
Rockefeller Foundation, 165, 171, 178, 183, 188, 189
Rockefeller Sr., John D, 165, 171, 178, 183, 186, 187, 188, 189, 190, 191, 196, 200
Rockefeller, William, 187

POSTSCRIPT
(June 2000)

As 'World Without AIDS' goes to print:

➤ Nelson Mandela has come out in support of President Thabo Mbeki's stand for an open debate on the AIDS issue.

➤ US president Bill Clinton, as predicted, has recently declared that AIDS in Africa is now officially a global security threat, and is seeking to put into place an appropriate military strategy.[435]

➤ Five of the world's largest pharmaceutical companies, including Glaxo-Wellcome, Bristol-Myers Squibb and Merck, have declared that they are to reduce the prices of their AIDS drugs to Africa by as much as 85%.[436]

➤ Dr Klaus Koehnlein, a German AIDS practitioner and a member of the recently convened AIDS specialist panel in South Africa, remarked at that gathering: "I remember vividly the early years, and seeing those AZT patients, and they just had no bone marrow left... they have no idea that we killed a whole generation of AIDS patients with AZT." [437]

➤ And finally, a Dr Mark Wainburg, president of the International AIDS Society, has declared that researchers such as those at Credence Publications should be jailed for daring to ask for an open and honest debate on the issues raised in this book. Says Wainburg: "If we could succeed and lock up a couple of these guys, I guarantee you, the HIV denier movement would die pretty damn quick." [438]

Let the reader decide who it is who should be incarcerated for the greater benefit of mankind.

---

[435] Washington Post, 30th April 2000. CNN report
[436] Boston Globe, 12th May 2000. Washington Post, 12th May 2000. New York Times, 15th May 2000.
[437] Farber, Celia. A Contrary Conference in Pretoria, ibid.
[438] Andre Picard, Montreal Health Report, Monday, 12th May 2000.

277

SPECIAL THANKS

Photographs

A very special thank you to photographer Loel Poor and colleague Jack Forest of the Forest Foundation for the photographs of Eddie and Arnie, and those featured in 'Loving Ministrations'. To Melissa Springer for 'Death of a Twelve Year Old'. To *Continuum* Magazine for 'Huw Christie, Joan Shenton, Stefan Lanka, Eleni Eleopulos, Paul B, Robert Gallo, Peter Duesberg, Luc Montagnier, Robert Giraldo, AIDSvax, Global Murder, Missing Virus'. To Christine Maggiore for 'Chris and Charlie'. To Philippe Krynen for 'Philippe, Lucy and Joseph, Deus and Jovina, Partage group, AIDS orphans'. To *Renewal* Magazine for 'Hungry'.

Editorial

Thank you to Huw, Alex, Joan and Stefan for their enthusiasm for the book and their invaluable editorial comments. To Michael, a fount of knowledge. To Edward for his invaluable support and encouragement. To Stewart at TVL for his technical crafting. And to Christine, for her help with and contribution to the 'Conquerors' chapter.

Inspiration

A big thank you to all who have encouraged us throughout the writing of this book. To our loved ones, who have borne with us as we burned the midnight oil. And finally, a special 'thank you' to our Beloved God, whose inspiration it was in the first place to believe in the possibility of a *World Without AIDS*.